Toni Morrison

Sula

With Essays in Criticism

Annotated with a Critical Introduction
by
Kim, Myung-Joo

Shinasa

CONTENTS

CRITICAL INTRODUCTION

1. 토니 모리슨의 삶과 작품들

모리슨(처녀 적 이름은 Chloe Anthony Wofford)은 1931년 2월 18일, 제철소로 알려진 오하이오주의 로레인(Lorain)에서 태어났다. 남부 죠지아(Georgia) 태생의 아버지는 백인에 대한 강한 반감을 지닌 사람으로서, 한 인종이 다른 인종보다 생래적으로 우월하다는 믿음이 인종차별주의라면 그도 역시 인종 차별자였다고 모리슨은 회고한다. 어머니 역시 남부의 알라바마(Alabama) 태생으로, 백인에게 사기 당한 후 남부에 염증을 느낀 부친과 함께 북부로 오게 된다.

오하이오주는 마치 전혀 다른 두개의 주가 합친 것처럼 각각 다른 특성을 지닌 두 부분으로 나뉘어져 있었다. 즉, 캔터키와 주경계를 두는 남쪽 지방은 KKK단의 폭력이 난무하는 곳이었고, 북쪽은 자유를 찾아 도망친 흑인노예의 탈출을 도왔던 "지하철도"(the Underground Railroad) 조직이 활동하던 곳이었다. 모리슨이 어린 시절을 보냈던 오하이오주의 로레인은 전형적인 중산층 미국 중소도시로서 제철소 산업을 중심으로 여러 나라에서 이민 온 다양한 인종이 모여 사는 곳이었다.

여러 인터뷰에서 밝히고 있듯이 모리슨은 특별히 작가가 되겠다는 꿈을 가진 적이 없으나, 어릴 적부터 도스토 예브스키, 톨스토이, 제인 오스틴, 그리고 유럽의 고전을 즐겨 읽곤 했다. 그리고 집안에서 자연스럽게 유령이야기를 비롯하여 여러 이야기를 말하고 듣는 것이 습관화되어 각종 민화와 신화, 그리고 노래에 익숙하게 자라났다.

로레인 고등학교를 우수하게 졸업한 모리슨은 유명한 흑인 지도자를 많이 배출한 미국 최고의 흑인대학 하워드 대학(Howard University)에 입학했고 여기에서 그녀는 자신의 이름을 토니로 바꾸었다. 영문학을 전공했으며 대학의 극단에서 적극적으로 활동했다. 졸업 후 그녀는 코

넬대학에서 석사학위를 받았는데, 그녀의 석사학위논문은 윌리엄 포크너와 버지니아 울프의 소설에서 자살이라는 주제를 다루었다. 다분히 어두운 주제를 선호하는, 이후 모리슨의 작품성향을 대체로 짐작케 하는 선택이었다. 그 후 휴스턴의 남부텍사스 대학에서 잠시 강의하다가 1957년 다시 하워드대학으로 돌아와 강의하게 된다.

하워드 대학에서 강의하는 동안 자마이카에서 온 건축가인 헤롤드 모리슨 (Harold Morrison) 을 만나 1958년 결혼하였고, 1961년 첫 아들 헤롤드 포드 모리슨 (Harold Ford Morrison)이 태어난다. 이때부터 그녀는 왠지 초초하게 느껴져서 작가들의 소모임에 참석하기 시작하는데, 딱히 작가가 되기 위해서는 아니고, 단지 흥미로운 사람을 만나고 싶다는 욕구 때문이었다. 이야기를 하나씩 쓰고 토론하는 그룹인데, 마땅히 가져갈 이야기가 궁색해진 모리슨은 자신이 오래 전에 대화를 나누었던 한 소녀에 대한 이야기를 썼고, 이것은 후에 『가장 푸른 눈』(*The Bluest Eye*)의 초고가 되었다.

1964년 두 번째 아이를 임신한 채, 강의를 그만두고 남편과 함께 유럽여행을 떠나게 된다. 여행에서 돌아온 후, 그녀는 자신의 미국적 자아와 남편의 자마이카 문화가 상치된다는, 간단한 설명만 남기고 이혼하게 된다. 직장도 없이 두 아이를 부양하게 된 모리슨은 매우 절망적인 상태에서 시라쿠즈 (Syracuse)에 있는 랜덤하우스에서 직장을 얻는다. 직장과 아이들 양육이라는 심신을 피폐케 하는 어려운 생활에서의 도피 내지는 해방의 출구로서 그녀는 글쓰기를 시도한다. 수년 전 처박아두었던 원고를 꺼내들어 완성하고 1970년 천신만고 끝에 출판한 것이 『가장 푸른 눈』이었다. 상업적 성공은 아니었지만, 권위 있는 문예비평가인 죤 레오날드 (John Leonard) 의 호평을 받았고, 민권운동이 자리잡기 시작한 호기를 타고 흑인의 경험을 리얼하게 묘사한 작품이라는 지속적인 평가를 누릴 수 있었다.

1973년에는 두 번째 작품, 『술라』(*Sula*)를 발표했다. 이 작품으로 모리슨은 전국적인 명성을 얻게 되었고 영예로운 문학상인 "최고작품상" (National Book Award) 의 후보로 지명되기도 하였다. 작품성에 대한 찬반이 엇갈렸지만 『술라』는 많은 비평가를 열광하게 하였고, 이후 모리슨은 흑인문제에 대한 전문가로 인식되었다.

1975년에는 모리슨의 기획으로 랜덤사에서 『흑인들의 삶』(*The Black Book*)이란 책을 출판했는데, 300년동안 미국의 흑인들의 삶이 담긴 신문기사, 사진, 요리법 등을 모아 만든 책이었다. 이 책은 삶에 허다한 고통과 폭력을 견디고 저항한 흑인들에 대한 자긍심을 불러일으키는 것으로 모리슨 자신에게도 깊은 영감을 주는 책이 되었다. 후에 『빌러비드』의 소재도 사실상 이 책에서 얻은 것이었다.

큰 아들로 인한 마음고생과 아버지의 죽음으로 큰 충격을 받은 모리슨은 1977년 『솔로몬의 노래』 (*Song of Solomon*) 를 발표한다. 이때 모리슨의 나이는 46세이지만 작가로서 활동한지는 10년이 채 안 되는 시기였는데도 불구하고 이 책은 대단한 성공을 거두었다. 보급판으로 570,000부가 팔리고, "비평가가 추천하는 최고문학상" (National Book Critics Circle Award) 을 수상했으며, 마침내 문학계의 거목으로 자리잡았다. 모리슨은 언론의 주목을 받고 각종 TV 인터뷰에 출연하여 특이하게도 작가로서 스타가 된 셈이었다. 사람들은 마치 마이클 잭슨의 새 앨범을 기다리듯 모리슨의 새 책을 기다렸고 1981년 『타르베이비』 (*Tar Baby*) 가 출판되어 베스트셀러의 목록에 연이어 넉 달 동안 오를 정도로 큰 성공을 거두었다. 같은 해 모리슨은 뉴스위크지의 표지모델로 세워졌고, 대체로 작가들에게 별로 주목하는 법이 없는 미국사람들에겐 예외적인 스타로서 헤밍웨이 이후 작가로서 최고의 영예를 누리게 되었다. 그리고 1984년에는 뉴욕주립대 알바니 캠퍼스의 알버트 슈바이쳐 교수가 되었다.

1987년, 모리슨이 오랫동안 쓰고 싶었지만 도저히 끝낼 수 없었던 책, 예술이라기보다는 삶일 수밖에 없었던 이야기, 그 이야기를 마침내 발표했는데, 이것이 바로 『빌러비드』였다. 이 책은 1988년 퓰리쳐 상을 받았고, 이어서 1989년엔 흑인여성으로서 최초로 아이비리그 대학인 프린스톤 대학의 로버트 고힌 교수가 되었다.

1992년에는 소설 『재즈』(*Jazz*)와 일종의 문학 비평서인 『어둠 속에서의 유희: 하얀 것과 문학적 상상력』(*Playing in the Dark: Whiteness and the Literary Imagination*)를 발표했다. 바로 이전의 『빌러비드』만큼 비평가를 열광하게 하는 소설은 못되었지만 더러 호감 어린 평가를 받기도 했다. 그리고 마침내 1993년 여성으로서는 여덟 번째, 흑인 여성으로서는 첫 번째로 노벨 문학상을 수상하는 영광을 얻게 된다. 호사다마인지, 노벨상을 수상하던 해의 크리스마스에 그녀의 집을 불타 전소하여 깊은 절망에 빠지지만, 그녀 특유의 강인함으로 극복한다. 그 후 오프라 윈프리 (Oprah Winfrey) 와의 계약으로 『빌러비드』를 영화화하고, 현재까지 가장 최근작인 1997년 『낙원』(*Paradise*)을 발표한다. 한 권의 책에 그렇게 많은 서평이 쓰여진 것은 어쩌면 처음일지도 모른다. 『낙원』이 출판되자, 주요 일간지, 문예지 등, 거의 모든 매체가 이 작품에 대한 견해를 실었고, 지나치게 어려운 책이라는 악평부터 가장 위대한 책이라는 찬사까지 다양한 평가가 지금까지 이루어지고 있다. 현재 프린스톤 대학 교수로서 뉴욕과 프린스톤, 뉴저지를 오가며 지내고 있다.

2. 『술라』 작품 해설

1) 작품의 줄거리

우선 『술라』의 줄거리를 요약해 보면, 이 이야기는 20세기 초, 도시화 산업화가 이루어지기 전 흑인들이 살고 있는 바텀(Bottom)이란 마을을 배경으로 시작된다. 어느 흑인농부가 백인 지주에게 속아서 바텀이라 불리는 산등성이에서 살기 시작한 것인데, 풍광이 아름답고 서로에 대한 관심이 지나칠 정도로 많아 모두가 서로를 알고 있는 공동체 의식이 강한 시골마을이다.

이야기는 연도별로 나뉘어져 1919년에서 시작하는데, 1차대전 적에게 포위되어 도망하던 중에 옆에서 뛰어가던 병사의 머리가 잘려나가고 몸만 앞으로 달려나가는 광경에 큰 충격을 받아 정신병원을 거쳐 바텀 마을로 돌아오는 쉐드랙(Shadrack)에 대한 이야기가 처음으로 나온다. 충격 후, 그는 손이 점점 커지는 환각에 사로잡히게 되지만, 변기에 비친 자신의 검은 얼굴을 보고 환각에서 벗어나게 된다. 그러나 여전히 죽음에 대한 두려움에 시달리는 듯, 그 두려움을 제어하기 위하여 "국민 자살일"을 만들어 매년 1월 3일만 되면 방울과 교수형 집행 밧줄을 들고 거리를 행진한다. 이러한 광기로 인해 마을 사람들과 떨어진 외딴 곳에서 살게 된다.

그리곤 주인공인 넬과 술라의 성장 배경이 나온다. 넬은 루이지애나 출신의 어머니 밑에서 엄격한 가정교육을 받고 자란다. 그러나 어머니 헬렌의 엄격함은 자신의 어머니가 창녀라는 사실에 대한 강한 반발로 이루어졌고, 이런 반발은 딸 넬에 대한 억압적 교육으로 나타난다. 그러나, 엄격하고 단정한 엄마가 루이지애나로 여행도중, 궁지에서 빠져나오기 위해 남자들의 음란한 눈과 그에 맞서 비굴한 미소를 띠는 엄마에게 넬은 큰 충격을 받고, 자신은 절대로 그런 음란한 눈길을 받지 않겠다고 다짐한다(22). 흔히 인용되는 "It's me. I'm not their daughter.

I'm not Nel. I'm me"(28)을 여기서 외치게 된다. 즉, 음탕한 자신의 할머니와 어머니와는 달리, 자신만큼은 정숙한 자아를 확립하겠다는 의지이고, 이는 흑인 마을에서 전통적으로 기대하는 여성적 가치를 내면화하여, 남편과 아이들을 돌보는 아내와 엄마의 역할에 충실할 것을 선언하는 것과도 같다. 따라서 자신의 보살핌과 남성적 자존심의 회복을 위해 결혼을 선택하는 쥬드를 넬이 선뜻 남편으로 받아들이는 것은, 흔히 말하듯 자아정체성의 탐색을 포기하는 넬의 변심이 아니라, 그녀의 결단에 따른 자연스런 귀결일 수도 있다.

이에 비해 술라의 가정환경은 언듯 보면 넬과 대조적이라 할 만하다. 술라의 할머니 이바(Eva)와 엄마 한나(Hanna)는 일찍 남편을 잃었으며, 남자 관계가 개방적이다. 그런데, 14살 때 우연히 엄마가 하는 말, "나는 술라는 사랑하지만 좋아하지는 않아"라는 말을 듣고 그녀는 더 이상 자신이 의지할 곳이 없다고 생각하게 된다("There was no other that you count on")(118-9). 이 말은 결국 자신의 삶이 모범을 삼을 만한 초자아가 부재한다는 것을 의미한다. 아버지의 부재에 이어 어머니의 의식적인 지움은, 그녀가 타인에 대한 어떠한 의존도 회피하고, 따라서 다른 사람과 관계 맺는 일이 어려워 질 것이라는 것을 의미한다. 흔히 넬과 술라가 자아정체성 탐구에 함께 나서지만, 넬은 실패하고 술라만 성공하는 것으로 해석하고, 그런 면에서 두 사람이 대조적이라고 말하지만 사실은 그렇지 않다. 두 사람은 모두 부모와 단절을 선언하고, 각자의 정체성 탐구에 몰두하나, 단지 그 양상이 다를 뿐인 것이다.

그리고 술라는 넬과 함께 우연한 사고로 한 소년(Chicken Little) 을 호수에 빠뜨려 죽이는 사건이 일어난다. 이후 술라는 더 이상 자신의 삶에 아무런 책임을 느끼지 않는다고 말한다(119). 그리곤 자신은 자아가 없다고 말한다 ("no ego") (119). 초자아에 이어 자아까지 상실했다는 의미인데, 무절제한 충동을 제어할 수 있는 능력을 상실했음을 의미한다. 이제 그녀에게 남아있는 것은 절제 없이 뻗어나가는 욕망의 그늘뿐이다. 친구 넬의 결혼을 마지막으로 마을을 떠난 후, 10여 년 만에 돌아오는 술라는 아름다운 얼굴과 지성을 갖춘 여성이지만, 마을 사람들은 그녀를 악녀로 취급한다. 왜냐하면 할머니 이바를 집에서 양로원으로 내쫓을 만큼 몰인정하고, 동네의 남자들과 동침하기를 다반사로 하고, 교회에 속옷도 입지 않고 나타나는 등, 그녀의 존재는 동네에서 확실한 악으로 인식된다. 마침내 친구 넬의 남편 쥬드의 남편과 아무런 죄의식 없이 동침하고, 이를 목격하는 넬과 결별하게 된다.

그 후 에이젝스를 만나고, 술라는 이전 남자들과의 관계에서는 느낄 수 없었던 독특한 감정을 경험하게 된다. 하지만, 술라의 독특한 감정이 독점적인 애욕이라고 생각한 에이젝스는 술라를 떠나고 만다. 상심한 술라는 병석에 눕는다. 이때 넬이 방문하는데, 서로 자신이 올바른 삶을 살아왔음을 고집하고, 확실한 자신을 찾았다고 각자 자신한다. 술라가 죽은 후 다시 "국민 자살일"이 되자, 이번 행진에는 마술에 홀린 듯, 많은 사람들이 행진에 가담하고 평소 흑인마을의 울분을 담고 있던 터널을 부숴뜨리고 이에 밀려드는 강물에 마을 사람들의 반 이상이 죽고 만다.

세월이 흘러, 자원 봉사자로 양로원을 방문한 넬은 여태 살아서 90세가 넘은 이바를 발견하지만, "너와 술라, 다 똑같아"(169)라는 이바의 말에 큰 충격을 받는다. 자신은 술라 보다 절제 있고 책임감 있는 선한 삶을 살았다고 자부했으며, 자신의 친구인 술라는 무책임하고 충동적인 악한 삶을 살아왔다는 넬의 확신이 허물어지는 순간이었다. 소년을 물에 빠뜨리고 이를 다소 즐기듯 바라보았던 과거의 자신을 그제 서야 발견하며 자신의 선이 독선이었음을 발견한다. 그리고 동병상련의 우정으로 죽은 술라를 그리워하는 장면으로 작품은 끝을 맺는다.

2) 작품에 대한 일반적 평가

작가는 일생동안 한 가지 주제를 다루기 마련이다. 모리슨이 지금까지 발표한 일곱 편의 소설에서 일관되게 천착하는 화두는 바로 흑인의 정체성에 관한 문제다. 따라서 첫 작품부터 끝까지 모리슨은 흑인여성으로서 강한 자의식을 가지고 소설을 썼고, 특별히 초기 작품인 『술라』는 백인이 아닌 흑인으로서의 정체성, 남성이 아닌 여성으로서의 정체성 문제를 깊이 다루고 있는 작품으로 알려져 있다. 그리하여 주인공 술라의 소위 "실험적" 삶은, 개인주의가 좀 지나쳤다는 약간의 우려를 토달면서도 미국적 평등과 자유를 성취하는 프론티어적 인물로 찬사 받는 경우가 꽤 많다. "실험적" 이란 말이 의미하는 우상파괴성, 즉 인습의 틀을 깨고 자신만의 영역을 개척하고, 타인이 아닌 내 스스로 자신을 정의한다는 독립성, "자유낙하"를 무릅쓴 용기와 대담성은 술라를 매우 매력적인 존재로 만들었다.

또한 바바라 크리스천 (Barbara Christian) 이나 로버트 스텝토(Robert Stepto) 같은 비평가가 지적하듯이, 『술라』는 앞선 작품인 『가장 푸른 눈』에 나오는 여자아이들 간의 우정이 성장하면서 어떤 형태로 만들어지는 지는가에 대한 자연스런 결과를 담고 있다고 볼 수 있다. 즉, 성격은 다르지만, 여성들간의 상호보완적 관계를 다루고 있다는 것이다. 모리슨 자신도 이들 비평가의 견해를 지지하면서, 클로디아나 프리다와 같은 작은 소녀들이 성장하여 어떤 모습을 갖게 될지 궁금해하는 것은 지극히 당연하다고 언급한 바 있다. 술라와 넬은 서로의 약점을 보완하는 상반된 성격을 지니면서 마치 서로의 반쪽인 것처럼 함께 같은 꿈을 꾸고 같은 경험을 공유하면서 성장한다. 비록, 그들의 다른 성격만큼이나 이후 서로 다른 길을 걷게 되지만 술라는 죽는 순간의 느낌조차 넬과 나누고 싶어 하고, 넬 역시 남편보다도 술라를 더욱 그리워하면 살았음을 깨닫게 된다. 죽음보다도 강하고, 결혼보다도 더욱 견고한 결속을 뒤늦게 깨닫게 되는 것이다.

흑인 소녀들의 정체성 형성과 여성간의 우정이라는 주제 이외에도 이 작품은 선악의 전통적인 정의에 대한 회의와 도전을 다루고 있다. 클로디아 테이트 (Claudia Tate) 와의 인터뷰에서, 작품을 쓴 모리슨 자신의 의도가 애초부터 선과 악의 모호한 경계에 대한 의문에서 출발했다고 말한 것을 보면 알 수 있다. 전통적으로 사람을 평가하는 잣대인 성실성과 책임감 같은 것이 과연 선악을 가르는 진정한 기준이 될 수 있는지에 대한 회의인 것이다. 전통적인 가치기준에 익숙한 눈으로 볼 때 넬은 분명 사랑하는 남편을 가장 친한 친구에게 빼앗긴 피해자이고, 남편이 무책임하게 떠난 후 세 아이들을 돌보는 성실한 가장임에 틀림없다. 이에 비해 술라는 친구의 남편을 빼앗고, 성적으로 문란하며, 타인에 대한 배려라고는 털끝만큼도 없는 사악한 존재일 수도 있다. 그러나 작품의 말미, 술라가 죽기 전 넬에게 던지는 말은 의미심장하다. 통념을 깨고, 어쩌면 술라가 선하고 넬이 악한 것인지도 모른다는 말은 모리슨 자신이 던지는 의문일 가능성이 많다.

『술라』에 대한 해석은 다양하다. 대체로 술라에 대한 시각과 평가면에서 엇갈리는 해석의 차이는 당연히 해석자의 가치관에 의해 달라질 수밖에 없다. 앞서 말한 대로 술라의 실험적 삶을 예찬하는 태도나, 술라의 우상파괴적 삶을 비난하는 쪽은 모두 해석자의 개인적 가치관에 따를 수밖에 없다는 뜻이다. 개인의 도덕적 판단에 따른 평가이외에도, 술라가 그렇게 밖에 될 수 없었던 사회적 상황을 비판하면서 술라에게 동정적인 시선을 던질 수도 있다. 또한, 시대적 컨텍스트와의 연관이라는 해석에서는 동일하지만, 술라를 1970년대의 미국적 상황의 산물로 보고, 동정이 아닌 비판적인 시선도 가능하다. 즉, 크리스토퍼 라쉬가 명명하는 1970년대의 미국문화 현상인 "나르시시스트의 문화"의 일부로 보는 것도 가능할 것이다.

3) 『술라』에서의 나르시시즘

앞서 말했듯이 해석은 부득이 해석자의 관점에 따라 달라질 수밖에 없다. 『술라』에 대한 일반적인 평가를 요약했으니, 이제 해설자의 관점에 따라 작품을 분석하려고 한다. 본 분석의 논점은 술라의 삶을 로울 모델(role model) 로 보려는 평가, 즉, 술라의 실험적 삶에 대한 매력에 몰입하는 일부 현상에 대한 반박이다. 다시 말해서 술라의 "실험적" 삶을 단순히 예찬하기 보다는, 그것을 예찬하게 만드는 시대정신과, 시대정신에 대한 무의식적 저항의 표출인 빙산의 일각에 주목할 필요가 있다고 본다.

그러므로, 술라의 실험적 삶을 미국이 스스로 낙관적으로 정의하는 미국적 특성 (평등, 독립성, 자유민주주의 등등...) 으로 단순하게 해석하기보다는, 크리스토퍼 라쉬 (Christopher Lasch) 가 1970년대의 미국 문화를 지칭하듯, "나르시시즘의 문화" 라는 병리적 문화현상으로 보는 것이 가능하다고 본다. 다시 말해, 모리슨의 초기소설 『술라』는 정체성을 탐색하되, 그녀의 정체성 탐색의 양상은 다분히 억압에서 자유로 탈피하는 과정에서 흔히 나타나는 부정적, 파괴적 실험으로 가득한데, 이는 이 소설들이 출판된 1970년대의 시대분위기를 반영하고 있다고 본다. 소위, 해방을 급기야 성취한 자[1]의 나르시시즘적 개인주의가 곳곳에 드러나 있는 것이다. 따라서 술라의 실험적 삶을 인습적인 여성의 틀에 도전하고 개인의 정체성을 찾으려는 긍정적인 시도로만 보기는 어려워진다.

물론, 모리슨의 작품들이 미국문화의 병리적 현상을 그대로 작품 속에 투영만 하는 것은 아니다. 다섯 번째 소설 『빌러비드』에 이르면, 흔히 말하듯 차별이 아닌 차이의 강조로서 흑인성과 여성성을 심도 있게 탐색·정의한 다음, 각각의 정체성 발견을 바탕으로 인종과 젠더를 넘어선, 자유로운 동시에 균형 있는 인간 삶에 대한 비전을 제시하게 된다. 비록 초기 소설에서 1970년대의 시대 분위기를 타고 실험적 인간

1 물론, 흑인들의 지위가 미국의 주류문화에 편입되는 목적을 이뤘다고 볼 수는 없다. 즉, 흑인들의 집단이 완전한 자유를 성취한 것은 결코 아니다. 그럼에도 불구하고 모리슨의 자아탐색이 백인 주류의 문화의 퇴폐적 양상을 띠는 것은 그녀 자신이 흑인이면서도 중산층 가정 출신에 탄탄한 출세가도를 달리고 있었던 개인적인 호황이 무의식적으로 작용한 것인지도 모른다.

에 대한 매료를 이끌어 내고, 그런 실험적 인간이 과연 정체성을 획득할 것인가를 작품 속에서 실험하는 작가적 실험정신을 발휘하고 있긴 하지만, 『술라』의 어딘 가에도 후에 나타날 비전에 대한 암시가 작품의 무의식 속에 잠겨 간간이 수면 위로 떠오르기도 한다. 즉, 후기소설에 나타나는 비전의 씨앗이 초기 나르시시즘의 흙더미 아래, 움트기 전 묻힌 모습으로 찾아 볼 수 있다는 뜻이다.

정체성의 확립은 나와 타자간의 부단한 충돌과 타협을 통해서 공통점과 차이를 구별해 내는 유동적인 과정이다. 이러한 과정에서 중요하고 필수적인 정신적 능력은 바로 공감적 상상력이라고 할 수 있다. 공감적 상상력이란 나의 욕망을 타인 안에서 읽고, 타인의 욕망을 내 안에 투영시킬 수 있는 능력이다. 그러나 나르시시스트는 자기 안이나 자기의 밖이나 오로지 자신의 욕망만이 반영될 뿐이어서 공감하는 능력은 턱없이 부족하고 따라서 올바른 정체성의 확립이란 불가능하다.

1960년대 민권운동 이후, 소수인종과 여성들이 앞다투어 권리를 주장할 때, 백인 주류문화가 나르시시트적으로 타락하고 있음은, 앞에서 언급된 크리스토퍼 라쉬의 『나르시시즘의 문화』에 잘 묘사되어 있다. 라쉬는 나르시시스트적 문화의 특성을 오늘날의 "해방된"(71)인간을 정확히 묘사하는 것으로 보고, "'해방된 자'의 매력, 자신의 상황에 대한 거짓 자각, 성적으로 문란한 범성애, 구강 섹스에의 매료, 거세적인 어머니에 대한 공포, 우울증, 자기 보호적인 천박성, 타인들에 대한 의존의 회피, 슬퍼할 수 없는 능력, 노령과 죽음의 공포 등"(71)을 특성으로 들고 있다. 라쉬는 미국이 1960년대를 지나 목표와 비전을 상실한 백인문화를 이렇게 묘사하고 있는데, 사실상, 1970년대에 대한 이러한 묘사는 70년대에 국한되지 않고, 80년대 90년대를 거쳐 2000대에 이르기까지 미국문화의 한 흐름, 타락한 개인주의의 한 면을 묘사하는데 적절하다고 본다. 이러한 미국문화의 어두운 일면에 대한 지적은 앨런 블룸의 『미국정신의 종말』(1987), 모리스 버만의 『미국문화의 종말』(2000)과

촘스키의 잇단 미국문화 비판과 맥을 함께 하고 있다. 다시 말해, 1970년대의 라쉬의 나르시시즘적 미국문화는 1980년대는 불룸이 비판하는 문화적 상대주의라는 체념적 허무주의로, 1990년대는 버만이 비판하는 소비 지향적인 기업문화의 형태로, 촘스키의 신제국주의 형태로 조금씩 모습을 바꾸면서 변화되지만, 근본적으로 극단적인 자기 중심성이란 면에서는 모두가 나르시시즘적 특성이라고 볼 수 있다는 뜻이다.

건국 초기, 그리고 초기 미국문학에서부터 끈질기게 탐구하는 미국과 개인의 정체성 문제[2]는 결핍이 창조하는 욕망의 형태로 계속되고 있는지도 모른다. 즉, 애초부터 여러 인종 여러 문화가 혼재하여 이를 하나로 묶는 동질성의 결핍은 정체성 탐구로의 욕망을 만들어 냈다는 뜻이다. 그리고 그러한 욕구는 어디까지나 건강한 욕구였다. 개인의 역사에서 의식이 싹트는 청년기에 정체성의 문제가 야기되는 것처럼 미국이 정체성으로 여전히 씨름하고 있음은 결핍된 정체성에 대한 욕망인 동시에 그들 문화의 젊음을 말해주는 것인지도 모른다. 1960년대 이후 소수민족과 여성의 자아 의식이 비로소 싹트면서 정체성의 문제가 크게 대두되었던 것은 바로 제각의 소수문화와 여성문화가 마찬가지로 젊은 청년기에 서 있음을 의미한다. 그렇기 때문에 정체성 탐구와 억압에서의 탈피라는 문제의식에 투철한 미국의 소수인종의 문화는 아직 건강함이 느껴진다. 스크리브너 출판사가 엮어낸 『1970년대 이후의 미국 단편소설집』(1999)은 이와 같은 견해를 뒷받침해 준다. 이 소설집은 미국의 굵직굵직한 상을 이미 받은 바 있는 촉망받는 현대 작가들의 대표작 50편으로 구성되어있는데, 미국문화의 다문화적 특색을 고려하여 각각 인종, 젠더, 그 외 소수그룹의 문화배경을 가진 작가를 고루 안배하려는 노력이 역력하다. 이 작품들을 꼼꼼히 읽어보면 재미있는 특색이 눈에 띤다. 즉, 소설이 일종의 이피퍼니(ephiphany)를

2 미국 소설의 정체성의 대략적인 윤곽은 부산대 정진농 교수의 『미국소설의 정체성 탐구』의 첫 논문 「미국소설의 미국적 특성」에 잘 요약되어 있다.

담고 소설의 재미와 지혜가 번득이는 작품은 대체로 소수민족, 혹은 여성작가들의 작품들이다. 소설의 재미와 지혜라는 것이 반드시 전통적인 일직선상의 소설적 내러티브에서만 생기는 것은 아니다. 비록 내러티브가 섬세하게 꼬여있어도 그 안에 담고있는 소설의 의미가 건강하기 때문에 재미와 지혜를 얻게 되는 것이다. 이에 반해, 소위 백인주류(WASP) 작가들의 작품들을 보면, 뛰어난 예술성에도 불구하고 그 의미는 애매모호하고, 의미해석을 의식적으로 거부하려는 유희성이 많이 눈에 띤다. 그들의 작품들은 더 나은 삶에 대한 뚜렷한 목표의식과 열망, 진지함, 그리고 건강한 투지가 결여되어 있다.

그러나 모든 소수 문화가 변함 없는 건강함을 유지하지 못할 수도 있다. 불룸의 지적대로 제각각의 소수문화가 "권리가 아닌 권력"(35)을 주장하기 시작하면, 다시 말해 그들의 개인주의가 극단적 이기주의로 타락하면, 그의 우려대로 문화적 상대주의는 오히려 폐쇄적인 독선으로 흐르기 쉽다. 너도 옳고 나도 옳다는 상대주의는 교묘하게도 자신의 결점을 은폐하는 장치가 될 수도 있기 때문이다. 이러한 폐쇄적 독선이 바로 나르시시즘이고, 흑인으로서 정체성을 추구하는 술라와 넬, 그리고 쉐드랙이 빠지는 함정이기도 하다.

작품의 주요 인물들이 왜 모두 나르시시스트적인지 먼저 구체적으로 증명할 필요가 있다. 흥미롭게도 쉐드랙, 넬, 술라 (내러티브의 순서에 따라), 모두 한결같이 한번씩 거울이나 물을 들여다보는 장면이 나온다. 거울이든 물이든, 모두는 자신을 반영하는 도구로서, 물에 비친 자신의 모습과 사랑에 빠지는 나르시시스트의 어원적 의미와 상통하는 바가 있다. 쉐드랙이 병원에서 변기의 물에 비친 자신의 모습을 바라보는 장면이 있다. 그 후에도 그는 날마다 강물에서 낚시질하면서 강물에 비친 자신을 들여다보면서 살아간다. 마찬가지로, 루이지애나 여행에서 돌아와 "나다움(Me-ness)"(28)을 성취하리라 결연하게 선언하는 장면에서도 어김없이 넬은 거울에 자신을 비춰보고 있다. 또한 술라 역시 에이젝스와 특별한 감정을 느낀 후 거울을 바라보는 장면이 있다. 거울이나 물을 바라보는 가각의 의미가 항상 똑같은 것은 아니다. 그러나 공통점은 한결같이 그들의 시야는 거울과 물 너머로 뻗어나가지 못하고, 그 공간 안에 갇힌다는 사실이다.

반드시 거울이나 물은 아니더라도, 한정된 공간에 스스로를 가두는 이미지는 여기에서 그치지 않는다. 이바가 마침내 가족의 생계를 웬만큼 해결한 후, 자신의 집의 3층에 스스로를 가두는 행동이나, 오로지 죽을 장소를 위해 이바의 집에 하숙하며 바깥출입을 그만두고 자신의 작은 방에 거처하는 타르 베이비(Tar Baby), 엄마의 컴컴한 자궁 안으로 다시 들어가고 싶어하는 풀룸(Plum), 술라의 임종시 널판자로 못질된 막혀진 창문과 벽안에서 느끼는 그녀의 평화, 물 속 깊은 죽음의 느낌 등, 갑갑하고 막힌, 고립된 공간으로의 욕망이 곳곳에 나타난다. 또한 상징적으로 흡사하게, 세 명의 서로 다른 개체인 듀이를 하나의 이름속에 가두는 행위나, 이상하게도 그들이 더 이상 키가 크지 않아서 소년의 키 안에 갇히는 것 역시, 비슷한 패턴의 이미지라고 볼 수 있다.

물론, 소통의 욕구가 없는 것은 아니다. 막힌 것을 털어 내고, 끊어진 것을 이으려는 노력이 나타나지만 모두 실패하고 만다. 갓난아기의 막힌 변을 통하기 위하여 손가락을 넣는 아비의 노력은 결국 사랑하는 아들을 죽이는 결과로 맺어진다. 소통이 끊어진 흑인 마을과 백인 마을을 잇는 터널의 시공은 결국 많은 사람들의 희생을 요구하면서 실패로 끝나고 만다. 자식을 사랑하지 않았다는 한나의 질책에 대해 자신의 끊어진 사랑을 증명이라도 하듯 창문을 넘어 불타는 한나를 구하려는 이바의 소통 노력도 수포로 돌아간다.

이처럼 『술라』는 막힌 한정된 공간 안에 자족하면서 그 너머를 보지 못하는 나르시시트적 인간들로 가득하다. 그러나 넬, 술라, 쉐드랙이 주요 인물일 수 있는 이유는, 그 이외의 인물들이 나르시시트로 끝까지 남는 반면에 이들은 나르시시즘을 극복하는 작은 여지를 남겨두기 때문이다. 즉, 위의 세 인물이 자신의 정체성을 찾아가는 양상은 다분히 나르시시스트적이지만, 아주 미묘하게 약화시키는(undercut) 장면에서 나르시시즘에 대한 저항을 읽어낼 수가 있는 것이다.

먼전 넬을 살펴보면, 그녀가 충격적인 루이지애나 여행에서 돌아왔을 때, 그녀는 엄마와는 다른 자신을 만들어 보리라고 결심한다. 이때 그녀의 결단은 술라와는 매우 다르다. 넬의 의식을 통해 표현되는 1920장에서 넬은 이렇게 말한다. "'Me,' She murmured. And then, sinking deeper into the guilts, 'I want. . . I want to be. . . wonderful. Oh, Jesus, make me wonderful'"(28-9). 여기서 "죄의식" ("guilts") 라는 표현은 그녀가 음란하다고 생각하는 할머니와 엄마에 대해 느끼는 죄의식을 말한다. 이 죄의식을 깊이 내면화한 넬은, 엄마와 할머니를 죄악시하는 사회의 판단을 그대로 내면화하고 사회가 "멋지다" ("wonderful") 하다고 믿는 또 하나의 사회적 통념을 실천하게 된다. 그래서 충동적인 술라 곁에서 넬은 언제나 이성적이고 침착하여, 호수에 빠져 죽은 아이를 보면서 느끼는 은근한 쾌감을 억누르고 재빠르게 사태를 수습하려는 문제해결사로, 성장하여서는 자신을 필요로 하는 남자의 헌신적인 아내로, 남편이 떠난 후엔 홀로 아이들을 키우는 성실한 가장으로 자신의 정체성을 확립해 간다. 그럼으로써 자신은 엄마와 할머니와는 달리 사회로부터 따돌림 받지 않고, 소위 원만하게 살아갈 수 있음에 큰 자부심을 느낀다. 남편이 떠난 자신은 외롭지만 자신의 선한 노고를 인정해주는 사회가 있기에 스스로 외롭지 않다고 생각한다. 술라가 몸져누운 뒤, 그들이 나누는 다음 대화에서 넬의 정체성이란 것이 다분히 나르시시트적 자기만족에 빠져 있음을 증명해 준다.

[Sula] " . . . I sure did live in this world."
[Nel] "Really" What have you got to show for it?"
[Sula] "Show? To who? Girl, I got my mind. And what goes on init. Which is to say, I got me."
[Nel] "Lonely, ain't it?"

[Sula] "Yes. But my lonely is mine. Now your lonely is somebody else's. Made by somebody else and handed to you. ain't that something? A secondhand lonely." (143)

이 대화에서 보면, 술라는 넬이 본래적인 자아가 원하는 방식으로 살지 못하고, 다른 사람들의 가치를 내면화하여 살았다고 비난하고 있다. 이러한 직설적 비난도 사실이지만, 술라의 비난에 대한 넬의 변명 속에 간접적으로 넬의 자기만족적 자긍심의 허위가 드러나 있다. 즉, 자기야말로 진짜 자아를 획득했다고 말하는 술라에게, 넬은 그 실험적 삶의 대가로 사회로부터 따돌림 받는 외로움이 오히려 실패를 의미하지 않느냐고 되받아 친다. 다시 말해서 자신 삶의 정당성은 바로, 사회가 자신을 따돌리지 않았다는 사실로 증명된다고 믿는 것이다. 삶의 질을 판단하는 준거로서 넬은 사회의 통념과의 동화 정도에 두고 있음이 분명하다. 따라서, 넬의 "Me-ness"란, 자신과 타자간의 아슬아슬한 외줄타기에서 어렵사리 얻어지는 정체성이 아니라, 자신을 타자 안에 전적으로 함몰시키거나, 타자의 욕망에는 무심한 자족적 만족감에서 얻어진 것인데, 넬은 이를 깨닫지 못하고 우월감과 독선에 빠져있다. 술라가 죽은 훨씬 뒤에 이바를 방문해서야 비로소, 경멸하고 미워했던 술라와 자신이 별반 차이가 없음을 깨닫고, 우월감과 독선을 버리게 된다.

위의 대화에서 술라가 하는 말, "I got me"는 그녀의 실험적 탐색을 긍정적으로 평가하는 증거로 흔히 인용된다. 그러나 그녀의 삶은 라쉬의 "해방된 인간"의 전형적인 증상을 보여주고 있기에 에이젝스를 만나기 전 그녀의 삶은 병리적 현상으로 해석하는 것이 오히려 타당하다. 넬 역시 엄마와의 "다름"을 선언하고 성취한다는 면에서 그녀 역시 "해방된 인간"으로 볼 수도 있으나, 해방된 자로서 그녀가 선택하는 삶은 사회의 가치를 그대로 내면화하는 삶인 것이다. 그러나, 술라의 경우는 좀 다르다. 앞서 언급한 대로 우연히 엿들은 엄마의 한 마디와 마찬가지로 우연한 소년의 죽음은 그녀 스스로 고백하듯, 관계와 과거의 자아와의 완전한 결별을 통하여 스스로를 해방시키는 것은 사실이다. 그러나, 해방 이후 그녀가 선택하는 삶은 넬과는 달리, 반사회적인 가치들이다. 그녀의 삶은 사회의 억압적 통념을 넘어선, 어찌 보면 매력적인 삶이다. 평범하게 결혼해서 엉덩이가 펑퍼짐해진 바텀 마을의 다른 여인들과는 달리, 그녀는 서른이 넘은 나이에도 여전히 남자들을 매혹시키는 마술적 몸을 지니고 있다. 그리고 스스로도 "I got me"라고 반박할 수 있을 만큼 자신이 선택한 삶에 자신감이 넘치고 있다. 여러 남자들과의 관계를 통해 자신의 욕구와 쾌락에 충실한 것도 일면 진솔한 삶으로 보일 수 있다. 결혼에 필수적인 독점적 형태의 사랑을 혐오 거부하고, 선과 악의 인위적 정의에 도전하며, 거꾸로 떨어져 파멸하더라도 낙하의 자유로움을 선호하는 술라는 진정 실험적 삶의 온갖 매력을 다 지닌 유혹적인 존재임에 틀림없다. 그리고 이러한 술라의 매력적인 도전정신에 많은 비평가들은 찬사를 보내왔다.

그러나 그녀의 도전은 반사회적 반항으로 인하여 사회질서를 유지하는데 위험한 존재라는 차원을 넘어서서, 그녀의 자아인식 자체에 문제가 있음을 보여준다. 앞서 말했듯이, 정체성이란 자아와 타자간의 부단한 충돌과 타협을 통하여 건전하게 형성되는 것인데, 술라는 자아인식 과정은 나와 타자간의 욕망을 반사하고 투영하는 단계를 거치지 못한, 철저한 고립 안에서 형성된 자아라는 사실이다. 라쉬에 따르면, 그렇게 형성된 자아는 자신의 상황에 대해서 자각하고 있다는 착각에 빠져 있고, 성적으로 문란한 경향이 있고, "거세적인 어머니에 대한 공포, 우울증, 자기 보호적인 천박성, 타인들에 대한 의존의 회피, 슬퍼할 수 있는 능력의 상실, 노령과 죽음의 공포"등의 현상을 보이게 된다. 술라는 이런 현상을 모두가 빠짐없이 보여주고 있다.

우선 술라의 자아인식의 착각과 문란한 성관계는 이미 언급한 바 있고, 그녀의 거세적인 어머니에 대한 공포는, 어린 시절, 자신과 엄마의 경제적인 가장으로서 권위를 지녀왔던 이바를 뚜렷한 이유 없이 양로원으로 쫓아낸다는 사실이다. 자신의 다리를 절단한 대가로 가정을 부양해왔고, 온전한 개인으로 살지 못할 것 같은 자신의 아들을 불태워 죽일 만큼 독선적인 할머니, 그러나 불타는 딸을 살리기 위해 이층에서 뛰어내릴 만큼 지극한 모성을 지닌 이바의 강인함에 대한 본능적 두려움이라고 할 수 있다. 또한 술라의 남성 편력은 다분히 우울증적이어서 자신이 남자들과 끊임없이, 가능하면 많은 관계를 맺으려 하는 것은 슬픔과 비참함을 느끼기 위해서라고 말한다(122). 관계를 통해서 타인에게 나아가려는 욕망대신, 모든 대상은 자신에게도 되돌아오는 메아리처럼 반향으로서만 가치를 지니는 것이다. 타인으로부터 자신을 보호하기 위한 술라의 행위는 자해하는 방법이나 교회에 속옷을 입지 않는 방식으로 뒤틀린 형태로 나타난다. 자신의 엄마가 불에 타죽는 모습을 바라보며 기괴한 웃음을 띠는 술라는 역시 슬퍼할 수 있는 능력을 상실한 사람이다. 특별히, 자신의 절친한 친구의 남편과 동침하는 것이 넬의 마음속에 어떤 파문을 일으킬 지 이해할 수 없는 술라는 매력적인 실험정신을 지나쳐, 도덕적으로 불감증이라는 결론을 내리지 않을 수 없다.

술라와 비슷하게, 자아인식이라는 착각을 거쳐 "국민 자살일"을 제정하는 마을의 광인 쉐드랙도 나르시시스트적 인간이다. 전쟁의 충격 때문에 손이 커지는 착시현상을 경험하는 그는 변기의 물에 비친 확실한 자신의 검은 얼굴을 보고 자신의 존재를 확인하게 된다. 많은 비평가들은 이 순간 쉐드랙이 자아 정체성을 얻게 되고 그러한 인식의 결과로 손의 커지는 착시현상에서 벗어나게 된다고 말한다. 그러한 그의 인식은 정체성이 확립되었다고 해석하기보다는 자신의 존재가 죽지 않고 살아있다는 확인에 불과한 것이다. 즉, 실존에 대한 확인이 아닌, 생존에 대한 확인인 것이다. 마을 사람들로부터의 고립은 콜린 윌슨 식의 "아웃사이더," 지혜인이라기 보다는, 말 그대로 타자와의 충돌을 피함으로써 부단한 대화와 타협을 통한 정체성확립의 과정에서 벗어나 있음을 의미한다. 사람들과의 부대낌 대신, 날마다 강에서 낚시질하는 그는 세상을 포월하여 유유자적하는 동양의 현인과는 다르다. 그의 자아는 강에 반영되는 자신의 얼굴만을 바라보는 까닭에, 타자의 무수한 욕망을 경험하면서 자신의 작음을 인식하고, 그에 따른 자아의 확대를 경험하는 것은 불가능하다. 작품의 말미에서 추운 겨울 끝, 햇볕을 만끽하며 쉐드랙의 "국민자살일" 행렬을 따른 마을사람의 파괴적 결말은 그의 자아 인식이 자신뿐 아니라, 다른 사람들도 오도하고 있었음을 의미한다. 또한 소년의 죽음이후, 살인 장면을 목격했을지도 모른다는 우려로 자신을 방문한 술라를 평생 동안 자신의 연인으로 삼아온 쉐드랙의 모습은 그가 여전히 환상 속에 살고 있었음을 의미한다. 술라의 주검을 보고 "항상" 존재한다는 것이 불가능한 환상이었음을 알게 된다. 죽음에 대한 공포를 제어하기 위한 방편으로 그가 제정한 "국민자살일"은 이제 아무런 소용이 없고, 이제 술라의 무덤을 매일 방문하면서 죽음을 매일 대면하는 일로 소일하고, 낚시 대신 마을에서 쓰레기 버리는 일을 하는 그는 이제 현실인식이 한 단계 성숙해진 듯하다.

지금까지 보면, 주요 인물들 중 넬과 쉐드랙은 작품의 끝에서 어느 정도 변화하고 성숙하는 모습을 보이지만, 술라의 경우는 죽는 순간까지 넬의 독선을 비난하고 자신을 옹호하는 듯해 보인다. 그러나 술라도 변화한다. 에이젝스와의 만남 후, 술라가 변화하는 장면을, 술라의 실험정신을 예찬하는 비평가들은 술라의 사랑이 예전의 자유로운 독립적 사랑으로부터 독점적이고 의존적인 사랑으로 변화한 흔적이고 그녀의 정체성 획득이 실패한 지점이라고 말한다. 물론, "술라는 독점이 무엇인지 발견하기 시작했다"(131)고 다분히 전지적인 목소리로 쓰여진 직접적 언설이 있긴 하다. 그리고 그 전지적 화자에게 포착된 술라의 변화는, 집으로 찾아올 에이젝스를 맞을 준비로 녹색 리본을 머리에 달고 목욕탕의 바닥을 깨끗하게 닦는 등, 흔히 남자의 마음을 잡으려는 여성의 행동으로 묘사된다. 따라서 이러한 행동은 실험적 삶을 예찬하는 사람들에겐 참을 수 없이 굴욕적인 행동이고, 술라는 마침내 이런 굴욕적인 변화로 인하여 죽음을 맞는다고 말한다.

그러나 술라의 갈망은 단순히 남자의 마음을 사로잡고 자신에게 머물게 하려는 독점적 행동 그 이상의 의미가 있다. 이것은 직접적 언술로 표현되진 않지만, 에이젝스와의 성관계가 예외적으로 길게 묘사되는 장면들에 가득한 상징들 속에서 찾아 볼 수 있다. 작품 속에 이탤릭으로 된 부분만, 길지만 인용한다.

> 노란 색 쎄무 가죽을 집어들고 그의 뼈에 대고 세게 문지르면, 바로 그의 광대뼈 불쑥 나온 곳을 문지르면, 검은 색이 어느 정도 없어질 거야. 검은 것은 쎄무 가죽 속으로 벗겨져 버리고, 그리곤 그 밑으로 황금빛 나무 잎사귀가 나타나겠지. 그 황금빛 잎사귀는 검은 빛 사이로 반짝거리고 있을 거야. 분명히 거기에 있을 거야...
>
> 그리고 이번엔 손톱 다듬는 줄이나, 할머니의 낡은 손톱 깎는 칼을 꺼내서 그래. 그것이면 될 거야 황금을 긁어내 버려야지. 그러면 황금이 떨어져 나가고 하얏 석고가 나타날 거야. 그 석고야 말로 얼굴의 윤곽을 만들어주는 것이지. 그 석고 때문에 입가의 미소가 눈에 닿지 않는 거야. 석고야 말로 얼굴 전체가 웃는 것을 막는 중심이 되는 것이다.
>
> 그리곤 이번엔 끌과 작은 망치를 들고 하얀 석고를 깨버리는 거다. 송곳아래 깨지는 얼음처럼, 석고는 깨져 버리겠지. 그 깨진 틈 사이로 기름진 흙이 보일 것이다. 자갈이나 나무뿌리가 섞이지 않는 기름진 옥토 말이다. 이 흙이야말로 너의 향기지.
>
> 너의 흙 속으로 내 손을 깊숙이 넣을 거야. 그래서 그 흙을 집어 올리고 내 손가락 사이로 체 치듯 떨어뜨리는 거다. 그리고 그 흙의 따뜻함과 그 밑에 이술 맺힌 서늘함을 느낄 것이다.
>
> 그리고 너의 흙에 물을 주어 더욱 기름지고 촉촉하게 만들 거야. 그렇지만 물을 얼마나 줘야 하지? 물을 촉촉하게 하려면 물의 양을 얼마나 해야하지? 내 물이 출렁이지 않으려면 또 흙은 양은 얼마큼 필요한 것일까? 그리고 언제, 우리 둘이 섞어 진흙이 될 수 있을까? (130-1)

—

검은 피부, 황금빛 잎사귀, 하얀 석고 등은 타자의 가장 정직한 진수에 다가가는데 장애가 되는 것들을 의미한다고 볼 수 있다. 그것을 하나하나 파괴하는 작업은 말 그대로 파괴적이다. 부드러운 쎄무 가죽에서 시작하여 금속성의 끌과 망치로 부수는 작업은 분명 파괴적이지만, 확실한 목표를 지니고 있다. 검고, 노랗고, 하얀 표면—어쩌면 인종의 빛깔을 의미할 수도 있는 겉 표면의 빛깔—그리고 딱딱한 것들의 표면아래 있는 흙과의 결합이 최종 목표다. 즉 파괴는 창조를 위한 것이다. 흙은 인간의 시원과 끝이며, 인간의 본질이라는 상징적 의미를 지닌다고 볼 수 있다. 즉 인종, 지위, 역할 등의 겉모양으로 규정하는 정체성이 아니라, 가장 본질적 진수에 다가가고자 하는 갈망으로 해석할 수 있다는 뜻이다. 그리고 마지막 물과 흙이 결합하는 장면은 본질적 관계에 대한 갈망으로 또한 해석할 수 있다. 물과 흙이 적절히 합쳐져서 진흙이 되면, 드디어 마음대로 형상을 빚을 수 있는 창조성이 생성된다. 진흙을 만드는데, 흙과 물의 양을 어떻게 조절할 것인가에 대한 염려는 자아와 타자와의 결합과 관계맺음이 아슬아슬한 외줄타기 곡예처럼 절묘한 균형과 조화를 필요로 함을 의미한다.

결국 술라는 끝까지 독선적 자아를 주장하는 듯하지만, 위의 독백을 보면 그녀의 갈망이 타자와의 진실한 결합을 향하고 있음이 분명해진다. 그렇게 본다면, 술라가 죽기 직전, 넬에게 "I got me"라고 말하는 것은 예전 실험적이고 파괴적 자아의 성취를 의미하는 것이 아니라, 에이젝스와의 관계에서 느꼈던 갈망의 확인 의미하는 것인지도 모른다. 비록 에이젝스가 이를 깨닫지 못하고 떠나기 때문에 실질적이고 지속적인 성취는 이루지 못하지만, 최소한 자신이 원했던 것이 타자와의 관계임을 확인하고 이를 상징을 통해 드러내고 있다고 본다.

그러므로 소설 『술라』는 1970년대 나르시시즘적 자아를 극한으로 실험하는 소설인 동시에, 20세기 후반부터 현재에 이르기까지 미국사회를 관통하는 특성인 나르시시즘의 한계를 깨닫고 후기 소설에게 활짝

개화할 모리슨의 삶의 비전이 상징을 통해 간접적으로 드러난 소설이라고 결론짓는다. 분명히 실험적 소설이긴 하나, 술라의 실험적 삶을 마냥 찬양 일변도로 보는 견해는 문제가 있다는 말이다. 이제까지 말했듯이 술라의 삶은 나르시시즘적 자아의 극한이고, 모리슨은 그런 삶의 한계를 짚고 다른 대안을 상징적으로 보여주고 있는 것이다.

모리슨은 인종과 젠더라는 시대의 화두를 자신의 작가적 문제의식으로 삼으면서도, 전체의 맥락을 놓치지 않으려는 보편성을 지니기 때문에 그녀의 작품은 언제나 즐거운 만남이다. 게다가, 내러티브를 이끄는 치열한 산문정신과 그 밑에서 말갛게 떠오르는 서정적 시성은 모리슨을 읽는 기쁨을 배가한다.

*위에서 표시된 『술라』의 쪽 번호는 1982년 풀룸(Plume) 판에 근거한다.

Sula

"Nobody knew my rose of the world
but me. . . . I had too much glory.
They don't want glory like that
in nobody's hearts."
— *The Rose Tattoo*[1]

Part One

In that place, where they tore the nightshade and blackberry patches from their roots to make room for the Medallion City Golf Course, there was once a neighborhood.[2] It[3] stood in the hills above the valley town of Medallion and spread all the way to the river. It is called the suburbs now, but when black people lived there it was called the Bottom[4]. One road, shaded by beeches, oakes, maples and chestnuts, connected it to the valley[5]. The beeches are gone now, and so are[6] the pear trees where children sat and yelled down through the blossoms to passersby. Generous funds have been allotted to level the

1 테네시 윌리엄스의 희곡 *The Rose Tatto* (1951)에서 발췌된 인용문으로 과거에 대한 향수와 상실감이 진하게 배어 있다.

2 벨라도나(가짓과 식물)와 블루베리가 자라는 밭을 뿌리 채 뽑아내고 메달리온 시립골프장을 만들었던 그 장소에 한때는 사람들이 살고 있었다.

3 여기서 It는 앞의 neighborhood, 즉 사람들을 가리킴.

4 The Bottom: 고유명사이지만 "밑바닥"이란 뜻인데, 대체로 가장 빈곤하고 소외된 지역이란 의미를 함축하고 있다.

5 골짜기로 마을을 연결하는 길 하나가 있었는데, 이는 너도밤나무와 참나무, 그리고 단풍나무와 밤나무가 우거져 있는 길이었다.

6 도치된 문장으로, 배나무도 없어졌다는 뜻임.

stripped and faded buildings that clutter the road from Medallion up to the golf course[7]. They are going to raze the Time and a Half Pool Hall[8], where feet in long tan shoes once pointed down from chair rungs[9]. A steel ball[10] will knock to dust Irene's Palace of Cosmetology, where women used to lean their heads on sink trays and doze while Irene lathered Nu Nile[11] into their hair. Men in khaki work clothes will pry loose the slats of Reba's Grill[12], where the owner cooked in her hat because she couldn't remember the ingredients without it.

There will be nothing left of the Bottom[13] (the footbridge that crossed the river is already gone), but perhaps it is just as well, since it Wasn't a town anyway: just a neighborhood where on quiet days people in valley houses could hear singing sometimes, banjos sometimes, and, if a valley man happened to have business up in those hills—collecting rent or insurance payments—he might see a dark woman in flowered dress doing a bit of cakewalk[14], a bit of black bottom[15], a bit of "messing around" to the lively notes of a mouth organ[16]. Her bare feet would raise the saffron dust[17] that floated down on the

7 메달리온에서 골프장까지 연결되는 길에는 칠이 벗겨지고 퇴색한 건물들이 어지럽게 서 있었는데, 많은 돈을 들여 이 건물들을 허물어뜨렸다.

8 The Time and a Half Pool Hall: 바텀 마을의 공동회관으로서 마을 사람들이 모여들던 곳을 의미한다.

9 기다란 황갈 색 구두를 신은 발이 의자 밑의 가로대에 걸쳐 있던 곳.

10 건물을 무너뜨릴 때 쓰는 커다랗고 둥그런 강철 덩어리를 말함.

11 Nu Nile: 샴프의 이름

12 레베카 그릴(식당이름)의 지붕을 뜯어낼 것이다.

13 "밑바닥" 마을의 아무 것도 남지 않을 것이다.

14 일종의 스텝댄스

15 엉덩이를 흔들며 춤추는 모양.

16 입으로 흥얼거리는 소리에 맞춰 그저 몸을 흔들어대는 모습.

17 노란색(사프란 색) 먼지

coveralls and bunion-split shoes[18] of the man breathing music in and out of his harmonica. The black people watching her would laugh and rub their knees, and it would be easy for the valley man to hear the laughter and not notice the adult pain[19] that rested somewhere under the eyelids, somewhere under their head rags and soft felt hats, somewhere in the palm of the hand, somewhere behind the frayed lapels[20], somewhere in the sinew's curve[21]. He'd have to stand in the back of Greater Saint Matthew's and let the tenor's voice dress him in silk, or touch the hands of the spoon carvers (who had not worked in eight years) and let the fingers that danced on wood kiss his skin.[22] Otherwise the pain would escape him even though the laughter was part of the pain.

A shucking, knee-slapping, wet-eyed laughter that could even describe and explain how they came to be where they were.[23]

A joke. A nigger joke. That was the way it[24] got started. Not the town, of course, but that part of town where the Negroes lived, the part they called the Bottom in spite of the fact that it was up in the hills. Just a nigger joke. The kind[25] white folks

18 coverall: 벨트가 달린 내리닫이 작업복. bunion-split: 엄지발가락 부분이 떨어진 신발.

19 어른들만의 고통.

20 닳아빠진 옷깃

21 불쑥 드러난 곡선의 힘줄

22 그는 마태오 성당의 뒤뜰에 서서 비단처럼 부드러운 테너음성에 감싸여 보거나, 지난 8년 동안 손을 놓은 스푼 깎는 사람의 손을 만져 보거나, 나무 위에서 춤추는 (고된 나무일로 거칠어진) 그의 손가락이 피부에 닿도록 해서야 비로소 그 고통을 느낄 수 있었을 것이다.

23 호들갑스럽고, 무릎을 치고, 눈물까지 찔끔거리며 웃어대는 그 웃음은 바로 그들이 왜 거기까지 오게 되었는지를 설명하고 묘사해주는 것이었다. (이 문장은 fragment 이지만 위처럼 해석해야 매끄럽다.)

24 여기서 it는 neighborhood를 가리킴.

tell when the mill closes down and they're looking for a little comfort somewhere. The kind[26] colored folks tell on themselves when the rain doesn't come, or comes for weeks, and they're looking for a little comfort somehow.

A good[27] white farmer promised freedom and a piece of bottom land to his slave if he would perform some very difficult chores. When the slave completed the work, he asked the farmer to keep his end of the bargain[28]. Freedom was easy[29] — the farmer had no objection to that. But he didn't want to give up any land. So he told the slave that he was very sorry that he had to give him valley land. He had hoped to give him a piece of the Bottom. The slave blinked and said he thought valley land was bottom land. The master said, "Oh, no! See those hills? That's bottom land, rich and fertile."

"But It's high up in the hills," said the slave.

"High up from us," said the master, "but when God looks down, It's the bottom. That's why we call it so. It's the bottom of heaven — best land there is."

So the slave pressed his master to try to get him some[30]. He preferred it[31] to the valley. And it was done. The nigger got the hilly land, where planting was backbreaking, where the soil slid down and washed away the seeds, and where the wind lingered

25 kind와 white 사이에 that(관계대명사)가 생략 된 것으로 보아 해석함. 즉, 방앗간이 문을 닫고 이제 다른 곳에 가서 살아야 할 때, 백인들이 말하는 종류의 농담. 문장은 역시 fragment이다.

26 주석 24번과 같은 방법으로 해석함.

27 "good"이란 형용사는 아이러니칼하게 쓰임. 일을 시키고도 약속을 지키지 않은 백인들의 악함을 아이러니컬하게 비판함.

28 약속된 거래를 지킬 것을 농부에게 요청했다.

29 노예에게 자유를 주는 것은 어렵지 않았다.

30 땅을 좀 얻을 수 있도록 노예는 주인을 압박했다.

31 it는 Bottom을 가리킴

all through the winter.

Which accounted for the fact that white people lived on the rich valley floor in that little river town in Ohio[32], and the blacks populated the hills above it, taking small consolation in the fact that every day they could literally look down on the white folks.

Still, it was lovely up in the Bottom. After the town grew and the farm land turned into a village and the village into a town and the streets of Medallion were hot and dusty with progress, those heavy trees that sheltered the shacks up in the Bottom were wonderful to see. And the hunters who went there sometimes wondered in private if maybe the white farmer was right after all[33]. Maybe it was the bottom of heaven.

The black people would have disagreed, but they had no time to think about it. They were mightily preoccupied with earthly things — and each other, wondering even as early as 1920 what Shadrack was all about, what that little girl Sula who grew into a woman in their town was all about, and what they themselves were all about, tucked up there in the Bottom.[34]

---

32 그리하여 백인들은 오하이오의 작은 강물이 흐르는 비옥한 골짜기에 자리를 잡게 되었던 것이다. 문두의 Which는 앞의 단락, 전체를 가리킴.

33 가끔 그곳을 지나는 사냥꾼들은 속으로 백인 농부의 말이 옳았는지도 모른다고 생각했다. 즉, 흑인노예에게 "밑바닥" 지역이 비옥하다고 속였는데, 실제로 그 곳이 아름답고 비옥했다는 뜻임.

34 먼 옛날 1920년에 조차, 쉐드랙이 도대체 누구인지, 이 마을에서 장성한 작은 소녀 술라가 누구인지, 이 밑바닥에 틀어박혀 살고 있는 그들 모두가 대체 누구인지 의아해하면서 오직 일상적인 일에만 골몰해 있었다.

1919

Except for World War II, nothing ever interfered with the celebration of National Suicide Day. It had taken place every January third since 1920, although Shadrack, its founder, was for many years the only celebrant. Blasted and permanently astonished by the events of 1917, he had returned to Medallion handsome but ravaged, and even the most fastidious people in the town sometimes caught themselves dreaming of what he must have been like a few years back before he went off to war. A young man of hardly twenty, his head full of nothing and his mouth recalling the taste of lipstick[1], Shadrack had found himself in December, 1917, running with his comrades across a field in France. It was his first encounter with the enemy and he didn't know whether his company was running toward them or away[2]. For several days they had been marching, keeping close to a stream that was frozen at its edges. At one point they crossed it[3], and no sooner had he stepped foot on the other side than the day was adangle with shouts and explosions[4]. Shellfire was all around him, and though he knew that this was something called *it*, he could not muster up the proper feeling —the feeling that would accommodate *it*[5]. He expected to

1 쉐드랙을 수식하는 말. 쉐드랙은 텅 빈 머리 속에다 계집애의 립스틱의 맛만 떠올리는 스무살도 채 안된 젊은이였다.

2 그의 동료가 적을 향해 뛰어가는지, 혹은 도망가 버리는 것인지 알지 못했다.

3 stream을 가리킴

4 시냇가의 저편으로 발을 내딛자마자, 그 날 하루는 온통 고함과 폭발음으로 가득했다.

be terrified or exhilarated — to feel *something* very strong. In fact, he felt only the bite of a nail in his boot, which pierced the ball of his foot whenever he came down on it[6]. The day was cold enough to make his breath visible[7], and he wondered for a moment at the purity and whiteness of his own breath among the dirty, gray explosions surrounding him. He ran, bayonet fixed[8], deep in the great sweep of men flying across this field[9]. Wincing at the pain in his foot, he turned his head a little to the right and saw the face of a soldier near him fly off[10]. Before he could register shock, the rest of the soldier's head disappeared under the inverted soup bowl of his helmet[11]. But stubbornly, taking no direction from the brain, the body of the headless soldier ran on, with energy and grace, ignoring altogether the drip and slide of brain tissue down its back[12].

When Shadrack opened his eyes he was propped up in a small bed. Before him on a tray was a large tin plate divided into three triangles[13]. In one triangle was rice, in another meat, and

5 이것이 바로 "그것," 즉, 전투라는 사실을 알면서도, "그것"을 이해해서 수용할 적절한 느낌을 이끌어낼 수 없었다.

6 그가 느낄 수 있는 오로지, 신발에 박힌 못에 발이 닿을 때마다 발바닥을 찌르는 그 느낌뿐이었다.

7 날씨가 추워서 입김이 하얗게 보였다.

8 총검을 세운 채

9 들판을 가로질러 휙휙 날아가는 사람들의 거대한 물결 깊숙한 곳에서

10 fly off: 증발해 버리다.

11 충격을 미처 인식하기도 전에, 그 군인의 나머지 머리 부분이 뒤집어진 국그릇 모양의 헬멧아래서 아예 사라져 버렸다.

12 두뇌의 지시를 받지 않는 상태에서, 머리가 잘려나간 군인의 몸은 그래도 끈질기게 계속 달리고 있었다. 여전히 힘이 넘치고 우아한 모습으로, 등뒤에 두뇌의 남은 조직이 흘러내리는 것에 아랑곳하지 않고 달리고 있었다.

in the third stewed tomatoes. A small round depression held a cup of whitish liquid[14]. Shadrack stared at the soft colors that filled these triangles: the lumpy whiteness of rice, the quivering blood tomatoes, the grayish-brown meat. All their repugnance was contained in the neat balance of the triangles — a balance that soothed him, transferred some of its equilibrium to him[15]. Thus reassured that the white, the red and the brown would stay where they were — would not explode or burst forth from their restricted zones[16] — he suddenly felt hungry and looked around for his hands. His glance was cautious at first, for he had to be very careful — anything could be anywhere. Then he noticed two lumps[17] beneath the beige blanket on either side of his hips. With extreme care he lifted one arm and was relieved to find his hand attached to his wrist[18]. He tried the other and found it also. Slowly he directed one hand toward the cup and, just as he was about to spread his fingers, they began to grow in higgledy-piggledy fashion like Jack's beanstalk all over the tray and the bed[19]. With a shriek he closed his eyes and thrust his huge growing hands under the covers. Once

---

13 그의 앞에 놓인 쟁반 위에는 세 개의 삼각형으로 나눠진 커다란 함석 접시가 놓여 있었다.

14 함석 그릇 안, 작고 동그랗게 옴폭 들어간 곳엔 희끄무레한 액체가 담긴 컵이 놓여 있었다.

15 음식들은 모두 맛없어 보였지만, 삼각형의 가지런한 균형 안에 담겨 있어서, 그의 마음을 달래주었고, 마음의 균형을 어느 정도 잡아 주었다.

16 하얀 것, 빨간 것, 갈색 음식은 바로 제자리에 있으리라, 제한된 장소를 떠나 폭발하거나 터져 버리지 않으리라, 그가 확신했을 때.

17 그의 두 손을 의미함.

18 조심스럽게 한 손을 들어올려, 손이 손목에 붙어 있는 것을 보고는 안심했다.

19 손가락을 막 펴려고 했을 때, 손가락은 마치 잭의 콩나무처럼 뒤죽박죽 쟁반과 침대위로 커져나가기 시작했다.

out of sight they seemed to shrink back to their normal size[20]. But the yell had brought a male nurse.

"Private?[21] We're not going to have any trouble today, are we? Are we, Private?"

Shadrack looked up at a balding man dressed in a green-cotton jacket and trousers. His hair was parted low on the right side[22] so that some twenty or thirty yellow hairs could discreetly cover the nakedness of his head.

"come on. Pick up that spoon. Pick it up, Private. Nobody is going to feed you forever."

Sweat slid from Shadrack's armpits down his sides. He could not bear to see his hands grow again and he was frightened of the voice in the apple-green suit.

"Pick it up, I said. There's no point to this . . . " The nurse reached under the cover for Shadrack's wrist to pull out the monstrous hand[23]. Shadrack jerked it back and overturned the tray. In panic he raised himself to his knees and tried to fling off and away his terrible fingers[24], but succeeded only in knocking the nurse into the next bed.

When they bound Shadrack into a straitjacket[25], he was both relieved and grateful, for his hands were at last hidden and confined to whatever size they had attained.

Laced and silent in his small bed, he tried to tie the loose

---

20 일단 시선을 거두자, 두 손은 원래 크기로 줄어드는 것 같았다.

21 미국 육군에서는 이등병을 말하는데, 위생병이 쉐드랙을 부르는 호칭이다.

22 대머리라서 오른쪽 밑으로 가르마를 탔다는 말임.

23 위생병은 쉐드랙이 숟가락을 집어들도록 담요 밑에 놓인 손을 당기려고 쉐드랙의 손목을 잡으려 했다.

24 공포에 사로잡혀 무릎을 들어 올려 잔뜩 웅크리고는 자기 자신의 무시무시한 손가락을 제치려고 했다.

25 straitjacket: 미친 사람이나 거친 죄수에게 입히는 죄수복

cords in his mind[26]. He wanted desperately to see his own face and connect it with the word "private" — the word the nurse (and the others who helped bind him) had called him. "Private" he thought was something secret, and he wondered why they looked at him and called him a secret. Still, if his hands behaved as they had done, what might he expect from his face? The fear and longing were too much for him, so he began to think of other things. That is, he let his mind slip into whatever cave mouths of memory it chose[27].

He saw a window that looked out on a river which he knew was full of fish. Someone was speaking softly just outside the door. . .

Shadrack's earlier violence had coincided with a memorandum from the hospital executive staff in reference to the distribution of patients in high-risk areas[28]. There was clearly a demand for space. The priority or the violence earned Shadrack his release, $217 in cash, a full suit of clothes and copies of very official- looking papers.

When he stepped out of the hospital door the grounds[29] overwhelmed him: the cropped shrubbery, the edged lawns, the undeviating walks[30]. Shadrack looked at the cement stretches[31]: each one leading clearheadedly to some presumably desirable

26 작은 침대에 묶여져 잠잠한 가운데, 그의 마음 속에 풀려진 기억의 끈을 다시 묶어보려 애썼다.

27 기억이라는 동굴의 어느 입구든지 마음이 제멋대로 향하도록 내버려두었다.

28 쉐드랙의 이와 같은 폭력적 행동을 보면, 위험한 환자들은 격리 수용하자고 말했던 병원 관계자의 말이 일리가 있었음을 증명했다.

29 grounds: 병원 구내를 의미함

30 잘 깎인 관목과 잔디, 반듯반듯한 길.

31 쭉 뻗은 시멘트 길들을 말함

destination. There were no fences, no warnings, no obstacles at all between concrete and green grass, so one could easily ignore the tidy sweep of stone[32] and cut out[33] in another direction — a direction of one's own.

Shadrack stood at the foot of the hospital steps watching the heads of trees tossing ruefully but harmlessly, since their trunks were rooted too deeply in the earth to threaten him[34]. Only the walks made him uneasy. He shifted his weight, wondering how he could get to the gate without stepping on the concrete. While plotting his course — where he would have to leap, where to skirt a clump of bushes — a loud guffaw startled him[35]. Two men were going up the steps. Then he noticed that there were many people about, and that he was just now seeing them, or else they had just materialized[36]. They were thin slips, like paper dolls floating down the walks[37]. Some were seated in chairs with wheels, propelled by other paper figures from behind. All seemed to be smoking, and their arms and legs curved in the breeze[38]. A good high wind would pull them up and away and they would land perhaps among the tops of the trees[39].

---

32 단정하게 뻗은, 돌로 만든 길을 무시하고.

33 다른 방향으로 벗어나다.

34 나무가 바람에 심하게 흔들리는 모양을 바라본다. 그러나 나무뿌리가 든든히 박혀 있으니 걱정할 필요가 없다고 안심함.

35 어느 길로 갈 것인지 계획하고 있는데 — 어디에서 펄쩍 뛰고, 또 덤불을 피할려면 어디로 가야할지 — 갑자기 들리는 커다란 너털웃음에 그는 깜짝 놀랐다.

36 그렇지 않으면, 그 사람들은 방금 어디선가 솟아난지도 모를 일이었다.

37 그들은 마치 보도 위에 둥둥 떠다니는 종이인형처럼, 실팍한 젊은이들이었다.

38 그들의 팔과 다리는 미풍에 휘어져 있었다.

39 바람이 조금만 세게 불어도 그들의 몸은 붕 떠올라 나무 꼭대기에 내려앉을 것만 같았다. (가정법문장임)

Shadrack took the plunge[40]. Four steps and he was on the grass heading for the gate. He kept his head down to avoid seeing the paper people swerving and bending here and there, and he lost his way. When he looked up, he was standing by a low red building separated from the main building by a covered walkway. From somewhere came a sweetish smell which reminded him of something painful. He looked around for the gate and saw that he had gone directly away from it[41] in his complicated journey over the grass. Just to the left of the low building was a graveled driveway that appeared to lead outside the grounds[42]. He trotted quickly to it and left, at last, a haven of more than a year, only eight days of which he fully recollected[43].

Once on the road, he headed west. The long stay in the hospital had left him weak — too weak to walk steadily on the gravel shoulders of the road[44]. He shuffled, grew dizzy, stopped for breath, started again, stumbling and sweating but refusing to wipe his temples, still afraid to look at his hands. Passengers in dark, square cars shuttered their eyes at what they took to be a drunken man.

The sun was already directly over his head when he came to a town. A few blocks of shaded streets and he was already at its heart — a pretty, quietly regulated downtown[45].

---

40 과감히 앞으로 나아갔다.

41 it: 문을 의미함.

42 나즈막한 빌딩의 왼쪽으로 자갈이 깔린 차도가 보였는데, 구내 밖으로 나가는 길처럼 보였다.

43 1년이 넘게 병원에 입원해 있었고, 그가 의식을 차린 지는 겨우 8일 되었음을 알 수 있다.

44 the gravel shoulders of the road: 자갈이 깔린 도로변

45 명사 "A few blocks of shaded streets" 다음에 등위접속사인 "and"로 연결되

Exhausted, his feet clotted with pain[46], he sat down at the curbside to take off his shoes. He closed his eyes to avoid seeing his hands and fumbled with the laces of the heavy high-topped shoes[47]. The nurse had tied them into a double knot[48], the way one docs for children, and Shadrack, long unaccustomed to the manipulation of intricate things, could not get them loose. Uncoordinated[49], his fingernails tore away at the knots. He fought a rising hysteria that was not merely anxiety to free his aching feet; his very life depended on the release of the knots. Suddenly without raising his eyelids, he began to cry. Twenty-two years old, weak, hot, frightened, not daring to acknowledge the fact that he didn't even know who or what he was. . . with no past, no language, no tribe, no source, no address book, no comb, no pencil, no clock, no pocket handkerchief, no rug, no bed, no can opener, no faded postcard, no soap, no key, no tobacco pouch, no soiled underwear and nothing nothing nothing to do. . . he was sure of one thing only: the unchecked monstrosity of his hands[50]. He cried soundlessly at the curbside of a small Midwestern town wondering where the window was, and the river, and the soft voices just outside the door. . .

Through his tears he saw the fingers joining the laces,

는 것이 문법적으로는 맞지 않지만 모리슨의 텍스트에서 자주 나타나는 문형이다. 해석은, "그늘진 거리를 몇 블럭 걸어가니 그는 이미 마을의 한복판에 서 있었다. 아름답고 조용한, 잘 정돈된 중심가였다."

46 고통으로 엉겨 붙은 발. 피가 엉겨붙고 고통스럽다는 뜻인데, 이를 짧게 표현함.

47 fumbled...: 발목이 높이 올라오는 무거운 구두 끈을 풀려고 만지작거리고 있었다.

48 두 겹으로 맨 매듭.

49 한 목적을 위해 근육이 잘 작동될 수 없는 상태, 즉, 신발 끈을 푸는데 몸이 제대로 집중하지 못하는 상태를 말한다.

50 괴물처럼 자라는 손을 제어할 수 없다는 사실.

tentatively at first, then rapidly. The four fingers of each hand fused into the fabric, knotted themselves and zigzagged in and out of the tiny eyeholes[51].

By the time the police drove up, Shadrack was suffering from a blinding headache[52], which was not abated by the comfort he felt when the policemen pulled his hands away from what he thought was a permanent entanglement with his shoelaces. They took him to jail, booked him for vagrancy and intoxication, and locked him in a cell[53]. Lying on a cot, Shadrack could only stare helplessly at the wall, so paralyzing was the pain in his head[54]. He lay in this agony for a long while and then realized he was staring at the painted-over letters[55] of a command to fuck himself. He studied the phrase as the pain in his head subsided.

Like moonlight stealing under a window shade an idea insinuated itself: his earlier desire to see his own face[56]. He looked for a mirror; there was none. Finally, keeping his hands carefully behind his back he made his way to the toilet bowl and peeped in. The water was unevenly lit by the sun so he could make nothing out[57]. Returning to his cot he took the blanket and covered his head, rendering the water dark enough to see his reflection[58]. There in the toilet water he saw a grave black

51 양손의 각각 네 개의 손가락이 신발 끈과 합쳐져서 스스로를 묶으면서, 신발 끈이 작은 구멍 속으로 들락날락 거렸다.

52 아찔한 두통

53 취한 채 집 없이 떠도는 죄목으로 감옥으로 데려가 가두었다.

54 so 이하는 도치된 문장. 머리 속의 고통은 멎어가고 있었다.

55 글자위로 페인트가 칠해졌으나 글씨가 보이는 상태를 말함.

56 창문의 그늘 밑으로 스미는 달빛처럼, 자신을 얼굴을 보고 싶다는 예전의 생각이 문득 다시 떠올랐다.

57 태양 빛이 고르지 않아서 물에 그의 얼굴을 비춰볼 수 없었다.

58 물에 비치는 자신을 모습을 볼 수 있도록, 머리에 담요를 뒤집어쓰고 물 주변을 어둡게 만들었다.

face. A black so definite, so unequivocal, it astonished him[59]. He had been harboring a skittish[60] apprehension that he was not real — that he didn't exist at all. But when the blackness greeted him with its indisputable presence, he wanted nothing more[61]. In his joy he took the risk of letting one edge of the blanket drop[62] and glanced at his hands. They were still. Courteously still.

Shadrack rose and returned to the cot, where he fell into the first sleep of his new life. A sleep deeper than the hospital drugs; deeper than the pits of plums, steadier than the condor's wing; more tranquil than the curve of eggs[63].

The sheriff looked through the bars at the young man with the matted hair[64]. He had read through his prisoner's papers[65] and hailed a farmer. When Shadrack awoke, the sheriff handed him back his papers and escorted him to the back of a wagon. Shadrack got in and in less than three hours he was back in Medallion, for he had been only twenty-two miles from his window, his river, and his soft voices just outside the door.

In the back of the wagon, supported by sacks of squash and hills of pumpkins[66], Shadrack began a struggle that was to

59 너무나 분명한, 너무나 확실한 검은 얼굴이 그를 놀라게 했다.

60 skittish: 조심스러운

61 자신이 흑인이라는 사실이 의심할 여지없는 확실함으로 인식되자, 더 이상 원하는 것이 없었다.

62 기쁨에 넘쳐 담요의 한 쪽 끝을 감히 내려놓고 자신의 손을 바라보았다.

63 모리슨 특유의 섬세한 감성이 느껴지는 묘사다. "병원의 수면제보다 더 깊은 잠, 자두 속 씨보다 깊고, 콘도르 독수리의 날개 짓처럼 천천히, 그리고 달걀의 곡선처럼 고요한 잠을 잘 수 있었다."

64 헝클어진 머리

65 병원에서 작성한 쉐드랙의 병에 관한 기록.

66 긴 호박이 든 자루와 높이 쌓인 둥근 호박 더미에 기대어.

last for twelve days, a struggle to order and focus experience. It had to do with making a place for fear as a way of controlling it[67]. He knew the smell of death and was terrified of it, for he could not anticipate it[68]. It was not death or dying that frightened him but the unexpectedness of both. In sorting it all out, he hit on the notion that if one day a year were devoted to it, everybody could get it out of the way and the rest of the year would be safe and free. In this manner he instituted National Suicide Day[69].

On the third day of the new year, he walked through the Bottom down Carpenter's Road with a cowbell and a hangman's rope[70] calling the people together. Telling them that this was their only chance to kill themselves or each other.

At first the people in the town were frightened; they knew Shadrack was crazy but that did not mean that he didn't have any sense or, even more important, that he had no power. His eyes were so wild, his hair so long and matted, his voice was so full of authority and thunder that he caused panic on the first, or Charter[71], National Suicide Day in 1920. The next one, in 1921, was less frightening but still worrisome. The people had seen him a year now in between[72]. He lived in a shack on the riverbank that had once belonged to his grandfather longtime

67 두려움을 조절하기 위해서(즉, 없애기 위해서) 두려움을 위한 자리를 마련해야 했다.

68 죽음이 언제 올지 예측할 수 없기 때문에 두려워했다.

69 국민 자살일.

70 소목에 매는 방울과 교수대에서 목을 매는 밧줄, 모두가 죽음을 일깨우는 물건들임.

71 국민 자살일이 설립된 첫날.

72 첫 번째 국민 자살 일로부터 올해까지 그 사이 일년 동안 그를 보아왔다.

dead. On Tuesday and Friday he sold the fish he had caught that morning, the rest of the week he was drunk, loud, obscene, funny and outrageous. But he never touched anybody, never fought, never caressed. Once the people understood the boundaries and nature of his madness, they could fit him, so to speak, into the scheme of things[73].

Then, on subsequent National Suicide Days, the grown people looked out from behind curtains as he rang his bell; a few stragglers increased their speed, and little children screamed and ran. The tetter heads[74] tried goading him (although he was only four or five years older than they) but not for long, for his curses were stingingly personal[75].

As time went along, the people took less notice of these January thirds, or rather they thought they did[76], thought they had no attitudes or feelings one way or another about Shadrack's annual solitary parade. In fact they had simply stopped remarking on the holiday[77] because they had absorbed it into their thoughts, into their language, into their lives.

Someone said to a friend, "You sure was a long time delivering that baby. How long was you in labor?"

And the friend answered, " 'Bout three days. The pains started on Suicide Day and kept up till the following Sunday. Was borned on Sunday. All my boys is Sunday boys."

---

73 fit him... : 일상의 한 부분으로 자연스럽게 그를 받아들일 수 있었다.

74 tetter head는 본래 피진이라는 피부병이 있는 까까머리 아이들을 가리킨다. 여기서는, 10대 전반쯤의 장난기가 많은 악동들을 의미한다.

75 그의 욕설이 신랄하게 인신 공격적이었기 때문이다.

76 여기서 did는 take less notice를 다시 받는 대동사임. 문장 전체를 해석하면, "시간이 지남에 따라 사람들은 1월 3일에 이루어지는 행사를 덜 신경 쓰게 되었다. 덜 신경 쓰고, 아예 아무런 느낌도 없다고 생각하게 되었다."

77 그 날에 특별히 신경 쓰지 않게 되었다.

Some lover said to his bride-to-be, "Let's do it after New Years, 'stead of before. I get paid New Year's Eve."

And his sweetheart answered, "OK, but make sure it ain't on Suicide Day. I ain't 'bout to be listening to no cowbells[78] whilst the weddin's going on."

Somebody's grandmother said her hens always started a laying of double yolks right after Suicide Day[79].

Then Reverend Deal took it up[80], saying the same folks who had sense enough to avoid Shadrack's call were the ones who insisted on drinking themselves to death or womanizing themselves to death[81]. "May's well go on with Shad and save the Lamb the trouble of redemption."[82]

Easily, quietly, Suicide Day became a part of the fabric of life up in the Bottom of Medallion, Ohio.

---

78 이중 부정이지만, 부정문으로 해석하면 된다. 즉, "결혼식을 하는 중에 그 방울소리를 듣고 싶지는 않아."

79 "suicide Day"이 지난 바로 후에 노른자가 두개 있는 계란을 낳기 시작했다는 뜻.

80 딜목사 조차도 "자살일"을 거론했다.

81 쉐드랙의 부름을 피할 만한 센스가 있는 자들은 죽도록 술 먹고 죽도록 계집질이나 하는 사람들이라고 목사는 말했다.

82 It may as well go on with Shad...가 구어체로 줄여진 형태다. 번역하면, "이제 자살의 날 행렬에 모두 쉐드랙과 더불어 참여하고, 이 날이 예수의 구원 사역을 대신하게 될 것이다."

1920

It had to be as far away from the Sundown House[1] as possible. And her grandmother's middle-aged nephew who lived in a Northern town called Medallion was the one chance she had to make sure it would be. The red shutters[2] had haunted both Helene Sabat and her grandmother for sixteen years. Helene was born behind those shutters, daughter of a Creol[3] whore who worked there. The grandmother took Helene away from the soft lights and flowered carpets of the Sundown House and raised her under the dolesome eyes of a multicolored Virgin Mary, counseling her to be constantly on guard for any sign of her mother's wild blood.

So when Wiley Wright came to visit his Great Aunt Cecile in New Orleans, his enchantment with the pretty Helene became a marriage proposal — under the pressure of both women. He was a seaman (or rather a lakeman, for he was a ship's cook on one of the Great Lakes lines[4]), in port only three days out of every sixteen[5].

He took his bride to his home in Medallion and put her in a lovely house with a brick porch and real lace curtains at the window. His long absences were quite bearable for Helene

1 사창가의 이름

2 선정적인 빨간색으로 칠해진 사창가의 출입문 셔터를 의미함.

3 미국 루이지애나 주에 이주한 프랑스사람의 자손을 일컬음. 자유분방하고 성적으로 개방적이라는 함축성이 담겨있다.

4 미국 오대호를 오고가는 정기선.

5 16일 마다 한번, 항구에 3일 동안 머문다.

Wright, especially when, after some nine years of marriage, her daughter was born.

Her daughter was more comfort and purpose than she had ever hoped to find in this life[6]. She rose grandly to the occasion of motherhood[7] — grateful, deep down in her heart, that[8] the child had not inherited the great beauty that was hers: that her skin had dusk in it[9], that her lashes were substantial but not undignified in their length[10], that she had taken the broad flat nose of Wiley (although Helene expected to improve it somewhat) and his generous lips.

Under Helene's hand the girl became obedient and polite. Any enthusiasm that little Nel showed were calmed by the mother until she drove her daughter's imagination underground[11].

Helene Wright was an impressive woman, at least in Medallion she was. Heavy hair in a bun, dark eyes arched in a perpetual query about other people's manners[12]. A woman who won all social battles with presence[13] and a conviction of the legitimacy of her authority[14]. Since there was no Catholic church in

6 그의 딸의 존재는 삶에서 얻고 싶었던 어떤 것보다도 더 많은 행복과 목적의식을 가져다주었다.

7 그녀는 기품 있게 엄마의 역할을 해냈다.

8 4번 계속되는 접속사 that은 헬렌이 마음 깊이 감사하는 내용들을 열거한 것이다.

9 피부색이 검다는 뜻.

10 눈썹은 숱이 많았지만, 눈썹의 길이가 품위 없이 긴 것은 아니었다.

11 딸의 상상력을 억누름으로써, 넬이 보여주는 어떠한 열정도 엄마가 잠잠케 만들었다.

12 Helene Wright의 외모에 대한 묘사. "둥글게 말아 올린 숱 많은 머리, 다른 사람들의 매너에 대한 끊임없는 관심으로 늘 동그랗게 뜬 까만 눈."

13 with presence: 침착하게

14 자신의 기품을 당당하게 인정받았음을 확신했다. a conviction은 won의 목적어임.

Medallion then, she joined the most conservative black church. And held sway[15]. It was Helene who never turned her head in church when latecomers arrived; Helene who established the practice of seasonal altar flowers; Helene who introduced the giving of banquets of welcome to returning negro veterans. She lost only one battle — the pronunciation of her name. The people in the Bottom refused to say Helene. They called her Helen Wright and left it at that[16].

All in all her life was a satisfactory one. She loved her house and enjoyed manipulating her daughter and her husband[17]. She would sigh sometimes just before falling asleep, thinking that she had indeed come far enough away from the Sundown House.

So it was with extremely mixed emotions that she read a letter from Mr. Henri Martin describing the illness of her grandmother, and suggesting she come down right away. She didn't want to go, but could not bring herself to ignore the silent plea of the woman who had rescued her.

It was November. November, 1920. Even in Medallion there was a victorious swagger in the legs of white men[18] and a dull-eyed excitement in the eyes of colored veterans.

Helene thought about the trip South with heavy misgiving[19] but decided that she had the best protection: her manner and

15 헬렌은 교회에서 당당하게 자신의 뜻대로 행동했다는 뜻임.
Hold sway: (...를) 마음대로 하다.

16 끝의 N을 길게 끌어 발음해서 Helene을 불어식으로 발음해 주기를 그녀는 원했지만 사람들은 미국식으로 발음했다는 뜻이다. 그리고 헬렌은 그것을 내버려두었다.

17 자신의 뜻대로 딸과 남편을 조정하는 것을 즐겼다.

18 1차대전의 승리로 메달리온에도 승리를 으스대며 걸어가는 백인들이 있었다.

19 흑인에 대한 인종차별이 심한 남부에 가는 것에 대한 두려움과 더불어 자신의 엄마가 창녀였던 고장에 가는 것에 대한 두려움이다.

her bearing, to which she would add a beautiful dress[20]. She bought some deep-brown wool and three-fourths of a yard of matching velvet. Out of this she made herself a heavy but elegant dress with velvet collar and pockets.

Nel watched her mother cutting the pattern from newspapers and moving her eyes rapidly from a magazine model to her own hands. She watched her turn up the kerosene lamp at sunset to sew far into the night.

The day they were ready, Helene cooked a smoked ham, left a note for her lake-bound husband[21], in case he docked early, and walked head high and arms stiff with luggage ahead of her daughter to the train depot.

It was a longer walk than she remembered, and they saw the train steaming up just as they turned the corner. They ran along the track looking for the coach pointed out to them by the colored porter. Even at that they made a mistake. Helene and her daughter entered a coach peopled by some twenty white men and women. Rather than go back and down the three wooden steps again, Helene decided to spare herself some embarrassment and walk on through to the colored car[22]. She carried two pieces of luggage and a string purse; her daughter carried a covered basket of food.

As they opened the door marked COLORED ONLY, they saw a white conductor coming toward them. It was a chilly day but a

20 남부로의 여행에 헬렌은 상당히 겁을 먹었지만, 자신의 (우아한) 매너와 행동거지, 게다가 아름다운 옷을 입으면 자신을 충분히 보호할 수 있으리라 생각했다.

21 호수로 일하러 떠난 남편

22 당혹감을 면하기 위해서, 세 개의 나무 계단을 다시 내려가기보다는 (즉, 기차를 내려 흑인 전용 칸을 찾기보다는) 흑인 전용 칸까지 기차 안을 통해 가기로 했다.

light skim of sweat glistened on the woman's face as she and the little girl struggled to hold the door open, hang on to their luggage and enter all at once. The conductor let his eyes travel over the pale yellow woman and then stuck his little finger into his ear, jiggling it free of wax[23]. "What you think you doin', gal?"

Helene looked up at him.

So soon. So soon[24]. She hadn't even begun the trip back. Back to her grandmother's house in the city where the red shutters glowed, and already she had been called "gal." All the old vulnerabilities, all the old fears of being somehow flawed gathered in her stomach and made her hands tremble. She had heard only that one word; it dangled above her wide-brimmed hat, which had slipped, in her exertions, from its carefully leveled placement and was now tilted in a bit of a jaunt over her eye[25].

Thinking he wanted her tickets, she quickly dropped both the cowhide suitcase and the straw one in order to search for them in her purse. An eagerness to please and an apology for living[26] met in her voice. "I have them. Right here somewhere, sir. . ."

The conductor looked at the bit of wax his fingernail had

23 역무원은 창백하고 노란 얼굴의 여자(헬렌)를 훑어보더니 새끼손가락으로 귀를 후벼 귓밥을 털어 냈다.

24 인종 차별로 인한 자기 위엄이 비하되는 것을 두려워해 왔는데, 그 상황이 이렇게 일찍 왔다는 뜻임. 헬렌이 자신이 숙녀로 대접받기를 원하는데, 역무원이 "gal"이라고 불렀을 때, 자존심에 상처를 받게 된다. 여기서 "gal"이란 단순히 비하하는 말일 뿐 아니라, 속어로 "매춘부"를 의미하는 경우도 있으므로, 매춘부를 엄마로 둔 헬렌은 자격지심으로 더욱 듣기 괴로운 단어다.

25 "여자"란 단어가 챙이 커다란 모자 위에 대롱대롱 매달려 있었다. 그녀가 움찔하는 바람에 반듯하게 놓여있던 모자가 눈 위로 살짝 기울어졌다.

26 apology for living: 변명조

retrieved. “What was you doin’ back in there? What was you doin’ in that coach yonder?”

Helene licked her lips. “Oh. . . I. . .” Her glance moved beyond the white man’s face to the passengers seated behind him. Four or five black-faces were watching, two belonging to soldiers still in their shit-colored uniforms and peaked caps. She saw their closed faces, their locked eyes[27], and turned for compassion to the gray eyes of the conductor.

“We made a mistake, sir. You see, there wasn’t no sign. We just got in the wrong car, that’s all. Sir.”

“We don’t ’low no mistakes[28] on this train. Now git your butt on in there[29].”

He stood there staring at her until she realized that he wanted her to move aside. Pulling Nel by the arm, she pressed herself and her daughter into the foot space in front of a wooden seat[30]. Then, for no earthly reason, at least no reason that anybody could understand, certainly no reason that Nel understood then or later, she smiled. Like a street pup that wags its tail at the very doorjamb of the butcher shop he has been kicked away from only moments before[31], Helene smiled. Smiled[32] dazzlingly and coquettishly at the salmon-colored[33] face of the conductor.

---

27 전쟁군인들인데 그들의 얼굴과 눈이 모두 헬렌의 곤경에 무심했다는 뜻이다.

28 “We don’t allow any mistakes on this train.”

29 “당장 꺼져버려!”라는 뜻. 매우 무례한 표현이다.

30 넬의 손을 잡아끌면서 헬렌은 자신과 딸 모두를 나무의자 앞에 발을 놓는 작은 공간으로 비집고 들어갔다.

31 방금 전 쫓겨난 푸줏간 문설주에 대고 꼬리를 흔드는 집 없는 강아지처럼 (비굴하게).

32 주어가 다시 반복되지 않고 바로 동사가 나오는 이런 문장을 모리슨의 소설에서 흔히 볼 수 있다.

33 연어처럼 붉은 얼굴

Nel looked away from the flash of pretty teeth[34] to the other passengers. The two black soldiers, who had been watching the scene with what appeared to be indifferent, now looked stricken. Behind Nel was the bright and blazing light of her mother's smile; before her the midnight eyes of the soldiers. She saw the muscles of their faces tighten, a movement under the skin from blood to marble. No change in the expression of the eyes, but a hard wetness[35] that veiled them as they looked at the stretch of her mother's foolish smile.

As the door slammed on the conductor's exit, Helene walked down the aisle to a seat. She looked about for a second to see whether any of the men would help her put the suitcases in the overhead rack. Not a man moved. Helene sat down, fussily, her back toward the men. Nel sat opposite, facing both her mother and the soldiers, neither of whom she could look at. She felt both pleased and ashamed to sense that these men, unlike her father, who worshiped his graceful, beautiful wife, were bubbling with a hatred for her mother[36] that had not been there in the beginning but had been born with the dazzling smile[37]. In the silence that preceded the train's heave[38], she looked deeply at the folds of her mother's dress. There in the fall of the heavy brown wool she held her eyes. She could not risk letting them travel upward for fear of seeing that the hooks and eyes in the placket of the dress had come undone and exposed the custard-colored skin underneath[39]. She stared

34 이빨을 하얗게 드러내고 웃는 엄마의 얼굴.

35 딱딱하게 긴장한 얼굴 밑에 스민 음습함

36 어머니에 대한 미움으로 그들의 마음이 부글부글 끓고 있었다.

37 처음부터 흑인칸에 들어오지 못하고, 빛나는 미소를 띠고 있는 엄마에 대하여.

38 기차가 들썩이기 전 조용한 가운데서

at the hem, wanting to believe in its weight but knowing that custard was all that it hid[40]. If this tall, proud woman, this woman who was very particular about her friends, who slipped into church with unequaled elegance, who could quell a roustabout with a look, if *she* were really custard, then there was a chance that Nel was too[41].

It was on that train, shuffling toward Cincinnati, that she resolved to be on guard — always. She wanted to make certain that no man ever looked at her that way. That no midnight eyes or marbled flesh would ever accost her and turn her into jelly[42].

For two days they rode; two days of watching sleet turn to rain, turn to purple sunsets, and one night knotted on the wooden seats[43] (their heads on folded coats), trying not to hear the snoring soldiers. When they changed trains in Birmingham for the last leg of the trip[44], they discovered what luxury they had been in through Kentucky and Tennessee, where the rest stops had all had colored toilets[45]. After Birmingham there were

39 넬은 감히 눈길을 위로 들어올릴 수 없었다. 엄마의 옷의 옆, 트여진 곳의 호크와 구멍이 열려져 그 밑으로 커스타드(갈색) 색의 속살이 보일까봐 두려웠기 때문이었다.

40 넬은 엄마의 치마 자락을 바라보았다. 치마의 무게 때문에 치마가 들춰지지 않을 거라고 믿고 싶어하면서. 그러나 그 치마 밑에는 엄마의 담황색 속살이 숨겨져 있다는 것을 잘 알고 있다,

41 if she were really custard, then there was a chance that Nel was too: 여기서 custard란 단순한 담황색이 아니라, 남자를 유혹하는 정숙하지 못한 자아를 상징적으로 의미한다. 그리고 엄마가 그런 자아를 지녔다면 자신도 마찬가지로 정숙하지 못할 지도 모른다는 생각을 하게 된다.

42 make certain that으로 이어지는 문장. 응큼한 눈과 대리석 같은 몸이 그녀에게 다가와 흐물거리게 만드는 일이 절대로 없을 거라고 확신하고 싶었다.

43 하룻밤엔 나무 좌석에 웅크린 채

44 여행의 마지막 구간.

45 colored toilets: 흑인들을 위한 화장실

none. Helene's face was drawn with the need to relieve herself[46], and so intense was her distress she finally brought herself to speak about her problem to a black woman with four children who had got on in Tuscaloosa.

"Is there somewhere we can go to use the restroom?"

The woman looked up at her and seemed not to understand. "Ma'am?" Her eyes fastened on[47] the thick velvet collar, the fair skin, the high-tone voice.

"The restroom," Helene repeated. Then, in a whisper, "The toilet."

The woman pointed out the window and said, "Yes, ma'am. Yonder."

Helene looked out of the window halfway expecting to see a comfort station in the distance[48]; instead she saw graygreen trees leaning over tangled grass. "Where?"

"Yonder," the woman said. "Meridian[49]. We be pullin' in direc'lin.[50]" Then she smiled sympathetically and asked, "Kin you make it?[51]"

Helene nodded and went back to her seat trying to think of other things — for the surest way to have an accident would be to remember her full bladder[52].

At Meridian the women got out with their children. While Helene looked about the tiny stationhouse for a door that said

---

46 소변 마려운 표정이 얼굴에 역력했다.

47 눈이 ...에 고정되었다.

48 저 멀리 어딘가에 휴게소가 있으리라 기대하며 창 밖을 내다보았다.

49 미시시피주의 동쪽에 있는 도시 이름

50 메리디안, 그 쪽으로 가서 잠시 열차가 멈출 겁니다.

51 거기까지 참을 수 있겠어요?

52 자꾸만 꽉 찬 방광을 떠올리면 실수를 해버릴 것 같아서 다른 생각을 하기로 했다.

COLORED WOMEN[53], the other woman stalked off[54] to a field of high grass on the far side of the track. Some white men were leaning on the railing in front of the stationhouse. It was not only their tongues curling around toothpicks that kept Helene from asking information of them[55]. She looked around for the other woman and, seeing just the top of her head rag in the grass, slowly realized where "Yonder" was. All of them, the fat woman and her four children, three boys and a girl, Helene and her daughter, squatted there in the four o'clock Meridian sun[56]. They did it again in Ellisville, again in Hattiesburg, and by the time they reached Slidell, not too far from Lake Pontchartrain, Helene could not only fold leaves as well as the fat woman[57], she never felt a stir[58] as she passed the muddy eyes of the men who stood like wrecked Dorics[59] under the station roofs of those towns.

The lift in spirit that such an accomplishment produced in her[60] quickly disappeared when the train finally pulled into New Orleans.

Cecile Sabat's house leaned between two others just like it on

---

53 흑인 전용 화장실이란 팻말을 찾기 위해 조그만 역원 주위를 둘러보는 동안.

54 stalk off: 성큼 성큼 걸어 나가다.

55 그 남자들에게 흑인용 화장실이 어디인가 물을 수 없는 이유는 단순히 그들이 혀로 이쑤시개를 핥고 있는 탓만은 아니었다.

56 오후 4시 벌건 대낮에 덤불 속에서 모두 소변을 보고 있었다는 뜻임.

57 다른 여자와 마찬가지로 덤불숲에서 잎사귀를 꺾어 젖힐 수 있었다. 즉, 별 부끄럼 없이 방뇨했다는 뜻임.

58 조금도 동요하지 않았다.

59 wrecked Dorics: 허물어진 도리스 양식의 건물

60 길거리에서도 아무렇지도 방뇨를 한 사실이 묘하게도 홀가분하게 느껴졌다는 뜻임.

Elysian Fields[61]. A Frenchified shotgun house[62], it sported[63] a magnificent garden in the back and a tiny wrought-iron fence in the front. On the door hung a black crepe wreath[64] with purple ribbon. They were too late. Helene reached up to touch the ribbon, hesitated, and knocked. A man in a collarless shirt opened the door. Helene identified herself and he said he was Henri Martin and that he was there for the settin'-up[65]. They stepped into the house. The Virgin Mary clasped her hands in front of her neck three times in the front room and once in the bedroom where Cecile's body lay[66]. The old woman had died without seeing or blessing her granddaughter.

No one other than Mr. Martin seemed to be in the house, but a sweet odor as of gardenias[67] told them that someone else had been. Blotting her lashes with a white handkerchief, Helene walked through the kitchen to the back bedroom where she had slept for sixteen years. Nel trotted along behind, enchanted with the smell, the candles and the strangeness. When Helene bent to loosen the ribbons of Nel's hat, a woman in a yellow dress came out of the garden and onto the back porch that opened into the bedroom. The two women looked at each other. There was no recognition in the eyes of either. Then Helene said, "This is your... grandmother, Nel." Nel looked at her mother and then quickly back at the door they had just come out of.

---

61 엘리지움. 영웅이나 선인이 사후에 가는 낙원.

62 불란서풍의 뚜쟁이 집.

63 과시하다

64 검은 크레이프 상장(喪章)이 달린 화환

65 장례식 준비

66 응접실에 세 개의 마리아 상이 두 손을 합장하고 있었고, 세실의 시체가 누워있는 방에 또 하나의 마리아 상이 놓여 있었다.

67 치자나무

"No. That was your great-grandmother. This is your grandmother. My... mother."

Before the child could think, her words were hanging in the gardenia air. "But she looks so young."

The woman in the canary-yellow dress laughed and said she was forty-eight, "an old forty-eight."

Then it was she who carried the gardenia smell. This tiny woman with the softness and glare of a canary. In that somber house that held four Virgin Marys, where death sighed in every corner and candles puttered, the gardenia smell and canary-yellow dress emphasized the funeral atmosphere surrounding them.

The woman smiled, glanced in the mirror and said, throwing her voice toward Helene, "That your only one?[68]"

"Yes," said Helene.

"Pretty. A lot like you."

"Yes. Well. She's ten now."

"Ten? Vrai[69]? Small for her age, no?"

Helene shrugged and looked at her daughter's questioning eyes. The woman in the yellow dress leaned forward. "come. Come, chere[70]."

Helene interrupted. "We have to get cleaned up. We been three days on the train with no chance to wash or..."

"Comment t'appelle?"[71]

"She doesn't talk Creole."

"Then you ask her."

"She wants to know your name, honey."

68 아이는 하나 뿐이니?

69 크레올 여성인 탓에 불어를 자주 사용한다. "정말이니?" 라는 뜻임.

70 영어로 "dear"의 뜻임.

71 이름이 뭐지?

With her head pressed into her mother's heavy brown dress, Nel told her and then asked, "What's yours?"

"Mine's Rochelle. Well. I must be going on." She moved closer to the mirror and stood there sweeping hair up from her neck back into its halo-like roll, and wetting with spit the ringlets that fell over her ears[72]. "I been here, you know, most of the day. She pass on yesterday. The funeral tomorrow. Henri takin' care." She struck a match, blew it out and darkened her eyebrows with the burnt head[73]. All the while Helene and Nel watched her. The one in a rage at the folded leaves she had endured, the wooden benches she had slept on, all to miss seeing her grandmother and seeing instead that painted canary who never said a word of greeting or affection or...[74]

Rochelle continued. "I don't know what happen to de house[75]. Long time paid for. You be thinkin' on it[76]? Oui?" Her newly darkened eyebrows queried Helene.

"Oui." Helene's voice was chilly. "I be thinkin' on it."

"Oh, well. Not for me to say...[77]"

Suddenly she swept around and hugged Nel — a quick

72 그녀는 거울로 다가갔다. 목으로 흘러내린 머리를 후광처럼 둥그렇게 말아 올리고는 귀 양 편에 늘어진 곱슬머리에 침을 묻혔다.

73 성냥을 켠 다음 훅 불어 꺼 버리고, 타버린 성냥 끝으로 눈썹을 까맣게 칠했다.

74 한데서 나뭇잎을 제치고 소변보고, 나무 좌석 위에 웅크리고 잠자면서까지 모든 고통을 참아냈는데, 오로지 할머니를 보기 위해 모든 것을 감내했는데, 할머니 대신 화장한 카나리아라니... 환영이나 애정 어린 말 한마디 없는 카나리아를 보기 위해서였다니... (여기서 문두의 "The one"은 Helene 자신을 가리킴.

75 할머니가 돌아가셨으므로 집 처분 문제가 대두된다. 집은 할머니의 소유인 듯하고, 아마도 헬렌에게 물려주기로 약속한 듯함.

76 집을 네가 물려받았으니, 네가 해결할 생각을 하고 있겠지?

77 그럼, 내가 관여할 바가 아니구나.

embrace tighter and harder than one would have imagined her thin soft arms capable of.

"'Voir!' Voir![78]" and she was gone.

In the kitchen, being soaped head to toe by her mother, Nel ventured an observation. "she smelled so nice. And her skin was so soft."

Helene rinsed the cloth. "Much handled things are always soft."[79]

"What does 'vwah' mean?"

"I don't know," her mother said. "I don't talk Creole." She gazed at her daughter's wet buttocks. "and neither do you."

When they got back to Medallion and into the quiet house they saw the note exactly where they had left it and the ham dried out in the icebox.

"Lord, I've never been so glad to see this place. But look at the dust. Get the rags, Nel. Oh, never mind. Let's breathe awhile first. Lord, I never thought I'd get back here safe and sound. Whoo. Well, it's over. Good and over. Praise His name. Look at that. I told that old fool not to deliver any milk and there's the can curdled to beat all[80]. What gets into people?[81] I told him not to. Well, I got other things to worry 'bout. Got to get a fire started. I left it ready so I wouldn't have to do nothin' but light it. Lord, it's cold. Don't just sit there, honey. You could be pulling your nose..."[82]

78 voir는 영어로 see의 뜻인데, 여기서는 로쉘의 실망과 체념을 담은 감탄사임.

79 많이 손을 탄 것들은 의례 부드럽기 마련이지. 즉, 많은 남성을 상대하는 창녀이기 때문에 부드럽다는 뜻임.

80 정말 웃기게도 우유가 전부 엉겨 붙고 말았군.

81 도대체 사람들이 왜 이런 거지?

Nel sat on the red-velvet sofa listening to her mother but remembering the smell and the tight, tight hug of the woman in yellow who rubbed burned matches over her eyes.

Late that night after the fire was made, the cold supper eaten, the surface dust removed, Nel lay in bed thinking of her trip. She remembered clearly the urine running down and into her stockings until she learned how to squat properly; the disgust on the face of the dead woman and the sound of the funeral drums. It had been an exhilarating trip but a fearful one. She had been frightened of the soldiers' eyes on the train, the black wreath on the door, the custard pudding she believed lurked under her mother's heavy dress[83], the feel of unknown streets and unknown people. But she had gone on a real trip, and now she was different. She got out of bed and lit the lamp to look in the mirror. There was her face, plain brown eyes, three braids and the nose her mother hated. She looked for a long time and suddenly a shiver ran through her.

"I'm me," she whispered. "Me."

Nel didn't know quite what she meant, but on the other hand she knew exactly what she meant.

"I'm me. I'm not their daughter. I'm not Nel. I'm me. Me."

Each time she said the word *me* there was a gathering in her like power, like joy, like fear[84]. Back in bed with her discovery, she stared out the window at the dark leaves of the horse chestnut[85].

82 가만히 앉아 있지 말고 코를 당겨서 높게 만들어야지.

83 엄마의 두꺼운 옷 밑에서 일렁거렸다고 믿었던, 갈색 빛의 말랑거림

84 "나"라고 말할 때 마다, 힘 같기도 하고, 혹은 기쁨, 혹은 두려움 같은 뭔가가 마음속에 생겨나고 있었다.

85 마로니에

"Me," she murmured. And then, sinking deeper into the quilts, "I want...I want to be...wonderful. Oh, Jesus, make me wonderful."

The many experiences of her trip crowded in on her. She slept. It was the last as well as the first time she was ever to leave Medallion[86].

For days afterward she imagined other trips she would take, alone though, to faraway places. Contemplating them was delicious. Leaving Medallion would be her goal. But that was before she met Sula, the girl she had seen for five years at Garfield Primary[87] but never played with, never knew, because her mother said that Sula's mother was sooty[88]. The trip, perhaps, or her new found me-ness, gave her the strength to cultivate a friend in spite of her mother.

When Sula first visited the Wright house, Helene's curdled scorn turned to butter[89]. Her daughter's friend seemed to have none of the mother's slackness. Nel, who regarded the oppressive neatness of her home with dread, felt comfortable in it with Sula[90], who loved it and would sit on the red-velvet sofa for ten to twenty minutes at the time — still as dawn[91]. As for Nel, she preferred Sula's woolly[92] house, where a pot of something was always cooking on the stove; where the mother, Hannah, never scolded or gave directions; where all sorts of

---

86 이번 여행이 넬에게는 메달이온을 떠난 처음이자 마지막 여행이었다.

87 가필드 초등학교

88 거무스름한. 여기서 sooty라는 말은 거무스름한 피부색뿐 아니라, 성적으로 분방한 술라엄마에 대한 경멸도 함께 함축하고 있다.

89 헬렌의 확고한 경멸은 바로 버터처럼 녹아버렸다.

90 지나치게 정갈해서 억압적인 집을 두려워했던 넬은 술라와 함께 있으면 그 집에서도 편안하게 느꼈다.

91 feel에 연결되는 말로써, 여명처럼 고요하게 느꼈다는 뜻.

92 덥수룩한, 거친.

people dropped in; where newspapers were stacked in the hallway, and dirty dishes left for hours at a time in the sink, and where a one-legged grandmother named Eva handed you goobers[93] from deep inside her pockets or read you a dream[94].

93 땅콩
94 꿈 해몽을 해준다.

1921

Sula Peace lived in a house of many rooms that had been built over a period of five years to the specifications of its owner, who kept on adding things: more stairways — there were three sets to the second floor[1] — more rooms, doors and stoops. There were rooms that had three doors, others that opened out on the porch only and were inaccessible from any other part of the house; others that you could get to only by going through somebody's bedroom. The creator and sovereign of this enormous house with the four sickle-pear trees[2] in the front yard and the single elm in the back yard was Eva Peace, who sat in a wagon[3] on the third floor directing the lives of her children, friends, strays, and a constant stream of boarders. Fewer than nine people in the town remembered when Eva had two legs, and her oldest child, Hannah, was not one of them. Unless Eva herself introduced the subject, no one ever spoke of her disability; they pretended to ignore it, unless, in some mood of fancy, she began some fearful story about it — generally to entertain children. How the leg got up by itself one day and walked on off[4]. How she hobbled after it[5] but it ran too fast. Or how she had a corn[6] on her toe and it just grew and grew

1 이층으로 가는 계단이 세 개나 있었다.
2 낫 모양의 배나무.
3 wagon: 휠체어
4 다리 한쪽이 저절로 일어나 걸어가 버렸는지, 꼬마들에게 들려주었다.
5 다리를 좇으러 외다리로 절뚝거리며 걷다.
6 티눈

and grew until her whole foot was a corn and then it traveled on up her leg and wouldn't stop growing until she put a red rag at the top but by that time it was already at her knee.

Somebody said Eva stuck it under a train and made them pay off[7]. Another said she sold it to the hospital for $10,000 —at which Mr. Reed opened his eyes and asked, "Nigger gal legs goin' for $10,000 a *piece*?" as though he could understand $10,000 a *pair*—but for *one*[8]?

Whatever the fate of her lost leg, the remaining one[9] was magnificent. It was stockinged and shod at all times and in all weather. Once in a while she got a felt slipper for Christmas or her birthday, but they soon disappeared, for Eva always wore a black laced-up shoe that came well above her ankle. Nor did she wear overlong dresses to disguise the empty place on her left side. Her dresses were mid-calf so that her one glamorous leg was always in view as well as the long fall of space below her left thigh[10]. One of her men friends had fashioned a kind of wheelchair for her: a rocking-chair top fitted into a large child's wagon[11]. In this contraption she wheeled around the room, from bedside to dresser to the balcony that opened out the north side of her room or to the window that looked out on the back yard. The wagon was so low that

---

7 또 어떤 사람들은 말하길, 이바가 기차 밑에 일부러 다리를 집어넣어 보상을 받아냈다고 했다.

8 "다리 한 짝에 만달러라구요?" 마치 다리 두 짝에 만달러라면 이해해도 한 짝에 그만한 액수가 믿어지지 않는다는 듯이, 리드씨는 눈을 동그랗게 뜨고 물었다.

9 남아 있는 한 쪽 다리.

10 치마는 늘 종아리의 반쯤 닿게 입는 탓에 그녀의 멋진 외다리는 항상 드러나 있었고 다리가 없는 왼쪽의 기다란 빈 공간도 마찬가지로 드러났다.

11 이바 친구들 중 한 남자가 흔들의자의 윗부분을 어린아이용 수레에 붙여 휠체어를 만들어 주었다.

children who spoke to her standing up were eye level with her, and adults, standing or sitting, had to look down at her. But they didn't know it. They all had the impression that they were looking up at her, up into the open distances of her eyes, up into the soft black of her nostrils and up at the crest of her chin.

Eva had married a man named BoyBoy and had three children: Hannah, the eldest, and Eva, whom she named after herself but called Pearl, and a son named Ralph, whom she called Plum.

After five years of a sad and disgruntled marriage BoyBoy took off. During the time they were together he was very much preoccupied with other women and not home much. He did whatever he could that he liked, and he liked womanizing best, drinking second, and abusing Eva third. When he left in November, Eva had $1.65, five eggs, three beets[12] and no idea of what or how to feel. The children needed her; she needed money, and needed to get on with her life. But the demands of feeding her three children were so acute she had to postpone her anger for two years until she had both the time and the energy for it. She was confused and desperately hungry. There were very few black families in those low hills then. The Suggs, who lived two hundred yards down the road, brought her a warm bowl of peas, as soon as they found out, and a plate of cold bread. She thanked them and asked if they had a little milk for the older ones. They said no, but Mrs. Jackson, they knew, had a cow still giving[13]. Eva took

12 사탕무 세 개
13 잭슨부인의 암소로부터 우유를 얻을 수 있다는 사실을 알았다.

a bucket over and Mrs. Jackson told her to come back and fill it up in the morning, because the evening milking had already been done. In this way, things went on until near December. People were very willing to help, but Eva felt she would soon run her welcome out[14]; winters were hard and her neighbors were not that much better off[15]. She would lie in bed with baby boy, the two girls wrapped in quilts on the floor, thinking. The oldest child, Hannah, was five and too young to take care of the baby alone, and any housework Eva could find would keep her away from them from five thirty or earlier in the morning until dark—way past eight. The white people in the valley weren't rich enough then to want maids; they were small farmers and tradesmen and wanted hard-labor help if anything. She thought also of returning to some of her people in Virginia, but to come home dragging three young ones would have to be a step one rung before death for Eva[16]. She would have to scrounge around and beg through the winter, until her baby was at least nine months old, then she could plant and maybe hire herself out to valley farms to weed or sow or feed stock until something steadier came along at harvest time. She thought she had probably been a fool to let BoyBoy haul her away from her people[17], but it had seemed so right at the time. He worked for a white carpenter and toolsmith who insisted on BoyBoy's accompanying him when he went West and set up in a squinchy[18]

14 이웃들은 기꺼이 이바를 도와주었지만 그리 오래가지 않으리라 느꼈다.

15 겨울나기는 누구나 힘들었고 이웃도 그녀보다 그리 나을 것이 없었기 때문이다.

16 죽기 바로 직전에나 해야 할 일. 즉, 최후에 어쩔 수 없을 때의 선택이다.

17 남편을 따라 자신의 고향을 떠나버린 것이 바보짓이었다고 생각했었다.

18 웅크릴 정도로 매우 작다는 뜻임.

little town called Medallion. BoyBoy brought this new wife and built them a one-room cabin sixty feet back from the road that wound up out of the valley, on up into the hills[19] and was named for the man he worked for. They lived there a year before they had an outhouse[20].

Sometime before the middle of December, the baby, Plum, stopped having bowel movements. Eva massaged his stomach and gave him warm water. Something must be wrong with my milk, she thought. Mrs. Suggs gave her castor[21] oil, but even that didn't work. He cried and fought so they couldn't get much down his throat anyway[22].

He seemed in great pain and his shrieks were pitched high in outrage and suffering. At one point, maddened by his own crying, he gagged, choked and looked as though he was strangling to death. Eva rushed to him and kicked over the earthen slop jar[23], washing a small area of the floor with the child's urine. She managed to soothe him, but when he took up the cry again late that night, she resolved to end his misery once and for all. She wrapped him in blankets, ran her finger around the crevices and sides of the lard can[24] and stumbled[25] to the outhouse with him. Deep in its darkness and freezing stench[26] she squatted down, turned the baby over her knees,

19 골짜기에서 나와 언덕배기로 이어지는 구불구불한 한 길에서 60피트 떨어진 길가에 방 한 칸 자리 통나무집을 짓고 살았다.

20 딴 채

21 해리의 살에서 나오는 분비물로 대변에 대한 약제로 쓰임

22 계속 울고 힘들어하는 통에 우유조차 목으로 많이 넘기지 못했다.

23 질그릇으로 된 요강

24 ran the fingers... can: 깡통의 측면과 갈라진 틈까지 손가락으로 샅샅이 훑었다.

25 비틀거리며 걸어갔다.

26 어둠 깊숙이, 얼어붙는 듯한 고약한 냄새와 함께

exposed his buttocks and shoved the last bit of food she had in the world (besides three beets) up his ass[27]. Softening the insertion with the dab of lard, she probed with her middle finger to loosen his bowels[28]. Her fingernail snagged what felt like a pebble[29]; she pulled it out and others followed. Plum stopped crying as the black hard stools ricocheted[30] onto the frozen ground. And now that it was over[31], Eva squatted there wondering why she had come all the way out there to free his stools, and what was she doing down on her haunches[32] with her beloved baby boy warmed by her body in the almost total darkness, her shins and teeth freezing, her nostrils assailed[33]. She shook her head as though to juggle her brains around[34], then said aloud, "Uh uh. Nooo." Thereupon she returned to the house and her bed. As the grateful Plum slept, the silence allowed her to think.

Two days later she left all of her children with Mrs. Suggs, saying she would be back the next day.

Eighteen months later she swept down from a wagon with two crutches, a new black pocketbook[35], and one leg. First she reclaimed her children, next she gave the surprised Mrs. Suggs a ten-dollar bill, later she started building a house on

27 이 세상에서 남은 마지막 음식을 아기의 항문 속으로 밀어 넣었다.
28 돼지 기름덩어리로 삽입을 부드럽게 하면서, 가운데 손가락으로 대장을 이완시키려 했다.
29 손가락에는 작은 돌맹이 같은 것이 걸렸다.
30 ricochet: 탄환처럼 튀어나오다.
31 일단 일이 끝나자
32 웅크리고 앉아
33 차가운 냉기 때문에 콧구멍이 아프도록.
34 juggle her brains around: 두뇌로 곡예를 부리는 것처럼.
35 검은 색의 돈지갑

Carpenter's Road, sixty feet from BoyBoy's one-room cabin, which she rented out.

When Plum was three years old, BoyBoy came back to town and paid her a visit. When Eva got the word that he was on his way[36], she made some lemonade. She had no idea what she would do or feel during that encounter. Would she cry, cut his throat, beg him to make love to her? She couldn't imagine. So she just waited to see. She stirred lemonade in a green pitcher and waited.

BoyBoy danced up the steps and knocked on the door.

"Come on in," she hollered.

He opened the door and stood smiling, a picture of prosperity and good will. His shoes were a shiny orange, and he had on a citified straw hat, a light-blue suit, and a cat's-head stickpin in his tie[37]. Eva smiled and told him to sit himself down. He smiled too.

"How you been, girl?"

"Pretty fair. What you know good?[38]" When she heard those words come out of her own mouth she knew that their conversation would start off polite. Although it remained to be seen whether she would still run the ice pick through the cat's-head pin[39].

"Have some lemonade."

"Don't mind if I do." He swept his hat off with a satisfied gesture[40]. His nails were long and shiny. "sho[41] is hot, and I

---

36 남편이 집에 돌아오는 길이라는 전갈을 받았을 때.

37 고양이 머리 모양의 넥타이 핀.

38 How are you?의 뜻임.

39 그녀의 손에 들린 얼음 쪼개는 칼로 그의 고양이 머리처럼 생긴 넥타이핀을 찌를 것인지는 좀 두고 볼 일이지만.

been runnin' around all day."

Eva looked out of the screen door and saw a woman in a pea-green dress leaning on the smallest pear tree. Glancing back at him, she was reminded of Plum's face when he managed to get the meat out of a walnut all by himself[42]. Eva smiled again, and poured the lemonade.

Their conversation was easy: she catching him up on all the gossip[43], he asking about this one and that one, and like everybody else avoiding any reference to her leg. It was like talking to somebody's cousin who just stopped by to say howdy[44] before getting on back to wherever he came from. BoyBoy didn't ask to see the children, and Eva didn't bring them into the conversation.

After a while he rose to go. Talking about his appointments and exuding an odor of new money and idleness, he danced down the steps and strutted toward the pea-green dress. Eva watched. She looked at the back of his neck and the set of his shoulders. Underneath all of that shine she saw defeat in the stalk of his neck and the curious tight way he held his shoulders[45]. But still she was not sure what she felt. Then he leaned forward and whispered into the ear of the woman in the green dress. She was still for a moment and then threw back her head and laughed. A high-pitched big-city laugh that reminded Eva of Chicago. It hit her like a sledge hammer, and it

40 만족스러운 움직임으로 모자를 털었다.

41 Sure의 뜻.

42 when 이하의 문장: 플럼이 혼자서 호두를 까서 가까스로 빼먹게 되었을 때.

43 이바는 온갖 새로운 뉴스거리를 그에게 늘어놓고.

44 howdy: How are you의 뜻.

45 그의 번쩍거림 아래, 그의 목줄기와 어깨를 추스리는, 묘하게 긴장된 모양새에서 왠지 그의 실패가 느껴졌다.

was then that she knew what to feel. A liquid trail of hate flooded her chest[46].

Knowing that she would hate him long and well filled her with pleasant anticipation, like when you know you are going to fall in love with someone and you wait for the happy signs[47]. Hating BoyBoy, she could get on with it[48], and have the safety, the thrill, the consistency of that hatred as long as she wanted or needed it to define and strengthen her or protect her from routine vulnerabilities[49]. (Once when Hannah accused her of hating colored people, Eva said she only hated one, Hannah's father BoyBoy, and it was hating him that kept her alive and happy.)

Happy or not, after BoyBoy's visit she began her retreat to her bedroom, leaving the bottom of the house more and more to those who lived there: cousins who were passing through, stray folks, and the many, many newly married couples she let rooms to with housekeeping privileges[50], and after 1910 she didn't willingly set foot on the stairs but once and that was to light a fire, the smoke of which was in her hair for years.

Among the tenants in that big old house were the children Eva took in. Operating on a private scheme of preference and prejudice[51], she sent off for children she had seen from the

46 증오의 물길이 그녀의 가슴속에 밀려들었다.

47 앞으로 오래도록 그를 미워할 것이고, 그러한 예상은 그녀를 기쁨으로 가득하게 한다는 사실을 그녀는 알았다. 마치 누군가와 사랑에 빠져 행복한 소식을 기다리기라도 하는 것처럼 말이다.

48 보이보이를 미워하면서도 그럭저럭 잘 지낼 수 있었다.

49 남편에 대한 미움에 의하여 자신을 규정하고 자신을 강하게 만들거나, 혹은 흔한 마음의 상처로부터 자신을 보호할 수 있는 한.

50 many newly married couples... privileges: 집안 전체의 관리를 도맡는 특권을 주면서 젊은 신혼부부들에게 방을 세 주었다.

balcony of her bedroom or whose circumstances she had heard about from the gossipy old men who came to play checkers or read the *Courier*[52], or write her number[53]. In 1921, when her granddaughter Sula was eleven, Eva had three such children. They came with woolen caps and names given to them by their mothers, or grandmothers, or somebody's best friend. Eva snatched the caps off their heads and ignored their names. She looked at the first child closely, his wrists, the shape of his head and the temperament that showed in his eyes and said, "Well. Look at Dewey. My my mymymy." When later that same year she sent for a child who kept falling down off the porch across the street, she said the same thing. Somebody said, "But, Miss Eva, you calls the other one Dewey[54]."

"So? This here's another one."

When the third one was brought and Eva said "dewey" again, everybody thought she had simply run out of names or that her faculties had finally softened[55].

"How is anybody going to tell them apart?[56]" Hannah asked her.

"What you need to tell them apart for? They's all deweys."

When Hannah asked the question it didn't sound very bright, because each dewey was markedly different from the other two. Dewey one was a deeply black boy with a beautiful head and the golden eyes of chronic jaundice[57]. Dewey two was light-

51 전적으로 자신의 개인적인 선호와 편견에 의해 집을 세주면서.
52 신문
53 그녀의 장부를 대신 기입해 준다.
54 이바는 아이들을 모두 한 이름으로, 즉, 듀이라고 부름.
55 그녀의 지각 기능이 저조해졌다고 모두들 생각했다.
56 사람들이 아이들을 어떻게 구별하지요?

skinned with freckles everywhere and a head of tight red hair. Dewey three was half Mexican with chocolate skin and black bangs. Besides, they were one and two years apart in age. It was Eva saying things like, "send one of them deweys out to get me some Garret, if they don't have Garret, get Buttercup," or, "Tell them deweys to cut out that noise," or, "Come here, you dewey you," and, "Send me a dewey," that gave Hannah's question its weight[58].

Slowly each boy came out of whatever cocoon he was in at the time his mother or somebody gave him away, and accepted Eva's view, becoming in fact as well as in name a dewey—joining with the other two to become a trinity with a plural name. . . inseparable, loving nothing and no one but themselves[59]. When the handle from the icebox fell off, all the deweys got whipped[60], and in dry-eyed silence watched their own feet as they turned their behinds high up into the air for the stroke. When the golden-eyed dewey was ready for school he would not go without the others. He was seven, freckled dewey was five, and Mexican dewey was only four. Eva solved the problem by having them all sent off together. Mr. Buckland Reed said, "But one of them's only four."

"How you know? They all come here the same year," Eva said.

"But that one there was one year old when he came, and that was three years ago."

---

57 만성 황달로 인한 눈이 노란 색임.

58 that gave Hannah's ... weight: 한나의 질문에 일리가 있는 경우. that 은 관계대명사이고, 선행사는 "send me a dewey,"

59 소년들이 버림받았을 당시에 그들이 어떤 고치 안에 머물러 있었든지 간에 그들은 천천히 그 고치에서 벗어났다. 그리고 이바의 견해를 받아들여 이름뿐 아니라 실제로 듀이가 되어 있었다. 그래서 그들은 서로 서로 하나가 되어 복수의 이름을 지닌 삼위일체를 이루었고, 분리될 수 없었으며 그들 자신 이외에 아무것도 사랑하지 않게 되었다.

60 아이스박스의 손잡이 떨어져 나가면, 세 명이 모두 함께 회초리를 맞았다.

"You don't know how old he was when he come here and neither do the teacher. Send'em."

The teacher was startled but not unbelieving, for she had long ago given up trying to fathom[61] the ways of the colored people in town. So when Mrs. Reed said that their names were Dewey King, that they were cousins, and all were six years old, the teacher gave only a tiny sigh and wrote them in the record book for the first grade. She too thought she would have no problem distinguishing among them, because they looked nothing alike, but like everyone else before her, she gradually found that she could not tell one from the other. The deweys would not allow it. They got all mixed up in her head, and finally she could not literally believe her eyes. They spoke with one voice, thought with one mind, and maintained an annoying privacy. Stouthearted, surly, and wholly unpredictable, the deweys remained a mystery not only during all of their lives in Medallion but after as well.

The deweys came in 1921, but the year before[62] Eva had given a small room off the kitchen to Tar Baby, a beautiful, slight, quiet man who never spoke above a whisper. Most people said he was half white, but Eva said he was all white. That she knew blood when she saw it, and he didn't have none[63]. When he first came to Medallion, the people called him Pretty Johnnie, but Eva looked at his milky skin and cornsilk hair and out of a mixture of fun and meanness called him Tar Baby[64]. He was a mountain boy[65] who stayed to himself, bothering no one, intent

61 fathom: 이해하다.

62 1921년에 듀이 소년들이 왔고, 그들이 오기 1년 전에 이바는 타르 베이비에게 부엌에서 좀 떨어진 작은 방을 주었다.

63 이바는 보기만 하면 혈통을 알 수 있고 타르 베이비은 흑인 피가 없다고 말했다.

64 이바는 장난기와 골려줄 목적으로 그를 타르 베이비라고 불렀다.

solely on drinking himself to death. At first he worked in a poultry market, and after wringing the necks of chickens all day, he came home and drank until he slept. Later he began to miss days at work[66] and frequently did not have his rent money. When he lost his job altogether, he would go out in the morning, scrounge around for money doing odd jobs, bumming[67] or whatever, and come home to drink. Because he was no bother, ate little, required nothing, and was a lover of cheap wine, no one found him a nuisance. Besides, he frequently went to Wednesday-night prayer meetings and sang with the sweetest hill voice[68] imaginable "In the sweet By-and-By." He sent the deweys out for his liquor and spent most of his time in a heap on the floor or sitting in a chair staring at the wall.

Hannah worried about him a little, but only a very little. For it soon became clear that he simply wanted a place to die privately but not quite alone. No one thought of suggesting to him that he pull himself together[69] or see a doctor or anything. Even the women at prayer meeting who cried when he sang "In the Sweet By-and-By" never tried to get him to participate in the church activities. They just listened to him sing, wept and thought very graphically of their own imminent deaths. The people either accepted his own evaluation of his life, or were indifferent to it. There was, however, a measure of contempt in their indifference, for they had little patience with people who took themselves that seriously[70]. Seriously enough to try to die. And it was natural

65 mountain boy: 은자 (隱者).

66 그 후, 낮에 직장도 빠지기 시작했다.

67 놀고 지내며

68 달콤한 고음

69 pull himself together: 정신을 차리다.

70 스스로에 대해 그토록 심각한 사람을 참아낼 인내심이 없었다.

that he, after all, became the first one to join Shadrack — Tar Baby and the deweys — on National Suicide Day.

Under Eva's distant eye, and prey to her idiosyncrasies[71], her own children grew up stealthily: Pearl married at fourteen and moved to Flint, Michigan, from where she posted frail letters to her mother with two dollars folded into the writing paper. Sad little nonsense letters about minor troubles, her husband's job and who the children favored[72]. Hannah married a laughing man named Rekus who died when their daughter Sula was about three years old, at which time Hannah moved back into her mother's big house prepared to take care of it and her mother forever.

With the exception of BoyBoy, those Peace women loved all men. It was manlove that Eva bequeathed to her daughters[73]. Probably, people said, because there were no men in the house, no men to run it. But actually that was not true. The Peace women simply loved maleness, for its own sake. Eva, old as she was, and with one leg, had a regular flock of gentleman callers, and although she did not participate in the act of love, there was a good deal of teasing and pecking[74] and laughter. The men wanted to see her lovely calf, that neat shoe, and watch the focusing that sometimes swept down out of the distances in her eyes[75]. They wanted to see the joy in her face as they

71 이바의 무심함과 특이한 성격에 희생되어, 그녀의 자녀들은 남의 눈을 피해 커나갔다.

72 자잘한 문제들, 남편의 직장, 이이들이 누구를 더 좋아하는지... 등과 같은 슬프고도 말도 안되는 편지들을 엄마에게 보냈다.

73 남자를 좋아하는 것은 이바가 딸에게 물려준 것이었다.

74 형식적으로 입을 맞추는 행위

75 남자들은 그녀의 예쁜 각선미와 깔끔한 신발을 보고 싶었다. 또한, 그녀의

settled down to play checkers, knowing that even when she beat them, as she almost always did, somehow, in her presence, it was they who had won something. They would read the newspaper aloud to her and make observations on its content, and Eva would listen feeling no obligation to agree and, in fact, would take them to task about their interpretation of events[76]. But she argued with them with such an absence of bile, such a concentration of manlove, that they felt their convictions solidified by her disagreement[77].

With other people's affairs Eva was equally prejudiced about men[78]. She fussed interminably with the brides of the newly wed couples for not getting their men's supper ready on time; about how to launder shirts, press them, etc. "Yo' man be here direc'lin. Ain't it 'bout time you got busy?[79]"

"Aw, Miss Eva. It'll be ready. We just having spaghetti[80]."

"Again?" Eva's eyebrows fluted up[81] and the newlywed pressed her lips together in shame.

Hannah simply refused to live without the attentions of a man, and after Rekus' death had a steady sequence of lovers, mostly the husbands of her friends and neighbors. Her flirting was sweet, low and guileless. Without ever a pat of the hair[82],

---

눈 길이 먼 곳에 머물다가 갑자기 가까운 한곳으로 초점을 맞추기 위해 몰려오는 것을 보고 싶었다.

76 신문에 난 사건에 대한 견해를 말하도록 만들었다.

77 그녀는 언짢은 기색 없이 논쟁했고, 자신을 좋아한다는 집중적인 느낌으로 인하여, 그녀의 반론에 의해 자신들의 확신이 오히려 견고해지는 느낌이 들었다.

78 다른 사람들의 일에 관하여도 그녀는 마찬가지로 남자들에 대한 호의적인 편견을 가졌다.

79 당신의 남편이 집에 돌아오고 있잖아. 이제 바빠질 시간이잖아?

80 스파게티. 서양 음식 중 가장 쉽게 만들 수 있는 음식중의 하나다.

81 이바는 눈살을 찌푸렸다.

a rush to change clothes or a quick application of paint[83], with no gesture whatsoever, she rippled with sex[84]. In her same old print wraparound[85], barefoot in the summer, in the winter her feet in a man's leather slippers with the backs flattened under her heels[86], she made men aware of her behind, her slim ankles, the dew-smooth skin and the incredible length of neck. Then the smile-eyes, the turn of the head — all so welcoming, light and playful. Her voice trailed, dipped and bowed[87]; she gave a chord to the simplest words[88]. Nobody, but nobody, could say "Hey sugar" like Hannah[89]. When he heard it, the man tipped his hat down a little over his eyes, hoisted his trousers and thought about the hollow place at the base of her neck[90]. And all this without the slightest confusion about work and responsibilities[91]. While Eva tested and argued with her men, leaving them feeling as though they had been in combat with a worthy, if amiable, foe, Hannah rubbed no edges[92], made no demands, made the man feel as though he were complete and wonderful just as he was — he didn't need fixing — and so he relaxed and swooned in the Hannah-light that shone on him

82 머리 한번 매만지지 않고
83 재빠르게 화장을 고치는 법도 없이
84 물결이 일렁이듯 섹스를 즐겼다.
85 날염 들인 낡은 스커트
86 겨울에는 남자용 가죽 실내화 뒤를 꺾어 신고
87 그녀의 목소리는 길게 늘어지면서 잠겼다가 구부러지곤 했다(즉, 매우 애교 있는 목소리였다는 뜻임).
88 가장 단순한 단어에도 느낌이 실렸다.
89 어느 누구도 한나처럼 달콤하게 사람을 부를 수는 없었다.
90 그녀의 목 아래 옴폭 들어간 부분, 즉, 젖가슴을 생각했다.
91 직장이나 자신의 책임과 조금도 혼동하지 않은 채, 한나에게 호감을 품었다.
92 rub no edges: 성가시게 하지 않다.

simply because he was. If the man entered and Hannah was carrying a coal scuttle up from the basement[93], she handled it in such a way that it became a gesture of love. He made no move to help her with it simply because he wanted to see how her thighs looked when she bent to put it down, knowing that she wanted him to see them too.

But since in that crowded house there were no places for private and spontaneous lovemaking, Hannah would take the man down into the cellar in the summer where it was cool back behind the coal bin and the newspapers, or in the winter they would step into the pantry and stand up against the shelves she had filled with canned goods, or lie on the flour sack just under the rows of tiny green peppers. When those places were not available, she would slip into the seldom-used parlor, or even up to her bedroom. She liked the last place least[94], not because Sula slept in the room with her but because her love mate's tendency was always to fall asleep afterward and Hannah was fastidious about whom she slept with. She would fuck practically anything, but sleeping with someone implied for her a measure of trust and a definite commitment[95]. So she ended up a daylight lover[96], and it was only once actually that Sula came home from school and found her mother in the bed, curled spoon in the arms of a man[97].

93 남자가 집에 들어올 때 마침 한나가 지하실로부터 석탄을 들고 종종걸음으로 걷고 있다면.

94 그녀에게 마지막 장소, 즉 침실은 가장 덜 좋아하는 곳이었다.

95 그녀는 누구와든 성관계를 맺을 수 있었다. 그러나 누군가와 함께 잔다는 것은 신의와 절대적인 헌신을 의미했다.

96 대낮에 관계를 갖게 되었다. (왜냐하면 남자들이 관계 후 잠들지 않는 대낮을 선호했기 때문에.)

97 술라가 방과후 집에 돌아와 엄마가 다른 남자의 품안에서 애무하며 구부리고 있는 모습을 발견한 것은 실제로 한 번 뿐이었다.

Seeing her step so easily into the pantry and emerge looking precisely as she did when she entered, only happier, taught Sula that sex was pleasant and frequent, but otherwise unremarkable[98]. Outside the house, where children giggled about underwear, the message was different[99]. So she watched her mother's face and the face of the men when they opened the pantry door and made up her own mind.

Hannah exasperated the women in the town — the "good" women, who said, "One thing I can't stand is a nasty woman" ; the whores, who were hard put to find trade among black men anyway and who resented Hannah's generosity[1]; the middling[2] women, who had both husbands and affairs, because Hannah seemed too unlike them, having no passion attached to her relationships and being wholly incapable of jealousy. Hannah's friendships with women were, of course, seldom and short-lived, and the newly married couples whom her mother took in soon learned what a hazard she was. She could break up a marriage before it had even become one — she would make love the new groom and wash his wife's dishes all in an afternoon. What she wanted, after Rekus dies, and what she succeeded in having more often than not[3], was some touching every day.

The men, surprisingly, never gossiped about her. She was

98 엄마가 찬방으로 편안하게 들러간 다음, 나올 때도 똑같은 모습으로, 아니 더 행복해진 모습으로 나타나는 모습을 보면서, 술라는 섹스란 즐겁고 자주 하는 것이며, 그렇지 않은 경우엔 대수롭지 않은 일이라고 여기게 되었다.

99 속옷에 대해 아이들이 킥킥거리는 집 바깥에서는 그 의미가 달랐다.

1 어쨌거나 한나 때문에 흑인들 사이에 영업에 어렵고 더구나 한나가 돈을 받지 않기 때문에 분노하는 창녀들.

2 소위 "훌륭한" 여자들과 창녀 사이의 중간, 평범한 여자들.

3 종종

unquestionably a kind and generous woman and that, coupled with her extraordinary beauty and funky elegance of manner, made them defend her and protect her from any vitriol that newcomers or their wives might spill.

Eva's last child, Plum, to whom she hoped to bequeath everything, floated in a constant swaddle of love and affection[4], until 1917 when he went to war. He returned to the States in 1919 but did not get back to Medallion until 1920. He wrote letters from New York, Washington, D.C., and Chicago full of promises of homecomings, but there was obviously something wrong. Finally some two or three days after Christmas, he arrived with just the shadow of his old dip-down walk[5]. His hair had been neither cut nor combed in months, his clothes were pointless and he had no socks. But he did have a black bag, a paper sack, and a sweet, sweet smile. Everybody welcomed him and gave him a warm room next to Tar Baby's and waited for him to tell them whatever it was he wanted them to know. They waited in vain for his telling but not long for the knowing[6]. His habits were much like Tar Baby's but there were no bottles, and Plum was sometimes cheerful and animated. Hannah watched and Eva waited. Then he began to steal from them[7], take trips to Cincinnati and sleep for days in his room with the record player going[8]. He got even thinner, since he ate only snatches of things at

---

4 floated in... affection: 엄마의 지속적인 사랑과 애정의 품안에서 성장했다.

5 with just the shadow of ... walk: 예전의 건실한 걸음걸이는 거의 보이지 않은 채.

6 그가 말해주기를 헛되게 기다렸다, 그러나 알기 위해서 그다지 오래 기다린 것은 아니었다.

7 몰래 빠져나가다.

8 전축을 틀어 놓은 채.

beginnings or endings of meals. It was Hannah who found the bent spoon black from steady cooking[9].

So late on night in 1921, Eva got up from her bed and put on her clothes. Hoisting herself up on her crutches[10], she was amazed to find that she could still manage them, although the pain in her armpits was severe. She practiced a few steps around the room, and then opened the door. Slowly, she manipulated herself down the long flights of stairs, two crutches under her left arm, the right hand grasping the banister[11]. The sound of her foot booming in comparison to the delicate pat of the crutch tip[12]. On each landing she stopped for breath[13]. Annoyed at her physical condition, she closed her eyes and removed the crutches from under her arms to relieve the unaccustomed pressure. At the foot of the stairs she redistributed her weight between the crutches and swooped on through the front room, to the dining room, to the kitchen, swinging and swooping[14] like a giant heron, so graceful sailing about in its own habitat but awkward and comical when it folded its wings and tried to walk. With a swing and a swoop she arrived at Plum's door and pushed it open with the tip of one crutch. He was lying in bed barely visible in the light coming from a single bulb. Eva swung over to the bed

9 조리하는데 오랫동안 사용한 탓에 그을고 구부러진 스푼을 찾아낸 사람은 바로 한나였다.

10 목발로 딛고 일어서서

11 한 손으로는 계단의 난간을 잡고, 왼 쪽 팔 아래 두개의 목발을 짚으며 긴 계단을 간신히 내려갔다.

12 목발 끝이 살며시 바닥에 닿는데 반해 그녀의 발소리는 쾅쾅 울렸다.

13 한 칸씩 내릴 때마다 멈춰서 그녀는 숨을 몰아쉬었다.

14 휘두르고 잡아채듯 달려들며

and propped her crutches at its foot. She sat down and gathered Plum into her arms[15]. He woke, but only slightly.

"Hey, man. Hey. You holdin' me, Mamma?" His voice was drowsy and amused. He chuckled as though he had heard some private joke. Eva held him closer and began to rock. Back and forth she rocked him, her eyes wandering around his room. There in the corner was a half-eaten store-bought cherry pie. balled-up candy wrappers and empty pop bottles peeped from under the dresser. On the floor by her foot was a glass of strawberry crush and a *Liberty* magazine. Rocking, rocking, listening to Plum's occasional chuckles, Eva let her memory spin, loop and fall. Plum in the tub that time[16] as she leaned over him.[17] He reached up and dripped water into her bosom and laughed. She was angry, but not too, and laughed with him.

"Mamma, you so purty[18]. You so purty, Mamma."

Eva lifted her tongue to the edge of her lip to stop the tears from running into her mouth. Rocking, rocking. Later she laid him down and looked at him a long time. Suddenly she was thirsty and reached for the glass of strawberry crush. She put it to her lips and discovered it was blood-tainted water[19] and threw it to the floor. Plum woke up and said, "Hey, Mamma, whyn't you go on back to bed? I'm all right. Didn't I tell you. I'm all right. Go on, now."

"I'm going, Plum," she said. She shifted her weight and pulled her crutches toward her. Swinging and swooping, she left his room. She dragged herself to the kitchen and made grating

15 풀럼을 팔로 안았다.

16 욕조에 앉아 있던 플럼을 회상한다.

17 그녀가 플럼에게 기댈 때 그는 기억 속, 욕조 안에 있었다.

18 pretty

19 피가 섞여 있는 물.

noises[20].

Plum on the rim of a warm light sleep[21] was still chuckling. Mamma. She sure was somethin'. He felt twilight[22]. Now there seemed to be some kind of wet light traveling over his legs and stomach with a deeply attractive smell. It wound itself[23] — this wet light — all about him, splashing and running into his skin. He opened his eyes and saw what he imagined was the great wing of an eagle pouring a wet lightness over him. Some kind of baptism, some kind of blessing, he thought. Everything is going to be all right, it said. Knowing that it was so he closed his eyes and sank back into the bright hole of sleep.

Eva stepped back from the bed and let the crutches rest under her arms. She rolled a bit of newspaper into a tight stick about six inches long, lit it and threw it onto the bed where the kerosene-soaked Plum lay in snug delight[24]. Quickly, as the whoosh of flames engulfed him, she shut the door and made her slow and painful journey back to the top of the house.

Just as she got to the third landing[25] she could hear Hannah and some child's voice. She swung along[26], not even listening to the voices of alarm and the cries of the deweys. By the time she got to her bed someone was bounding up the stairs after her. Hannah opened the door. "Plum! Plum! He's

---

20 삐걱거리는 소리를 내다.

21 아직 잠이 얕게 든 상태에서

22 몽롱하게 느꼈다.

23 불길이 자신을 휘감는 상태를 묘사함.

24 신문지를 6인치 정도로 돌돌 말아 막대기를 만든 다음 그 위에 불을 붙인다. 그리고 등유에 폭 젖은 채 포근한 잠에 잠긴 플럼이 자고 있는 침대에 불붙은 신문지를 던졌다.

25 세 번째 계단에 발을 놓았을 때.

26 계속해서 계단을 올라갔다.

burning, Mamma! We can't even open the door! Mamma!"

Eva looked into Hannah's eyes. "Is? My baby? Burning?" The two women did not speak, for the eyes of each were enough for the other[27]. Then Hannah closed hers and ran toward the voices of neighbors calling for water.

27 두 눈으로 모든 것을 전하고 이해할 수 있기에 두 여자는 아무 말도 하지 않았다.

1922

It was too cool for ice cream. A hill wind was blowing dust and empty Camels wrappers about their ankles[1]. It pushed their dresses into the creases of their behinds, then lifted the hems to peek at their cotton underwear[2]. They[3] were on their way to Edna Finch's Mellow House, an ice cream parlor catering to nice folks — where even children would feel comfortable, you know, even though it was right next to Reba's Grill and just one block down from the Time and a Half Pool Hall. It[4] sat in the curve of Carpenter's Road, which, in four blocks, made up all the sporting life available in the Bottom[5]. Old men and young ones draped themselves in front of the Elmira Theater, Irene's Palace of Cosmetology, the pool hall, the grill and the other sagging business enterprises that lined the street. On sills[6], on stoops[7], on crates[8] and broken chairs they sat tasting their teeth and waiting for something to distract them. Every passerby, every motorcar, every alteration in stance caught their attention and was commented on. Particularly they watched women. When a

1 언덕에서 부는 바람이 먼지를 날리고, 그들이 발목까지 덮은 헐렁한 낙타털 치마를 펄럭였다.

2 바람은 엉덩이의 갈라진 틈새로 옷을 밀어 넣었고, 치마 끝을 들썩거리는 바람에 무명 속옷이 내 보였다.

3 술라와 넬

4 Edna Finch's Mellow House

5 네 개의 블록에 걸쳐 바텀 마을에서 가능한 모든 오락을 제공하는 거리.

6 문턱

7 현관 입구의 계단

8 포장용 상자

woman approached, the older men tipped their hats; the younger ones opened and closed their thighs. But all of them, whatever their age, watched her retreating view with interest.

Nel and Sula walked through this valley of eyes chilled by the wind and heated by the embarrassment of appraising stares[9]. The old men looked at their stalklike legs[10], dwelled on the cords[11] in the backs of their knees and remembered old dance steps they had not done in twenty years. In their lust, which age had turned to kindness[12], they moved their lips as though to stir up the taste of young sweat on tight skin.

Pig meat[13]. The words were in all their minds. And one of them, one of the young ones, said it aloud. Softly but definitively and there was no mistaking the compliment[14]. His name was Ajax, a twenty-one-year-old pool haunt of sinister beauty[15]. Graceful and economical in every movement, he held a place of envy with men of all ages for his magnificently foul mouth[16]. In fact he seldom cursed, and the epithets he chose were dull, even harmless. His reputation was derived from the way he handled the words. When he said "Hell" he hit the *h* with his lungs[17]

---

9 바람 때문에 차갑지만 뚫어지게 쳐다보는 뜨거운 눈길에 당황하면서 시선으로 가득한 길 위를 넬과 술라는 걸어가고 있었다.

10 늘씬한 다리

11 cords: 힘줄

12 시간이 지나면서 친절로 변한 욕정 속에서

13 돼지 고기. 여자를 욕정의 단순한 대상으로 여기는 욕설에 가까운 언어. 여성의 입장에서는 비하적인 언어로 들릴 수 있으나, 남자들의 입장에서 매혹적인 여자라는 뜻에서 사용했다면, 다소 칭찬조로 들릴 수도 있는 애매모호한 말이다.

14 부드럽지만 확실하게 말했다. 그리고 그 말(Pig meat)이 칭찬임에는 분명했다.

15 사악한 아름다움을 지닌, 스물 한 살의 당구광이었다.

16 걸쩍지근한 말씨.

and the impact was greater than the achievement of the most imaginative foul mouth in the town. He could say "shit" with a nastiness impossible to imitate. So, when he said "Pig meat" as Nel and Sula passed, they guarded their eyes lest someone see their delight.

It was not really Edna Finch's ice cream that made them brave the stretch of those panther eyes[18]. Years later their own eyes would glaze as they cupped their chins in remembrance of the inchworm smiles, the squatting haunches, the track-rail legs straddling broken chairs[19]. The cream-colored trousers marking with a mere seam the place where the mystery curled[20]. Those smooth vanilla crotches[21] invited them; those lemon-yellow gabardines[22] beckoned to them.

They moved toward the ice-cream parlor like tightrope walkers, as thrilled by the possibility of a slip as by the maintenance of tension and balance[23]. The least sideways glance, the merest toe stub, could pitch them into those creamy haunches spread wide with welcome[24]. Somewhere beneath all of that daintiness, chambered in all that neatness, lay the thing that clotted their

17 H를 발음할 때, 폐부 깊숙한 곳으로부터 잡아끄는 소리를 냈다.

18 표범 같은 눈길이 뻗친 곳으로 감히 걸어가게 된 것은 에드나 핀치의 아이스크림 때문은 아니었다.

19 몇 년이 지나면, 턱을 괴고 앉아 자벌레 같은 남자들의 웃음, 잔뜩 웅크린 모습, 부러진 의자에 선로처럼 벌리고 앉은 모양새를 기억하면서 그들 자신의 눈길도 그 (남자들처럼) 욕망에 가득 찬 눈길이 될 터였다.

20 안쪽에 신비(성기)가 웅크리고 있을 홑솔기 크림색 바지.

21 남자의 성기를 말함.

22 개버딘 바지. 역시 남자들을 의미함.

23 균형과 긴장의 유지에 의해 전율을 느끼는 만큼이나 미끄러져 떨어지는 실수에도 재미가 있는 줄타는 곡예사처럼.

24 조금만 눈길을 빗겨도, 약간만 발이 삐끗해도, 언제든지 환영한 태세를 갖추고 다리를 활짝 벌리고 웅크린 크림빛 남자들에게 내던져질 판이었다.

dreams.[25]

Which was only fitting, for it was in dreams that the two girls had first met. Long before Edna Finch's Mellow House opened, even before they marched through the chocolate halls of Garfield Primary School out onto the playground and stood facing each other through the ropes of the one vacant swing ("Go on." "No. You go."), they had already made each other's acquaintance in the delirium of their noon dreams. They were solitary little girls whose loneliness was so profound it intoxicated them and sent them stumbling into Technicolored visions[26] that always included a presence, a someone, who, quite like the dreamer, shared the delight of the dream. When Nel, an only child, sat on the steps of her back porch surrounded by the high silence of her mother's incredibly orderly house, feeling the neatness pointing at her back, she studied the poplars and fell easily into a picture of herself lying on a flowered bed, tangled in her own hair, waiting for some fiery prince. He approached but never quite arrived. But always, watching the dream along with her, were some smiling sympathetic eyes. Someone as interested as she herself in the flow of her imagined hair, the thickness of the mattress of flowers, the voile sleeves that closed below her elbows in gold-threaded cuffs[27].

Similarly, Sula, also an only child, but wedged into a household of throbbing disorder constantly awry with things, people, voices and the slamming of doors, spent hours in the attic behind a roll of linoleum galloping through her own mind

---

25 그들의 고상함 아래 어딘가에, 정갈함 속 깊숙한 곳에, 그들의 꿈을 엉겨 게 하는 뭔가가 있었다.

26 천연색의, 선명한 빛깔의 비전

27 머리모양을 상상할 때, 풍성한 꽃밭, 금실로 박은 소매가 팔꿈치까지 달려 늘어진 보일 옷소매, 등에 자신만큼 관심 있는 누군가가 있었다.

on a gray-and-white horse tasting sugar and smelling roses in full view of a someone who shared both the taste and the speed.

So when they met, first in those chocolate halls and next through the ropes of the swing, they felt the ease and comfort of old friends. Because each had discovered years before that they were neither white nor male, and that all freedom and triumph was forbidden to them, they had set about creating something else to be[28]. Their meeting was fortunate, for it let them use each other to grow on. Daughters of distant mothers and incomprehensible fathers[29] (Sula's because he was dead; Nel's because he wasn't), they found in each other's eyes the intimacy they were looking for.

Nel Wright and Sula Peace were both twelve in 1922, wishbone thin and easy-assed[30]. Nel was the color of wet sandpaper[31] — just dark enough to escape the blows of the pitch-black truebloods[32] and the contempt of old women who worried about such things as bad blood mixtures and knew that the origins of a mule and a mulatto were one and the same[33]. Had she been any lighter-skinned she would have needed either her mother's protection on the way to school or a streak of mean[34] to defend herself. Sula was a heavy brown with large quiet eyes, one of

28 그들 모두가 백인도 남자도 아닌 까닭에 또 다른 자아를 만들어야 할 필요를 느꼈다.

29 전혀 성격이 다른 엄마를 가지고 있으면, 아빠에 대해서는 아는 바가 없는 딸들.

30 새다리에 엉덩이가 납작한.

31 까맣지만 완전히 까맣지는 않다는 뜻.

32 the blows of the pitch-black truebloods: 새까만 흑인 순수혈통이라는 자만심.

33 백인피가 섞이는 것을 우려하고, 노새와 혼혈은 근원이 똑같이 미련하다고 믿는 늙은 여자의 경멸을 피하기에 충분할 만큼 새까만 피부색을 지녔다.

34 a streak of mean: 좀 괴팍한, 혹은 비열하고 강한 성향.

which featured a birthmark that spread from the middle of the lid toward the eyebrow, shaped something like a stemmed rose[35]. It gave her otherwise plain face a broken excitement and blue-blade threat[36] like the keloid scar[37] of the razored[38] man who sometimes played checkers with her grandmother. The birthmark was to grow darker as the years passed, but now it was the same shade as her gold-flecked eyes[39], which, to the end, were as steady and clean as rain.

Their friendship was as intense as it was sudden. They found relief in each other's personality. Although both were unshaped, formless things[40], Nel seemed stronger and more consistent than Sula, who could hardly be counted on to sustain any emotion for more than three minutes[41]. Yet there was one time when that was not true, when she held on to a mood for weeks, but even that was in defense of Nel[42].

Four white boys in their early teens, sons of some newly arrived Irish people, occasionally entertained themselves in the afternoon by harassing black schoolchildren. With shoes that pinched and woolen knickers that made red rings on their calves[43], they had come to this valley with their parents

35 한쪽 눈의 속눈썹 가운데로부터 윗눈썹으로 뻗친, 줄기가 달린 장미 모양의 모반이 있었다.

36 반점이 없었다면 평범할 얼굴에 반점은 번득이는 자극과 시퍼렇게 날선 듯한 위협적인 인상을 만들었다.

37 피부 조직이 과도하게 자람으로써 생긴 흉터

38 면도날로 상처를 입은 사람.

39 노란 빛 반점이 있는 눈과 같은 정도의 색조가 되었다.

40 몸매도 형편없고, 볼품없었다.

41 어떤 감정이든, 3분 이상 지속할 수 없는 성격을 지닌 술라 보다는 넬이 한결 강하고 일관성 있는 성격이었다.

42 딱 한번, 그렇지 않은 적인 있는데, 수 주 동안 같은 감정이 지속되었다. 그때조차 넬을 보호하려는 의도에서 비롯된 것이었다.

believing as they did that it was a promised land — green and shimmering with welcome. What they found was a strange accent, a pervasive fear of their religion and firm resistance to their attempts to find work. With one exception the older residents of Medallion scorned them[44]. The one exception was the black community. Although some of the negroes had been in Medallion before the Civil War (the town didn't even have a name then), if they had any hatred for these newcomers it didn't matter because it didn't show. As a matter of fact, baiting them was the one activity that the white Protestant residents concurred in[45]. In part their place in this world was secured only when they echoed the old residents' attitude toward blacks.

These particular boys caught Nel once, and pushed her from hand to hand until they grew tired of the frightened helpless face. Because of that incident, Nel's route home from school became elaborate. She, and then Sula, managed to duck[46] them for weeks until a chilly day in November when Sula said, "Let's us go on home the shortest way."

Nel blinked, but acquiesced. They walked up the street until they got to the bend of Carpenter's Road where the boys lounged on a disused well. Spotting their prey[47], the boys sauntered forward as though there were nothing in the world on

---

43 너무 꽉 쪼여서 종아리에 빨간 줄을 남기는 모직 긴 양말에다가 꼭 끼는 신발을 신고.

44 단 한 부류를 제외하고 메달리온에 오랫동안 살아온 사람들은 모두 그들을 얕잡아 봤다.

45 그들을 괴롭히는 것이야말로 백인 개신교인들이 공동으로 합의한 단 하나의 행동이었다.

46 duck: 피하다.

47 놀림감으로 소녀들을 주목하고는

their minds but the gray sky[48]. Hardly able to control their grins, they stood like a gate blocking the path. When the girls were three feet in front of the boys, Sula reached into her coat pocket and pulled out Eva' paring knife[49]. The boys stopped short, exchanged looks and dropped all pretense of innocence. This was going to be better than they thought. They were going to try and fight back, and with a knife. Maybe they could get an arm around one of their waists, or tear. . .

Sula squatted down in the dirt road and put everything down on the ground: her lunchpail, her reader, her mittens, her slate[50]. Holding the knife in her right hand, she pulled the slate toward her and pressed her left forefinger down hard on its edge. Her aim was determined but inaccurate. She slashed off only the tip of her finger[51]. The four boys stared open-mouthed at the wound and the scrap of flesh, like a button mushroom, curling in the cherry blood that ran into the corners of the slate[52].

Sula raised her eyes to them. Her voice was quiet. "If I can do that to myself, what you suppose I'll do to you?"

The shifting dirt was the only way Nel knew that they were moving away[53]; she was looking at Sula's face, which seemed miles and miles away.

But toughness was not their quality—adventuresomeness was

48 아무 해 끼칠 생각이 없는 척하고

49 손톱 깎는 칼

50 slate: 예정표, 즉 계획표.

51 손가락 끝을 조금 베어 버렸다.

52 the scrap of flesh... the slate: 예정표의 한 모서리로 흘러 들어가는 버찌빛 피 속에서 마치 단추 버섯처럼 꼬부라진 살점.

53 넬은 술라의 자해행위에 너무 놀라서 소년들을 직접 쳐다보지는 못하고, 먼지가 풀풀 일어나는 것만을 보며 소년들이 물러나고 있음에 안심한다는 뜻이다.

— and a mean determination to explore everything that interested them, from one-eyed chickens highstepping in their penned yards to Mr. Buckland Reed's gold teeth[54], from the sound of sheets flapping in the wind to the labels on Tar Baby's wine bottles[55]. And they had no priorities. They could be distracted from watching a fight with mean razors by the glorious smell of hot tar being poured by roadmen two hundred yards away.

In the safe harbor of each other's company they could afford to abandon the ways of other people and concentrate on their own perceptions of things. When Mrs. Wright reminded Nel to pull her nose, she would do it enthusiastically but without the least hope in the world[56].

"While you sittin' there, honey, go 'head and pull your nose."

"It hurts, Mamma."

"Don't you want a nice nose when you grow up?"

After she met Sula, Nel slid the clothespin[57] under blanket as soon as she got in the bed. And although there was still the hateful hot comb to suffer through each Saturday evening[58], its consequences — smooth hair — no longer interested her.

Joined in mutual admiration they watched each day as though it were a movie arranged for their amusement. The new theme they were now discovering was men. So they met regularly,

---

54 from one-eyed chickens... gold teeth: 울 쳐진 뒷마당에서 펄떡거리는 외눈박이 닭에서 시작하여 버클랜드 리드씨의 금이빨에 이르기까지.

55 from the sound... wine bottles: 바람에 침대시트가 펄럭거리는 소리에서부터 타르베이비의 술병딱지에 이르기까지.

56 엄마가 코를 예쁘게 만들려면 당겨줘야 한다고 일러줄 때, 넬은 열심히 당겼지만, 꼭 그렇게 될거라는 어떤 희망이 있어서 하는 것은 아니었다.

57 코를 높이기 위해 사용한 빨래집게

58 흑인의 머리카락은 지나치게 꼬불꼬불하기 때문에 부드럽게 해주기 위해서 토요일 저녁 빗으로 빗는데, 그것이 매우 고통스러웠다는 뜻.

without even planning it, to walk down the road to Edna Finch's Mellow House, even though it was too cool for ice cream.

Then summer came. A summer limp with the weight of blossomed things. Heavy sunflowers weeping over fences; iris curling and browning at the edges far away from their purple hearts; ears of corn letting their auburn hair wind down to their stalks. And the boys. The beautiful, beautiful boys who dotted the landscape like jewels, split the air with their shouts in the field, and thickened the river with their shining wet backs. Even their footsteps left a smell of smoke behind.

It was in that summer, the summer of their twelfth year, the summer of the beautiful black boys, that they became shittish[59], frightened and bold—all at the same time.

In that mercury mood[60] in July, Sula and Nel wandered about the Bottom barefoot looking for mischief. They decided to go down by the river where the boys sometimes swam. Nel waited on the porch of 7 Carpenter's Road while Sula ran into the house to go to the toilet. On the way up the stairs, she passed the kitchen where Hannah sat with two friends, Patsy and Valentine. The two women were fanning themselves and watching Hannah put down some dough, all talking casually about one thing and another, and had gotten around, when Sula passed by, to the problems of child rearing[61].

"They a pain."[62]

"Yeh. Wish I'd listened to mamma[63]. She told me not to have

59 실없고

60 민활하면서도 변덕스러운 분위기

61 술라가 지나치고 있을 때 마침, 아이들 키우는 문제를 거론하고 있었다.

62 아이들은 골치거리야.

63 나도 엄마 말을 잘 들었으면 나았을 텐데...

'em too soon.[64]"

"Any time atall is too soon for me."[65]

"Oh, I don't know. My Rudy minds his daddy[66]. He just wild with me. Be glad when he growed and gone."

Hannah smiled and said, "shut your mouth. You love the ground he pee on."[67]

"Sure I do. But he still a pain. Can't help loving your own child. No matter what they do."

"Well, Hester grown now and I can't say love is exactly what I feel."

"Sure you do. You love her, like I love Sula. I just don't like her. That's the difference."

"Guess so. Likin' them is another thing."

"Sure. They different people[68], you know..."

She only heard Hannah's words, and the pronouncement sent her flying up the stairs. In bewilderment, she stood at the window fingering[69] the curtain edge, aware of a sting in her eye[70]. Nel's call floated up and into the window, pulling her away from dark thoughts back into the bright, hot daylight.

They ran most of the way.

Heading toward the wide part of the river where trees grouped themselves in families darkening the earth below. They passed some boys swimming and clowning in the water, shrouding their

64 엄마는 너무 일찍 아이를 갖지 말라고 했었지.
65 언제 아이들 갖든지 언제라도 내겐 너무 빠른 것이었어.
66 내 아들 루비는 꼭 제 아빠를 닮았어.
67 그 애가 오줌 눈 곳조차 사랑하잖아.
68 they와 different 사이에 "are"가 생략되어 있음.
69 fingering: 만지작거리다.
70 눈이 따끔거리는 것을 느끼며

words in laughter.

They ran in the sunlight, creating their own breeze, which pressed their dresses into their damp skin. Reaching a kind of square of four leaf-locked trees which promised cooling, they flung themselves into the four-cornered shade to taste their lip sweat and contemplate the wildness that had come upon them so suddenly. They lay in the grass, their foreheads almost touching, their bodies stretched away from each other at a 180-degree angle. Sula's head rested on her arm, an undone braid coiled around her wrist[71]. Nel leaned on her elbows and worried[72] long blades of grass with her fingers. Underneath their dresses flesh tightened and shivered in the high coolness[73], their small breasts just now beginning to create some pleasant discomfort when they were lying on their stomachs[74].

Sula lifted her head and joined Nel in the grass play[75]. In concert, without ever meeting each other's eyes, they stroked the blades[76] up and down, up and down. Nel found a thick twig and, with her thumbnail, pulled away its bark until it was stripped to a smooth, creamy innocence[77]. Sula looked about and found one too. When both twigs were undressed[78] Nel moved easily to the next stage and began tearing up rooted grass to make a bare spot of earth[79]. When a generous clearing

71 팔베개를 베고 누웠고, 땋은 머리가 팔목 근처에 풀려져 있었다.

72 쑤석거리다.

73 갑작스런 서늘함에 옷 밑으로 살이 오그라들면서 떨렸다.

74 분사구문. 배를 깔고 눕자 이제 막 커지기 시작한 젖가슴 때문에 불편하게 느꼈다.

75 풀을 가지고 장난치는 일.

76 풀잎

77 넬은 굵은 나무뿌리를 찾아내어 엄지손톱으로 그 껍질을 벗겨냈다. 그러자, 부드럽고 하얀 순수(껍질이 벗어져 하얗게 드러난 줄기)가 드러났다.

78 나무 꼬챙이의 껍질을 다 벗겨냈을 때.

was made, Sula traced intricate patterns in it with her twig. At first Nel was content to do the same. But soon she grew impatient and poked her twig rhythmically and intensely into the earth, making a small neat hole that grew deeper and wider with the least manipulation of her twig. Sula copied her, and soon each had a hole the size of a cup. Nel began a more strenuous digging and, rising to her knee[80], was careful to scoop out the dirt as she made her hole deeper. Together they worked until the two holes were one and the same. When the depression was the size of a small dishpan, Nel's twig broke. With a gesture of disgust she threw the pieces into the hole they had made. Sula threw hers in too. Nel saw a bottle cap and tossed it in as well. Each then looked around for more debris to throw into the hole: paper, bits of glass, butts of cigarettes, until all of the small defiling things they could find were collected there. Carefully they replaced the soil and covered the entire grave with uprooted grass.

Neither one had spoken a word.

They stood up, stretched, then gazed out over the swift dull water as an unspeakable restlessness and agitation held them. At the same instant each girl heard footsteps in the grass. A little boy in too big knickers[81] was coming up from the lower bank of the river. He stopped when he saw them and picked his nose[82].

"Your mamma tole you to stop eatin' snot[83], Chicken," Nel hollered at him through cupped hands.

79 나무 꼬챙이로 풀을 뽑아, 흙만 있는 공간을 만들어냈다.
80 무릎을 꿇고 앉아
81 knickers: 무릎 아래서 졸라매는 낙낙한 짧은 바지.
82 코를 후볐다.
83 snot: 콧물

"Shut up," he said, still picking.

"Come up here and say that."

"Leave him 'lone, Nel. Come here, Chicken. Lemme show you something."

"Naw."

"You scared we gone take your bugger away?[84]"

"Leave him 'lone, I said. Come on, Chicken. Look. I'll help you climb a tree."

Chicken looked at the tree Sula was pointing to — a big double beech with low branches and lots of bends for sitting. He moved slowly toward her.

"Come on, Chicken, I'll help you up."

Still picking his nose, his eyes wide, he came to where they were standing. Sula took him by the hand and coaxed[85] him along. When they reached the base of the beech, she lifted him to the first branch, saying, "go on. Go on. I got you." She followed the boy, steadying him, when he needed it, with her hand and her reassuring voice. When they were as high as they could go, Sula pointed to the far side of the river.

"See? Bet you never saw that far before, did you?"

"Uh uh."

"Now look down there." They both leaned a little and peered through the leaves at Nel standing below, squinting up at them. From their height she looked small and foreshortened.

Chicken Little laughed.

"Y'all better come on down before you break your neck," Nel hollered.

"I ain't never coming down," the boy hollered back.

"Yeah. We better. Come on, Chicken."

---

84 bugger: 쓸모없는 하찮은 물건.

85 coax: 유혹하다.

"Naw. Lemme go."

"Yeah, Chicken. Come on, now."

Sula pulled his leg gently.

"Lemme go."

"OK, I'm leavin' you." She started on.

"Wait!" he screamed.

Sula stopped and together they slowly worked their way down. Chicken was still elated. "I was way up there, wasn't I? Wasn't I? I'm a tell my brovver[86]."

Sula and Nel began to mimic him: "I'm a tell my brovver; I'm a tell my brovver."

Sula picked him up by his hands and swung him outward then around and around[87]. His knickers ballooned[88] and his shrieks of frightened joy startled the birds and the fat grasshoppers. When he slipped from her hands and sailed away out over the water they could still hear his bubbly laughter[89].

The water darkened and closed quickly over the place where Chicken Little sank. The pressure of his hard and tight little fingers was still in Sula's palms as she stood looking at the closed place in the water. They expected him to come back up, laughing. Both girls stared at the water.

Nel spoke first. "Somebody saw." A figure appeared briefly on the opposite shore.

The only house over there was Shadrack's. Sula glanced at Nel. Terror widened her nostrils. Had he seen?

The water was so peaceful now. There was nothing but the

86 brother

87 팔을 잡고 들어 올려 빙빙 돌렸다.

88 무릎에서 잡아매는 반바지 속으로 바람이 들어가 불룩해졌다.

89 빙빙 돌리던 손을 놓아 버리자 아이는 물 속 저편으로 내던져졌다. 그리고 여전히 거품이 퐁퐁 솟는 듯한 아이의 웃음소리가 들렸다.

baking sun and something newly missing. Sula cupped her face for an instant, then turned and ran up to the little plank bridge that crossed the river to Shadrack's house. There was no path. It was as though neither Shadrack nor anyone else ever came this way.

Her running was swift and determined, but when she was close to the three little steps that led to his porch, fear crawled into her stomach and only the something newly missing back there in the river[90] made it possible for her to walk up the three steps and knock at the door.

No one answered. She started back, but thought again of the peace of the river. Shadrack would be inside, just behind the door ready to pounce on her. Still she could not go back. Ever so gently she pushed the door with the tips of her fingers and heard only the hinges weep[91]. More. And then she was inside. Alone. The neatness, the order startled her, but more surprising was the restfulness. Everything was so tiny, so common, so unthreatening. Perhaps this was not the house of the Shad. The terrible Shad who walked about with his penis out, who peed in front of ladies and girl-children, the only black who could curse white people and get away with it, who drank in the road from the mouth of the bottle, who shouted and shook in the streets. This cottage? This sweet old cottage? With its made-up bed[92]? With its rag rug and wooden table? Sula stood in the middle of the little room and in her wonder forgot what she had come for until a sound at the door made her jump. He was there in the doorway looking at her. She had not heard his coming and now he was looking at her.

---

90 something newly... : 방금 물에 빠진 Chicken Little을 가리킴.

91 문이 삐걱거리는 소리.

92 잘 정돈된 침대.

More in embarrassment than terror she averted her glance[93]. When she called up enough courage to look back at him, she saw his hand resting upon the door frame. His fingers, barely touching the wood, were arranged in a graceful arc. Relieved and encouraged (no one with hands like that, no one with fingers that curved around wood so tenderly could kill her), she walked past him out of the door, feeling his gaze turning, turning with her.

At the edge of the porch, gathering the wisps of courage that were fast leaving her, she turned once more to look at him, to ask him. . . had he. . .?

He was smiling, a great smile, heavy with lust and time to come[94]. He nodded his head as though answering a question, and said, in a pleasant conversational tone, a tone of cooled butter, "Always."

Sula fled down the steps, and shot through the greenness and the baking sun back to Nel and the dark closed place in the water. There she collapsed in tears.

Nel quieted her. "Sh, sh. Don't, don't. You didn't mean it. It ain't your fault. Sh. Sh. Come on, le's go, Sula. Come on, now. Was he there? Did he see? Where's the belt to your dress?"

Sula shook her head while she searched her waist for the belt.

Finally she stood up and allowed Nel to lead her away. "He said, 'Always. Always.' [95]"

---

93 시선을 돌렸다.

94 heavy with lust and time to come: 다가올 미래에 대한 기대와 욕정으로 가득한.

95 우연한 사건과 오해가 작중인물의 삶을 묘한 방향으로 이끌게 된다. "always"란 쉐드랙의 말은 술라에게서 전혀 엉뚱하게도 자신의 범죄 행위를 계속해서 보아왔다는 뜻으로 해석된다. 또한 술라의 방문 역시 쉐드랙에게 다른 해석을 야기하여 술라를 평생 동안 자신의 연인으로 삼게 된다.

"What?"

Sula covered her mouth as they walked down the hill. Always. He had answered a question she had not asked, and its promise[96] licked at her feet.

A bargeman, poling away from the shore, found Chicken late that afternoon stuck in some rocks and weeds, his knickers ballooning about his legs. He would have left him there but noticed that it was a child, not an old black man, as it first appeared, and he prodded the body loose, netted it and hauled it aboard[97]. He shook his head in disgust at the kind of parents who would drown their own children. When, he wondered, will those people ever be anything but animals, fit for nothing but substitutes for mules, only mules didn't kill each other the way niggers did. He dumped Chicken Little into a burlap sack[98] and tossed him next to some egg crates and boxes of wool cloth. Later, sitting down to smoke on an empty lard tin, still bemused by God's curse[99] and the terrible burden his own kind had of elevating Ham's sons[1], he suddenly became alarmed by the thought that the corpse in this heat would have a terrible odor, which might get into the fabric of his woolen cloth. He dragged the sack away and hooked it over the side[2], so that the

96 여기서 "always"란 말은 범죄행위가 미래에도 계속해서 기억될 것임을 의미한다. 그래서 "Promise"라는 단어가 사용된다. 따라서 이 사건은 술라의 이후 정체성 탐색의 방향에 커다란 영향을 미치게 된다.

97 시체를 바위틈에서 빼내어 그물로 건져 배 위에 올려놓았다.

98 burlap sag: 대마로 만들어진 포대

99 성경의 창세기에 나오는 이야기. 노아의 세 아들 중, 함에게 내린 신의 저주를 의미하는데, 함은 오늘날 흑인의 조상이 되었다는 해석이 있음.

1 함의 자손을 가르쳐야 하는 백인들의 부담. 즉 뱃사공이 자신이 백인이라는 사실에 대해 우월감을 느끼고 있음을 보여준다.

2 배의 옆에 달아맸다.

Chicken's body was half in and half out of the water.

Wiping the sweat from his neck, he reported his find to the sheriff at Porter's Landing, who said they didn't have no niggers in their county, but that some lived in those hills 'cross the river, up above Medallion. The bargeman said he couldn't go all the way back there, it was every bit of two miles[3]. The sheriff said whyn't he throw it on back into the water. The bargeman said he never shoulda taken it out in the first place[4]. Finally they got the man who ran the ferry twice a day to agree to take it over in the morning.

That was why Chicken Little was missing for three days and didn't get the embalmer's until the fourth day, by which time he was unrecognizable to almost everybody who once knew him, and even his mother wasn't deep down sure, except that it just had to be him since nobody could find him[5]. When she saw his clothes lying on the table in the basement of the mortuary, her mouth snapped shut[6], and when she saw his body her mouth flew wide open again and it was seven hours before she was able to close it and make the first sound.

So the coffin was closed.

The Junior Choir, dressed in white, sang "Nearer My God to Thee" and "Precious Memories," their eyes fastened on the songbooks they did not need[7], for this was the first time their voices had presided at a real-life event[8].

3 2 마일이 꼬박 걸리는 거리였다.
4 처음부터 강에서 건져내지 말았어야 하는 건데.
5 except that: 그를 찾을 수 없기에 그임에 틀림없다는 확신 이외에는.
6 입을 꽉 다물었다.
7 그들의 눈은 다 외우기 때문에 볼 필요가 없는데도 악보만 쳐다보고 있었다.
8 그들이 실제 장례식에서 노래 부르기는 처음이었다.

Nel and Sula did not touch hands or look at each other during the funeral. There was a space, a separateness, between them. Nel's legs had turned to granite and she expected the sheriff or Reverend Deal's pointing finger at any moment. Although she knew she had "done nothing," she felt convicted and hanged right there in the pew — two rows down from her parents in the children's section[9].

Sula simply cried. Soundlessly and with no heaving and gasping for breath[10], she let the tears roll into her mouth and slide down her chin to dot[11] the front of her dress.

As Reverend Deal moved into his sermon, the hands of the women unfolded like pairs of raven's wings and flew high above their hats in the air[12]. They did not hear all of what he said; they heard the one word, or phrase, or inflection that was for them the connection between the event and themselves[13]. For some it was the term "sweet Jesus." And they saw the Lamb's eye and the truly innocent victim: themselves. They acknowledged the innocent child hiding in the corner of their hearts, holding a sugar-and-butter sandwich[14]. That one. The one who lodged deep in their fat, thin, old, young skin, and was the one the world had hurt[15]. Or they thought of their son

---

9 그녀의 부모가 앉아 있는 곳에서 두 줄 떨어진, 주로 어린이들이 앉는 앞 좌석에서 당장에 교수형에 처해질 것처럼 느꼈다.

10 어깨를 들썩이거나 흐느끼지 않고

11 눈물이 방울방울 옷 위에 떨어졌다. to 이하는 결과적으로 해석함.

12 팔을 펴서 번쩍 들어올렸다는 뜻.

13 목사의 설교를 듣는 것이 아니라, 군데군데 자신들과 관련된 단어만 들릴 뿐이었다.

14 목사의 설교는 듣는 이에 따라 다른 해석을 생산하고, 죽은 소년에 대해 각각 다른 이미지를 떠올린다. 그들의 마음 속 한 구석에 숨어서 설탕과 버터 바른 빵을 들고 서 있는, 아무 것도 모르는 소년을 떠올리기도 했다.

newly killed and remembered his legs in short pants and wondered where the bullet went in. Or they remembered how dirty the room looked when their father left home and wondered if that is the way the slim, young Jew felt, he who for them was both son and lover and in whose downy face they could see the sugar-and-butter sandwiches and feel the oldest and most devastating pain there is: not the pain of childhood, but the remembrance of it.

Then they left their pews. For with some emotions one has to stand[16]. They spoke, for they were full and needed to say. They swayed, for the rivulets of grief or of ecstasy must be rocked[17]. And when they thought of all that life and death locked into that little closed coffin they danced and screamed, not to protest God's will but to acknowledge it and confirm once more their conviction that the only way to avoid the Hand of God is to get in it[18].

In the colored part of the cemetery[19], they sank Chicken Little in between his grandfather and an aunt. Butterflies flew in and out of the bunches of field flowers now loosened from the top of the bier[20] and lying in a small heap at the edge of the grave. The heat had gone, but there was still no breeze to lift

---

15 뚱뚱하거나 여위었거나, 늙거나 젊거나, 그들 맘속에 깊이 자리 잡은 이미지. 즉, 세상에 의해 상처 입은 소년의 이미지가 떠올랐다. 즉, 한 소년의 우연한 죽음은 흑인 가슴 깊이 자리 잡은 한과 피해의식을 일깨운다.

16 어떤 특정한 감정이 생길 때, 그들은 일어서야 한다.

17 강물처럼 흐르는 슬픔과 황홀을 조절하기 위함인 듯 그들은 몸을 이리저리 흔들었다.

18 신의 뜻에 도전하기 위해서가 아니라 인정하며, 신의 손(처벌)을 피하기 위한 유일한 방법은 신의 손안에 있어야 한다는 사실을 다시 확인하기 위하여 그들은 춤을 추고 소리를 질렀다.

19 흑인들을 위해 따로 마련된 공동묘지

20 관

the hair of the willows.

Nel and Sula stood some distance away from the grave, the space that had sat between them in the pews had dissolved. They held hands and knew that only the coffin would lie in the earth; the bubbly laughter and the press of fingers in the palm would stay aboveground forever. At first, as they stood there, their hands were clenched together. They relaxed slowly until during the walk back home their fingers were laced in as gentle a clasp as that of any two young girlfriends trotting up the road on a summer day wondering what happened to butterflies in the winter.

1923

The second strange thing was Hannah's coming into her mother's room with an empty bowl and a peck of Kentucky Wonders[1] and saying, "Mamma, did you ever love us?" She sang the words like a small child saying a piece[2] at Easter, then knelt to spread a newspaper on the floor and set the basket on it; the bowl she tucked in the space between her legs[3]. Eva, who was just sitting there fanning herself with the cardboard fan from Mr. Hodges' funeral parlor, listened to the silence that followed Hannah's words, then said, "Scat!"[4] to the deweys who were playing chain gang[5] near the window. With the shoelaces of each of them tied to the laces of the others, they stumbled and tumbled out of Eva's room.

"Now," Eva looked up across from her wagon at her daughter. "give me that again. Flat out to fit my head[6]."

"I mean, did you? You know. When we was little."

Eva's hand moved snail-like down her thigh toward her stump[7], but stopped short of it to realign a pleat[8]. "No. I don't reckon I did. Not the way you thinkin'."

1 Kentucky Wonders: 콩의 종류; a peck of: 많은...
2 학교에서 암송용으로 지정한 한 문장을 말하듯이.
3 the bowl... : 다리를 벌리고 그릇은 그 사이 공간에 놓았다.
4 듀이 소년들에게 조용히 하라고 소리침.
5 여러 사람을 한 줄로 묶는 게임
6 다시 한 번 말해 보아라. 내가 알아듣기 쉽게 말해 보아.
7 stump: 다리가 절단된 부분
8 옷의 주름을 가지런히 하느라, 절단된 부분까지 이르기 전에 손이 멈췄다.

"Oh, well. I was just wonderin'." Hannah appeared to be through with the subject[9].

"An evil wonderin' if I ever heard one[10]." Eva was not through.

"I didn't mean nothing by it, Mamma."

"What you mean you didn't *mean* nothing by it? How you gone not mean something by it?[11]"

Hannah pinched the tips off the Kentucky Wonders and snapped their long pods[12]. What with the sound of the cracking and snapping and her swift-fingered movements, she seemed to be playing a complicated instrument. Eva watched her a moment and then said, "You gone can them?[13]"

"No. They for tonight."

"Thought you was gone can some."

"Uncle Paul ain't brought me none yet. A peck ain't enough to can[14]. He say he got two bushels for me."

"Triflin'."[15]

"Oh, he all right."

"Sho he all right. Everybody all right. 'Cept Mamma. Mamma the only one ain't all right. Cause she didn't *love* us."

"Awww, Mamma."

"Awww, Mamma? Awww, Mamma? You settin' here with your healthy-ass self and ax[16] me did I love you? Them big old eyes

9 한나는 그 이야기를 이젠 끝낸 듯했다.

10 내가 들어본 말 중, 가장 못된 궁금증이로구나.

11 "그런 말을 하고는 어떻게 아무 것도 아니라고 말할 수가 있는 거지?" 여기서 gone은 say의 뜻으로 보면 된다.

12 한나는 캔터키원더 콩 끝을 쥐고 긴 콩깍지를 뒤틀었다.

13 그 콩은 캔으로 저장할 작정이니?

14 저장할 만큼 양이 충분하지 않아요.

15 너무 조금이군.

in your head would a been two holes full of maggots if I hadn't.[17]"

"I didn't mean that, Mamma. I know you fed us and all. I was talkin' 'bout something else. Like. Like. Playin' with us. Did you ever, you know, play with us?"

"Play? Wasn't nobody playin' in 1895. Just 'cause you got it good now you think it was always this good? 1895 was a killer, girl. Things was bad. Niggers was dying like flies. Stepping tall, ain't you[18]? Uncle Paul gone bring me *two* bushels. Yeh. And they's a melon downstairs, ain't they? And I bake every Saturday, and Shad brings fish on Friday, and they's a pork barrel full of meal, and we float eggs in a crock of vinegar...[19]"

"Mamma, what you talkin' 'bout?"

"I'm talkin' 'bout 18 and 95 when I set in that house five days with you and Pearl and Plum and three beets, you snake-eyed ungrateful hussy. What would I look like leapin' 'round that little old room playin' with youngins with three beets to my name[20]?"

"I know 'bout them beets, Mamma. You told us that a million times."

"Yeah? Well? Don't that count? Ain't that love? You want me to tinkle you under the jaw and forget 'bout them sores in your mouth? Pearl was shittin' worms[21] and I was supposed to play rang-around-the-rosie?

---

16 ax: ask의 속어

17 내가 너희들을 사랑하지 않았다면, 네 머리에 달린 커다란 두 눈은 구더기로 가득한 구멍 두개에 불과했을 거다.

18 너희들은 의기양양하게 살고 있는 거야. 그렇지 않니?.

19 식초 항아리에 계란을 절여둘 수도 있고 말야. 모든 것이 옛날에 비해 풍족하다는 뜻임.

20 내 소유라고는 근대 세 자루 밖에 없는데 애들과 함께 이리저리 뛰어 놀고만 있다면 내가 어찌 보였겠니.

21 worm은 고통의 원인이란 뜻.

"But Mamma, they had to be some time when you wasn't thinkin' 'bout..."

"No time. They wasn't no time. Not none. Soon as I got only day done here come a night[22]. With you all coughin' and me watchin' so TB wouldn't take you off[23] and if you was sleepin' quiet I thought, O Lord, they dead and put my hand over your mouth to feel if the breath was comin' what you talkin' 'bout did I love you girl I stayed alive for you can't you get that through your thick head or what is that between your ears, heifer?"

Hannah had enough beans now. With some tomatoes and hot bread, she thought, that would be enough for everybody, especially since the deweys didn't eat vegetables no how and Eva never made them and Tar Baby was living off air and music these days[24]. She picked up the basket and stood with it and the bowl of beans over her mother. Eva's face was still asking her last question. Hannah looked into her mother's eyes.

"But what about Plum? What'd you kill Plum for, Mamma?"

It was a Wednesday in August and the ice wagon was coming and coming. You could hear bits of the driver's song. Now Mrs. Jackson would be tipping down her porch steps[25]. "Jes[26] a piece. You got a lil ole piece layin' 'round in there you could spare[27]?" And as he had since the time of the pigeons[28], the iceman would hand her a lump of ice saying, "Watch it now,

---

22 하루 일을 다 마치면 이미 밤이었다.

23 항상 기침하는 너를 결핵이 널 앗아가지 않도록 지켜주고, 밤에 잠을 잘 자고 있는지 늘 지켜보아야 했다.

24 타르 베이비는 요즘 아무 것도 먹지 않고 공기와 음악이면 충분하다.

25 까치발을 딛고 현관 계단을 내려가다.

26 Just

27 당신이 가진 것이라곤 케케묵은 것 뿐 이지요?

28 비둘기로 소식을 전하던 그 옛날부터 늘 그래왔듯이.

Mrs. Jackson. That straw'll tickle your pretty neck to death[29]."

Eva listened to the wagon coming and thought about what it must be like in the icehouse. She leaned back a little and closed her eyes trying to see the insides of the icehouse. It was a dark, lovely picture in this heat, until it reminded her of that winter night in the outhouse holding her baby in the dark, her fingers searching for his asshole and the last bit of lard scooped from the sides of the can, held deliberately on the tip of her middle finger, the last bit of lard to keep from hurting him when she slid her finger in and all because she had broken the slop jar and the rags had frozen. The last food staple in the house[30] she had rammed up her baby's behind to keep from hurting him too much when she opened up his bowels to pull the stools out. He had been screaming fit[31] to kill, but when she found his hole at last and stuck her finger up in it, the shock was so great he was suddenly quiet. Even now on the hottest day anyone in Medallion could remember—a day so hot flies slept and cats were splaying[32] their fur like quills, a day so hot pregnant wives leaned up against trees and cried, and women remembering some three-month-old hurt put ground glass in their lovers' food[33] and the men looked at the food and wondered if there was glass in it and ate it anyway because it was too hot to resist eating it—even on this hottest of days in the hot spell, Eva shivered from the biting cold[34] and

29 하찮은 지푸라기 하나가 당신의 목을 부러뜨릴 수도 있어요.

30 문장의 목적어. 마지막 남은 음식원료

31 곧 ... 할 것같이 되어. 즉, 곧 죽을 것처럼 소리를 질렀다.

32 쭉 펴 벌리다.

33 임신 석달 째 여자들이 마음의 상처를 받고 연인의 음식에 깨진 유리를 넣었는데, 남자들이 이 음식을 보고 좀 의심하긴 해도 너무나 더워서 먹을 수밖에 없었던 일을 기억했다.

stench of that outhouse.

Hannah was waiting. Watching her mother's eyelids. When Eva spoke at last it was with two voices. Like two people were talking at the same time[35], saying the same thing, one a fraction of a second behind the other[36].

"He give me such a time[37]. Such a time. Look like he didn't even want to be born. But he come on out. Boys is hard to bear. You wouldn't know that but they is. It was such a carryin' on to get him born and to keep him alive[38]. Just to keep his little heart beating and his little old lungs cleared and look like when he came back from that war he wanted to git back in[39]. After all that carryin' on, just gettin' him out and keepin' him alive, he wanted to crawl back in my womb and well. . . I ain't got the room no more even if he could do it. There wasn't space for him in my womb. And he was crawlin' back. Being helpless and thinking baby thoughts and dreaming baby dreams and messing up his pants again and smiling all the time[40]. I had room enough in my heart, but not in my womb, not no more. I birthed him once. I couldn't do it again. He was growed, a big old thing. Godhavemercy[41], I couldn't birth him twice. I'd be laying here at night and he be downstairs

34 살을 에이는 듯한 추위

35 두 사람이 동시에 말하는 것처럼.

36 one a fraction of a second behind the other: 한 목소리에 이어 그 목소리의 작은 조각이 그 다음 목소리에 담겨.

37 그는 나를 정말 힘들게 했지.

38 그를 낳고 살아남게 하는 일이 정말 고된 일이었지.

39 look like...git back in: 전쟁에서 돌아 왔을 때 그는 마치 다시 전쟁으로 돌아가고 싶은 듯했지.

40 어쩔 도리 없이 유치한 생각에다 유치한 꿈을 꾸고, 다시금 바지에 쉬하고 늘상 웃기만 하는 아이였지.

41 신이여, 자비를 베푸소서. 여기는 같은 뜻을 지닌 감탄사임.

in that room, but when I closed my eyes I'd see him... six feet tall smilin' and crawlin' up the stairs quietlike[42] so I wouldn't hear and opening the door soft so I wouldn't hear and he'd be creepin' to the bed trying to spread my legs trying to get back up in my womb. He was a man, girl, a big old growed-up man. I didn't have that much room. I kept on dreaming it. Dreaming it and I knowed it was true. One night it wouldn't be no dream. It'd be true and I would have done it, would have let him if I'd've had the room but a big man can't be a baby all wrapped up inside his mamma no more, he suffocate. I done everything I could to make him leave me and go on and live and be a man but he wouldn't and I had to keep him out so I just thought of a way he could die like a man not all scrunched up inside my womb[43], but like a man."

Eva couldn't see Hannah clearly for the tears, but she looked up at her anyway and said, by way of apology or explanation or perhaps just by way of neatness, "But I held him close first. Real close. Sweet Plum. My baby boy."

Long after Hannah turned and walked out of the room, Eva continued to call his name while her fingers lined up the pleats in her dress.

Hannah went off to the kitchen, her old man's slippers plopping down the stairs and over the hardwood floors. She turned the spigot on, letting water break up the tight knots of Kentucky Wonders[44] and float them to the top of the bowl. She swirled them about with her fingers, poured the water off and

42 quietlike: quietly

43 내 자궁 안에서 우지끈거리지 않은 채(작은 공간에 큰 몸이 들어가서 생기는 현상) 사람처럼 죽을 수 있는 방법을 생각해냈다.

44 켄터키 원더스라고 불리 우는 콩 종류인데, 물을 세게 틀어 콩깍지를 깐다는 뜻임.

repeated the process. Each time the green tubes[45] rose to the surface she felt elated and collected whole handfuls at a time to drop in twos and threes back into the water.

Through the window over the sink she could see the deweys still playing chain gang; their ankles bound one to the other, they tumbled, struggled back to their feet and tried to walk single file[46]. Hens strutted by[47] with one suspicious eye on the deweys, another on the brick fireplace where sheets and mason jars were boiled[48]. Only the deweys could play in this heat. Hannah put the Kentucky Wonders over the fire and, struck by a sudden sleepiness, she went off to lie down in the front room. It was even hotter there, for the windows were shut to keep out the sunlight. Hannah straightened the shawl that draped the couch and lay down. She dreamed of a wedding in a red bridal gown until Sula came in and woke her.

But before the second strange thing, there had been the wind, which was the first. The very night before the day Hannah had asked Eva if she had ever loved them, the wind tore over the hills rattling roofs and loosening doors. Everything shook, and although the people were frightened they thought it meant rain and welcomed it. Windows fell out and trees lost arms. People waited up half the night for the first crack of lightning. Some had even uncovered barrels to catch the rain water, which they loved to drink and cook in. They waited in vain, for no lightning no thunder no rain came. The wind just swept through, took what dampness there was out of the air[49], messed up the

45 green tubes: 콩깍지.

46 walk single file: 일렬종대, 한 줄로 걷다.

47 점잔빼며 걸어지나가다.

48 brick fireplace... were boiled: 침대 시트와 식품 저장용 유리병을 삶는 화덕

yards, and went on. The hills of the Bottom, as always, protected the valley part of town where the white people lived, and the next morning all the people were grateful because there was a dryer heat[50]. So they set about their work early, for it was canning time[51], and who knew but what the wind would come back this time with a cooling rain[52]. The men who worked in the valley got up at four thirty in the morning and looked at the sky where the sun was already rising like a hot white bitch. They beat the brims of their hats against their legs before putting them on and trudged down the road like old promises nobody wanted kept.

On Thursday, when Hannah brought Eva her fried tomatoes and soft scrambled eggs with the white left out for good luck[53], she mentioned her dream of the wedding in the red dress. Neither one bothered to look it up for they both knew the number was 522[54]. Eva said she'd play it[55] when Mr. Buckland Reed came by. Later she would remember it as the third strange thing. She had thought it odd even then, but the red in the dream confused her. But she wasn't certain that it was third or not because Sula was acting up[56], fretting the

---

49 공기중의 습기란 습기는 바람이 몽땅 가져가 버렸다.

50 습기가 적은 더위.

51 식품을 저장하는 시기.

52 who knew... a cooling rain: 바람이 이번엔 시원한 비를 몰고 다시 오리라는 사실을 누가 알았겠는가.

53 행운을 빌며 계란의 흰자위를 빼고 만든 스크램블드 에그(요리 이름)와 튀긴 토마토를 이바에게 가져갔다.

54 두 사람 모두 꿈풀이 책을 찾아보려 하지 않았다. 왜냐하면 그 꿈에 대한 설명이 522번(꿈 종류의 일련번호)에 나온다는 사실을 알고 있었기 때문이었다.

55 play: 다루다. 즉, 버클랜드 리드씨가 오면 그 꿈에 대해 이야기해 본다는 뜻임.

deweys and meddling the newly married couple. Because she was thirteen, everybody supposed her nature was coming down[57], but it was hard to put up with her sulking and irritation. The birthmark over her eye was getting darker and looked more and more like a stem and rose. She was dropping things and eating food that belonged to the newly married couple and started in to worrying everybody[58] that the deweys needed a bath and she was going to give it to them[59]. The deweys, who went wild at the thought of water[60], were crying and thundering all over the house like colts.

"We ain't got to, do we[61]? Do we got to do what she says? It ain't Saturday." They even woke up Tar Baby, who came out of his room to look at them and then left the house in search of music.

Hannah ignored them and kept on bringing mason jars[62] out of the cellar and washing them. Eva banged on the floor with her stick but nobody came. By noon it was quiet. The deweys had escaped, Sula was either in her room or gone off somewhere. The newly married couple, energized by their morning lovemaking, had gone to look for a day's work happily certain that they would find none.

The air all over the Bottom got heavy with peeled fruit and oiling vegetables. Fresh corn, tomatoes, string beans, melon

---

56 제멋대로 행동하다.

57 타고난 성품이 이제 수그러질 때라고 모두들 생각했다.

58 start in to doing... : 호통치다. ...을 비난하기 시작하다. 즉, 듀이가 목욕을 해야할 만큼 더럽다고 모든 사람들을 비난하기 시작했다.

59 직접 목욕을 시키다.

60 물만 생각하면 질겁하는 듀이 아이들.

61 우린 목욕할 필요가 없지요. 그렇지요?

62 식품 저장용 유리병

rinds[63]. The women, the children and the old men who had no jobs were putting up for a winter[64] they understood so well. Peaches were stuffed into jars and black cherries (later, when it got cooler, they would put up jellies and preserves). The greedy canned as many as forty-two a day even though some of them, like Mrs. Jackson, who ate ice, had jars from 1920[65].

Before she trundled her wagon over to the dresser to get her comb, Eva looked out the window and saw Hannah bending to light the yard fire. And that was the fifth (or fourth, if you didn't count Sula's craziness) strange thing. She couldn't find her comb. Nobody moved stuff in Eva's room except to clean and then they put everything right back. But Eva couldn't find it anywhere. One hand pulling her braids loose, the other searching the dresser drawers, she had just begun to get irritated when she felt it in her blouse drawer. Then she trundled back to the window to catch a breeze, if one took a mind to come by, while she combed her hair. She rolled up to the window and it was then she saw Hannah burning. The flames from the yard fire were licking the blue cotton dress,[66] making her dance. Eva knew there was time for nothing in this world other than the time it took to get there and cover her daughter's body with her own[67]. She lifted her heavy frame up on her good leg[68], and with fists and arms smashed the

63 melon rinds: 멜론 껍질

64 겨우살이를 장만하다.

65 얼음을 먹는 잭슨 아주머니처럼 어떤 사람들은 1920년도 만든 저장음식을 내내 먹기도 하지만, 욕심이 많은 이들은 하루에 42개 정도의 유리병에 식품을 저장했다.

66 파란 무명옷에 불이 붙어 일렁이는 모습을 묘사함.

67 지금 이 순간, 딸에게 다가가 자신의 몸으로 덮는 것 보다 급한 것은 이 세상에 없었다.

windowpane. Using her stump as a support on the window sill, her good leg as a lever, she threw herself out of the window[69]. Cut and bleeding she clawed the air trying to aim her body toward the flaming, dancing figure. She missed and came crashing down some twelve feet from Hannah's smoke. Stunned but still conscious, Eva dragged herself toward her firstborn, but Hannah, her senses lost, went flying out of the yard gesturing and bobbing[70] like a sprung jack-in-the-box[71].

Mr. and Mrs. Suggs, who had set up their canning apparatus[72] in their front yard, saw her running, dancing toward them. They whispered, "Jesus, Jesus," and together hoisted up their tub of water in which tight red tomatoes floated[73] and threw it on the smoke-and-flame-bound woman[74]. The water did put out the flames, but it also made steam, which seared to sealing all that was left of the beautiful Hannah Peace[75]. She lay there on the wooden sidewalk planks, twitching lightly among the smashed tomatoes, her face a mask of agony so intense that for years the people who gathered 'round would shake their heads at the recollection of it.

Somebody covered her legs with a shirt. A woman unwrapped her head rag and placed it on Hannah's shoulder. Somebody else ran to Dick's Fresh Food and Sundries to call the

---

68 성한 다리 한쪽에 몸 전체를 의지해서 일으켜 세우고.

69 그녀의 다리 절단면을 창틀에 대고, 성한 다리를 지렛대 삼아 온몸을 창문 밖에 던졌다.

70 bob: 몸을 홱홱 움직이다.

71 상자를 열면 인형이 톡 튀어나오는 장난감.

72 apparatus: 장치, 기계

73 싱싱하고 빨간 토마토가 둥둥 떠 있는 양동이의 물을 들어올렸다.

74 연기와 불꽃에 휩싸여 펄펄 뛰는 여자.

75 which seared to sealing... : 예쁜 한나에서 남아 있는 모든 것을 모두 가둬버릴 만큼 완전히 그을렸다. Which의 선행사는 멀찌감치 앞에 있는 flames으로 보는 것이 적당함.

ambulance. The rest stood there as helpless as sunflowers leaning on a fence. The deweys came and stepped in the tomatoes, their eyes raked with wonder[76]. Two cats sidled through the legs of the crowd, sniffing the burned flesh. The vomiting of a young girl finally broke the profound silence and caused the women to talk to each other and to God. In the midst of calling Jesus they heard the hollow clang of the ambulance bell struggling up the hill, but not the "Help me, ya'll" that the dying woman whispered[77]. Then somebody remembered to go and see about Eva. They found her on her stomach by the forsythia[78] bushes calling Hannah's name and dragging her body through the sweet peas and clover that grew under the forsythia by the side of the house. Mother and daughter were placed on stretchers and carried to the ambulance. Eva was wide awake. The blood from her face cuts[79] filled her eyes so she could not see, could only smell the familiar odor of cooked flesh.

Hannah died on the way to the hospital. Or so they said. In any case, she had already begun to bubble and blister[80] so badly that the coffin had to be kept closed at the funeral and the women who washed the body and dressed it for death wept for her burned hair and wrinkled breasts as though they themselves had been her lovers.

When Eva got to the hospital they put her stretcher on the floor, so preoccupied with the hot and bubbling flesh of the

76 놀라움으로 눈을 잔뜩 치켜뜨고.

77 연민의 소리들 가운데, 언덕을 올라오는 요란한 앰블란스 소리가 들렸으나 사람들은 죽어 가는 여인이 신음하는 소리, "도와줘요"는 듣지 못했다.

78 개나리과 식물

79 face cuts: 얼굴의 상처

80 부글부글 끓고 부풀어 올라.

other (some of them had never seen so extreme a burn case before) they forgot Eva, who would have bled to death except Old Willy Fields, the orderly, saw blood staining his just-mopped floors and went to find out where it was coming from[81]. Recognizing Eva at once he shouted to a nurse, who came to see if the bloody one-legged black woman was alive or dead. From then on Willy boasted that he had saved Eva's life — an indisputable fact which she herself admitted and for which she cursed him every day for thirty-seven years thereafter and would have cursed him for the rest of her life except by then she was already ninety years old and forgot things[82].

Lying in the colored ward of the hospital[83], which was a screened corner of a larger ward, Eva mused over the perfection of the judgment against her[84]. She remembered the wedding dream and recalled that weddings always meant death. And the red gown, well that was the fire, as she should have known. She remembered something else too, and try as she might to deny it, she knew that as she lay on the ground trying to drag herself through the sweet peas and clover to get to Hannah, she had seen Sula standing on the back porch just looking. When Eva, who was never one to hide the faults of her children, mentioned what she thought she'd seen to a few friends, they said it was natural. Sula was probably struck dumb, as anybody would be who saw her own mamma burn up. Eva said yes, but inside she

81 who would have bled to death...: 청소부 윌리 필드가 방금 닦은 바닥에 흐르는 피를 보고 이 피가 어디서 흘러나오는지 발견하지 못했더라면 이바는 과다출혈도 죽었을지도 모른다.

82 90살이 되어 기억을 잃을 때까지 평생 동안 윌리를 저주했을 것이다.

83 병원 안에 흑인들만 따로 사용하는 입원실

84 Eva mused over... against her: 자신에 대한 저주가 극치에 이르렀음을 생각하고 있었다.

disagreed and remained convinced that Sula had watched Hannah burn not because she was paralyzed, but because she was interested.

1927

Old people were dancing with little children. Young boys with their sisters, and the church women who frowned on any bodily expression of joy (except when the hand of God commanded it) tapped their feet. Somebody (the groom's father, everybody said) had poured a whole pint[1] jar of cane liquor[2] into the punch, so even the men who did not sneak out the back door to have a shot, as well as the women who let nothing stronger than Black Draught enter their blood, were tipsy[3]. A small boy stood at the Victrola turning its handle[4] and smiling at the sound of Bert Williams' "Save a Little Dram for Me."

Even Helene Wright had mellowed with the cane, waving away apologies for drinks spilled on her rug and paying no attention whatever to the chocolate cake lying on the arm of her red-velvet sofa. The tea roses above her left breast had slipped from the brooch that fastened them and were hanging heads down. When her husband called her attention to the children wrapping themselves into her curtains[5], she merely smiled and said, "Oh, let them be." She was not only a little drunk, she was weary and had been for weeks. Her only child's wedding — the culmination of all she had been, thought or done in this world[6]

1 액량의 단위. 0.550 리터

2 등류(사탕수수, 등, 종려나무)식물로 만든 술.

3 (독한 술을 섞었기 때문에) 한 잔하러 뒷문으로 빠져나가지 않는 남자들조차, 블랙드라우트보다 센 술은 먹지 않는 여자들조차 취해서 비틀거렸다.

4 작은 소년이 축음기 옆에 서서 바늘을 돌리고 있다.

5 아이들이 커튼을 휘감으며 놀고 있는 모습을 남편이 알려 주어도.

6 그녀가 이 세상에서 존재하고, 생각하고, 일해 왔던 모든 것들의 최고점

— had dragged from her energy and stamina even she did not know she possessed. Her house had to be thoroughly cleaned, chickens had to be plucked[7], cakes and pies made, and for weeks she, her friends and her daughter had been sewing. Now it was all happening and it took only a little cane juice to snap the cords of fatigue and damn the white curtains that she had pinned on the stretcher only the morning before[8]. Once this day was over she would have a lifetime to rattle around in that house and repair the damage.

A real wedding, in a church, with a real reception afterward, was rare among the people of the Bottom. Expensive for one thing, and most newlyweds just went to the courthouse if they were not particular, or had the preacher come in and say a few words if they were. The rest just "Took up" with one another[9]. No invitations were sent. There was no need for that formality. Folks just came, bringing a gift if they had one, none if they didn't. Except for those who worked in valley houses, most of them had never been to a big wedding; they simply assumed it was rather like a funeral except afterward you didn't have to walk all the way out to Beechnut Cemetery.

This wedding offered a special attraction, for the bridegroom was a handsome, well-liked man — the tenor of Mount Zion's Men's Quartet, who had an enviable reputation among the girls and a comfortable one among men. His name was Jude Greene, and with the pick of some eight or ten girls who came regularly to services to hear him sing, he had chosen Nel Wright[10].

7 요리하기 위해 닭을 잡았다는 뜻.

8 전날 밤에 꽂은 하얀 커텐을 망가뜨리고, 피곤에 지쳐 쓰러져버리는데는 약간의 케인쥬스면 족했다.

9 나머지 사람들은 결혼식 없이 그냥 함께 살았다.

10 그의 노래를 듣기 위해 정기적으로 교회에 오는 여덟 명 내지 열 명 가량의

He wasn't really aiming to get married. He was twenty then, and although his job as a waiter at the Hotel Medallion was a blessing to his parents and their seven other children, it wasn't nearly enough to support a wife. He had brought the subject up first on the day the word got out that the town was building a new road, tarmac[11], that would wind through Medallion on down to the river, where a great new bridge was to be built to connect Medallion to Porter's Landing, the town on the other side. The war over, a fake prosperity was still around[12]. In a state of euphoria, with a hunger for more and more, the council of founders[13] cast its eye toward a future that would certainly include trade from cross-river towns. Towns that needed more than a house raft to get to the merchants of Medallion[14]. Work had already begun on the New River Road (the city had always meant to name it something else, something wonderful, but ten years later when the bridge idea was dropped for a tunnel it[15] was still called the New River Road).

Along with a few other young black men, Jude had gone down to the shack where they were hiring. Three old colored men had already been hired, but not for the road work, just to do the picking up[16], food bringing and other small errands. These old men were close to feeble, not good for much else, and everybody was pleased they were taken on[17]; still it was a shame to see

---

처녀들 중, 그는 넬을 선택했다.

11 아스팔트 도로.

12 전쟁이 끝나고, 아직도 경제적으로 풍요롭다는 착각이 만연해 있었다.

13 다리 만드는 기금의 기부자 협의회

14 앞 문장에서의 towns를 다시 설명하고 있다. 즉, 메달리온의 상인들에게 가려면 가정용 뗏목 이상이 것이 필요로 할, 강 건너 마을들.

15 다리를 놓는 대신 터널을 뚫기로 했을 때.

16 정돈하는 일.

those white men laughing with the grandfathers but shying away from the young black men who could tear that road up[18]. The men like Jude who could do real work. Jude himself longed more than anybody else to be taken[19]. Not just for the good money, more for the work itself. He wanted to swing the pick or kneel down with the string or shovel the gravel. His arms ached for something heavier than trays, for something dirtier than peelings; his feet wanted the heavy work shoes, not the thin- soled black shoes that the hotel required. More than anything he wanted the camaraderie[20] of the road men: the lunch buckets, the hollering, the body movement that in the end produced something real, something he could point to. "I built that road," he could say. How much better sundown would be than the end of a day in the restaurant[21], where a good day's work was marked by the number of dirty plates and the weight of the garbage bin. "I built that road." People would walk over his sweat for years. Perhaps a sledge hammer would come crashing down on his foot, and when people asked him how come he limped, he could say, "got that building the New Road[22]."

It was while he was full of such dreams, his body already feeling the rough work clothes, his hands already curved to the pick handle, that he spoke to Nel about getting married. She seemed receptive but hardly anxious. It was after he stood in

17 흑인 노인들이 일자리를 얻게 되어 모두들 기뻐하고 있었다.

18 백인들이 흑인 할아버지들과는 웃고 떠들면서도, 길을 갈기갈기 부숴 낼만큼 힘이 센 젊은 흑인들을 멀리한다는 것은 부끄러운 일이었다.

19 쥬드는 누구보다도 일자리를 얻기를 원했다.

20 동지애, 우정

21 식당에서 하루를 끝내는 것보다, 길 만드는 일을 한다면 그 황혼(하루의 끝)이 얼마나 보람 있겠는가.

22 새 도로를 만드느라 다쳤어요.

lines for six days running and saw the gang boss pick out thin- armed white boys from the Virginia hills and the bull-necked Greeks and Italians and heard over and over, "Nothing else today. Come back tomorrow," that he got the message[23]. So it was rage, rage and a determination to take on a man's role anyhow that made him press Nel about settling down[24]. He needed some of his appetites filled, some posture of adulthood recognized, but mostly he wanted someone to care about his hurt, to care very deeply. Deep enough to hold him, deep enough to rock him, deep enough to ask, "How you feel? You all right? Want some coffee?" And if he were to be a man, that someone could no longer be his mother[25]. He chose the girl who had always been kind, who had never seemed hell-bent to marry[26], who made the whole venture seem like his idea, his conquest.

The more he thought about marriage, the more attractive it became. Whatever his fortune, whatever the cut of his garment[27], there would always be the hem—the tuck and fold that hid his raveling edges[28]; a someone sweet, industrious and loyal to shore him up[29]. And in return he would shelter her, love her,

---

23 메시지(일자리를 얻을 수 없다는)를 받은 것은, 엿새나 줄서 기다리며 자기 대신 버지니아 촌구석에서 온 가느다란 백인 소년이나 굵고 짤막한 목을 가진 그리스인과 이태리인을 고용하고, 겨우 한다는 말이 오늘은 일거리가 없으니 내일 오라는 말을 반복해서 들고난 다음이었다.

24 앞 문장과 마찬가지로 it-that 용법이다. 결혼하자고 넬을 설득하게 만든 것은 (남자다운 일자리는 얻지 못했어도) 이제 남자의 역할을 하리라는 결심과, 또한 분노, 분노 때문이었다.

25 이제 그가 진짜 남자가 되려면, 자신을 위로해 줄 사람은 더 이상 엄마가 아니었다.

26 결혼하려고 안달하지 않는 듯한

27 옷의 어딘가 찢어진다 해도

28 찢긴 옷 솔기를 접어서 감쳐 줄 사람이 항상 있게 되는 것이다.

grow old with her. Without that someone he was a waiter hanging around a kitchen like a woman. With her he was head of a household pinned to an unsatisfactory job out of necessity. The two of them together would make one Jude.

His fears lest his burst dream of road building discourage her were never realized[30]. Nel's indifference to his hints about marriage disappeared altogether when she discovered his pain. Jude could see himself taking shape in her eyes[31]. She actually wanted to help, to soothe, and was it true what Ajax said in the Time and a Half Pool Hall? That "all they want, man, is they own misery. Ax em to die for you and they yours for life[32]."

Whether he was accurate in general, Ajax was right about Nel. Except for an occasional leadership role with Sula, she had no aggression[33]. Her parents had succeeded in rubbing down to a dull glow any sparkle or splutter she had[34]. Only with Sula did that quality have free reign, but their friendship was so close, they themselves had difficulty distinguishing one's thoughts from the other's. During all of her girlhood the only respite Nel had had from her stern and undemonstrative parents was Sula. When Jude began to hover around, she was flattered—all the girls like him—and Sula

---

29 shore up: 받쳐주다.

30 길을 닦는 꿈이 무산되었다는 사실에 넬이 실망할까봐 두려워했으나 실제로 그녀는 실망하지 않았다.

31 자신의 모습이 그녀의 눈에 선명히 투영되는 것을 보았다. 즉, 그녀가 골똘하게 관심을 써준다는 사실을 알았다는 뜻임.

32 they own misery: their own misery. Ax: Ask. "그들이 원하는 것이라곤, 자신들의 비참함 뿐이야

33 술라와 함께 있을 때 가끔 취하는 리더역할을 제외하고는 넬은 저돌적인 편은 아니었다.

34 넬의 부모는 그녀가 본래 가진 튀고 반짝거리는 성격이 조금이라도 있으면 모두 문질러서 둔하게 만들어 버렸다.

made the enjoyment of his attentions keener simply because she seemed always to want Nel to shine[35]. They never quarreled, those two, the way some girlfriends did over boys, or competed against each other for them. In those days a compliment to one was a compliment to the other, and cruelty to one was a challenge to the other.

Nel's response to Jude's shame and anger selected her away from Sula. And greater than her friendship was this new feeling of being needed by someone who saw her singly. She didn't even know she had a neck until Jude remarked on it, or that her smile was anything but the spreading of her lips until he saw it as a small miracle.

Sula was no less excited about the wedding. She thought it was the perfect thing to do following their graduation from general school. She wanted to be the bridesmaid. No others. And she encouraged Mrs. Wright to go all out, even to borrowing Eva's punch bowl. In fact, she handled most of the details very efficiently, capitalizing on[36] the fact that most people were anxious to please her since she had lost her mamma only a few years back and they still remembered the agony in Hannah's face and the blood on Eva's.

So they danced up in the Bottom on the second Saturday in June, danced at the wedding where everybody realized for the first time that except for their magnificent teeth, the deweys would never grow. They had been forty-eight inches tall for years now, and while their size was unusual it was not unheard of. The realization was based on the fact that they remained

35 술라가 곁에 있음으로 해서 넬은 더욱 쥬드의 관심을 즐길 수 있었다. 왜냐하면 술라는 넬이 한껏 빛을 내길 원했기 때문이다.

36 capitalize on: 이용하다.

boys in mind. Mischievous, cunning, private and completely unhousebroken[37], their games and interests had not changed since Hannah had them all put into the first grade together.

Nel and Jude, who had been the stars all during the wedding, were forgotten finally as the reception melted into a dance, a feed, a gossip session, a playground and a love nest. For the first time that day they relaxed and looked at each other, and liked what they saw. They began to dance, pressed in among the others, and each one turned his thoughts to the night that was coming on fast[38]. They had taken a housekeeping room with one of Jude's aunts (over the protest of Mrs. Wright, who had rooms to spare, but Nel didn't want to make love to her husband in her mother's house) and were getting restless to go there.

As if reading her thoughts, Jude leaned down and whispered, "Me too." Nel smiled and rested her cheek on his shoulder. The veil she wore was too heavy to allow her to feel the core of the kiss he pressed on her head. When she raised her eyes to him for one more look of reassurance, she saw through the open door a slim figure in blue, gliding, with just a hint of a strut, down the path toward the road. One hand was pressed to the head to hold down the large hat against the warm June breeze. Even from the rear Nel could tell that it was Sula and that she was smiling; that something deep down in that litheness was amused. It would be ten years before they saw each other again, and their meeting would be thick with birds[39].

37 항상 집에서만 지내는

38 넬과 쥬드는 마침내 빨리 다가오는 신혼 밤에 대해 생각하기에 이르렀다.

39 그들이 10년 후 재회할 즈음엔 온 마을이 새로 가득 차 있을 터였다.

Part Two

1937

Accompanied by a plague of robins[1], Sula came back to Medallion. The little yam-breasted shuddering birds were everywhere, exciting very small children away from their usual welcome into a vicious stoning[2]. Nobody knew why or from where they had come. What they did know was that you couldn't go anywhere without stepping in their pearly shit, and it was hard to hang up clothes, pull weeds or just sit on the front porch when robins were flying and dying all around you.

Although most of the people remembered the time when the sky was black for two hours with clouds and clouds of pigeons[3], and although they were accustomed to excesses in nature[4] — too much heat, too much cold, too little rain, rain to flooding — they still dreaded the way a relatively trivial phenomenon could become sovereign in their lives and bend their minds to its will[5].

In spite of their fear, they reacted to an oppressive oddity, or what they called evil days, with an acceptance that bordered on welcome[6]. Such evil must be avoided, they felt, and precautions

---

1 수많은 로빈 새떼들이 갑자기 마을에 나타나 골치 거리가 된 일.

2 평소처럼 새들을 환영하지 않고, 새떼를 향해 악한 마음으로 돌팔매질하게끔 자극하고 있었다.

3 수많은 비둘기 떼로 하늘이 뒤덮였을 때.

4 자연에서 지나친 것들, 즉, 자연재해를 이름

5 상대적으로 사소한 현상이 생활 전체를 지배하고 그 뜻대로 휘둘리게 될 수 있다는 사실에 그들은 두려워했다.

6 두려움에도 불구하고, 소위 불길한 기간으로 불리는 매우 힘들고 괴이한 사

must naturally be taken to protect themselves from it[7]. But they let it run its course, fulfill itself, and never invented ways either to alter it, to annihilate it or to prevent its happening again. So also were they with people.

What was taken by outsiders to be slackness, slovenliness or even generosity was in fact a full recognition of the legitimacy of forces other than good ones[8]. They did not believe doctors could heal — for them, none ever had done so[9]. They did not believe death was accidental — life might be, but death was deliberate[10]. They did not believe Nature was ever askew — only inconvenient[11]. Plague and drought were as "Natural" as springtime. If milk could curdle, God knows robins could fall[12]. The purpose of evil was to survive it[13] and they determined (without ever knowing they had made up their minds to do it) to survive floods, white people, tuberculosis, famine and ignorance. They knew anger well but not despair, and they didn't stone sinners for the same reason they didn't commit suicide[14] — it was beneath them[15].

건을 오히려 환영에 가까운 심정으로 받아들였다.

7 그런 사악함은 분명 피해야 하고, 자신을 보호하기 위해서는 마음을 단단히 먹고 준비해야 한다고 모두가 자연스레 느꼈다.

8 외부인들의 눈엔 느리고 추저분하고 혹은 관용이라고 보일지 모르지만, 사실은, 선한 것이 아닌 악한 세력조차 합법적으로 존재할 수 있음을 그들이 분명하게 인식하는 탓이었다.

9 병은 고치는 것은 의사가 아니라고 그들은 믿었다.

10 생명의 탄생은 우연적일 수 있지만, 죽음은 결코 우연적인 것이 아니라 계획된 것이라고 믿었다.

11 자연은 인간을 단지 불편하게 할 뿐, 그 자체가 사악하진 않다고 생각했다.

12 우유가 엉겨 못쓰게 될 수 있듯이 로빈 새들이 떨어져 죽을 수도 있는 일이었다.

13 악이 존재하는 목적은 그것을 이기고 살아남기 위함이다.

14 그들이 자살하지 않는 같은 이유로 다른 사람의 잘못을 응징하지도 않았다.

Sula stepped off the Cincinnati Flyer[16] into the robin shit and began the long climb up into the Bottom. She was dressed in a manner that was as close to a movie star as anyone would ever see. A black crepe dress splashed with pink and yellow zinnias[17], foxtails, a black felt hat with the veil of net lowered over one eye[18]. In her right hand was a black purse with a beaded clasp[19] and in her left a red leather traveling case, so small, so charming—no one had seen anything like it ever before, including the major's wife and the music teacher, both of whom had been to Rome.

Walking up the hill toward Carpenter's Road, the heels and sides of her pumps edged with drying bird shit[20], she attracted the glances of old men sitting on stone benches in front of the courthouse, housewives throwing buckets of water on their sidewalks, and high school students on their way home for lunch. By the time she reached the Bottom, the news of her return had brought the black people out on their porches or to their windows. There were scattered hellos and nods but mostly stares[21]. A little boy ran up to her saying, "Carry yo' bag, ma'am?[22]" Before Sula could answer his mother had called him, "You, John. Get back in here."

At Eva's house there were four dead robins on the walk. Sula stopped and with her toe pushed them into the bordering grass.

15 it는 앞 문장 전체를 받음. 절망하고 정죄하는 일은 그들이 할 일이 아니었다.
16 급행열차
17 분홍색 노랑색 백일초가 흐드러진 검은 색 축면사 옷.
18 망사가 한 쪽 눈 위에 드리워진 검은 펠트 모자.
19 beaded clasp: 구슬이 달린 잠금장치.
20 신발의 옆과 뒤꿈치에 새똥을 묻힌 채.
21 간간이 인사가 오고갔지만, 사람들은 대체로 빤히 쳐다보기만 했다.
22 짐 가방을 들어드릴까요?

Eva looked at Sula pretty much the same way she had looked at BoyBoy that time when he returned after he'd left her without a dime or a prospect of one. She was sitting in her wagon, her back to the window she had jumped out of (now all boarded up[23]) setting fire to the hair she had combed out of her head[24]. When Sula opened the door she raised her eyes and said, "I might have knowed them birds meant something. Where's your coat?"

Sula threw herself on Eva's bed. "The rest of my stuff will be on later."

"I should hope so. Them little old furry tails ain't going to do you no more good than they did the fox that was wearing them[25]."

"Don't you say hello to nobody when you ain't seen them for ten years?"

"If folks let somebody know where they is and when they coming, then other folks can get ready for them. If they don't — if they just pop in all sudden like — then they got to take whatever mood they find[26]."

"How you been doing, Big Mamma?"

"Gettin' by[27]. Sweet of you to ask. You was quick enough when you wanted something. When you needed a little change or. . ."

"Don't talk to me about how much you gave me, Big Mamma, and how much I owe you or none of that."

"Oh? I ain't supposed to mention it?"

---

23 지금은 모두 널판자로 막아 놓은 창문

24 setting fire to...: 머리카락을 불로 펴면서.

25 그 낡은 여우목도리는 여우에게 별 도움이 안되듯이 네게도 소용이 없을게다.

26 말도 없이 나타나면, 지금처럼 갑자기 튀어나오면, 내 기분대로 맞는 수밖에 별 도리가 없지.

27 그럭저럭 지낸다.

"OK. Mention it." Sula shrugged and turned over on her stomach, her buttocks toward Eva.

"You ain't been in this house ten seconds and already you starting something[28]."

"Takes two, Big Mamma[29]."

"Well, don't let your mouth start nothing that your ass can't stand[30]. When your ass can't stand. When you gone to get married? You need to have some babies. It'll settle you[31]."

"I don't want to make somebody else. I want to make myself."

"Selfish. Ain't no woman got no business floatin' around without no man."

"You did."

"Not by choice."

"Mamma did."

"Not by choice, I said. It ain't right for you to want to stay off by yourself. You need... I'm a tell you what you need."

Sula sat up. "I need you to shut your mouth."

"Don't nobody talk to me like that. Don't nobody..."

"This body does. Just 'cause you was bad enough to cut off your own leg you think you got a right to kick everybody with the stump."

"Who said I cut off my leg?"

"Well, you stuck it under a train to collect insurance."

"Hold on, you lyin' heifer!"

"I aim to."

---

28 이집에 들어온 지 10초도 지나지 않아 또 싸움을 시작하는구나.

29 싸움하는 데는 두 사람이 있어야지요. 즉, 자신만이 문제를 일으키는 것이 아니라, 할머니도 싸움에 책임이 있다는 뜻임.

30 네 엉덩이가 견뎌낼 수 없는 말을 입으로 시작하지 말아라. 즉, 엉덩이 맞을 만큼 버릇없는 말은 하지 말라는 뜻임.

31 결혼하고 아이를 가지면 안정될 게다.

"Bible say honor thy father and thy mother that thy days may be long upon the land thy God giveth thee."

"Mamma must have skipped that part. Her days wasn't too long.[32]"

"Pus mouth! God's going to strike you!"

"Which God? The one watched you burn Plum?"

"Don't talk to me about no burning. You watched your own mamma. You crazy roach! You the one should have been burnt!"

"But I ain't. Got that? I ain't. Any more fires in this house, I'm lighting them[33]!"

"Hellfire don't need lighting and it's already burning on you. . ."

"Whatever's burning in me is mine!"

"Amen!"

"And I'll split this town in two and everything in it before I'll let you put it out!"

"Pride goeth before a fall[34]."

"What the hell do I care about falling?"

"Amazing Grace."

"You sold your life for twenty-three dollars a month."

"You throwed yours away."

"It's mine to throw."

"One day you gone need it."

"But not you. I ain't never going to need you. And you know what? Maybe one night when you dozing in that wagon flicking flies and swallowing spit, maybe I'll just tip on up here with some kerosene and—who knows—you may make the brightest flame of them all[35]."

---

32 할머니는 한 부분을 빼놓고 읽었군요. 부모님의 삶이 그리 길지 않았다는 부분 말이에요.

33 이제 내가 불을 켤 겁니다.

34 교만하면 타락하는 법이지.

So Eva locked her door from then on. But it did no good. In April two men came with a stretcher and she didn't even have time to comb her hair before they strapped her to a piece of canvas[36].

When Mr. Buckland Reed came by to pick up the number[37], his mouth sagged at the sight of Eva being carried out and Sula holding some papers against the wall, at the bottom of which, just above the word "guardian," she very carefully wrote Miss Sula Mae Peace.

* * *

Nel alone noticed the peculiar quality of the May that followed the leaving of the birds. It had a sheen, a glimmering as of green, rain-soaked Saturday nights[38] (lit by the excitement of newly installed street lights); of lemon-yellow afternoons bright with iced drinks and splashes of daffodils. It showed in the damp faces of her children and the river-smoothness of their voices. Even her own body was not immune to the magic. She would sit on the floor to sew as she had done as a girl, fold her legs up under her or do a little dance that fitted some tune in her head. There were easy sun-washed days[39] and purple dusks in which Tar Baby sang "Abide With Me" at prayer meetings, his

35 할머니가 잠든 사이 등유를 들고 들어와 불을 지르겠다는 뜻임.

36 머리 빗을 시간도 없이 두 남자가 그녀를 캔버스에 묶어 버렸다.

37 여기서 number는 앞서 꿈풀이 책을 의미한 바 있으므로, 마찬가지로, "리드 씨가 이바할머니의 꿈 풀이 책을 보려고 왔을 때"로 해석하는 것이 적당할 것 같다.

38 그 해 5월에는 비에 촉촉이 젖은 초록빛의 토요일 밤과 같은 (as of) 희미하게 반짝거리는 빛이 있었다.

39 편안하고 화창한 날

lashes darkened by tears, his silhouette limp with regret against the whitewashed walls of Greater Saint Matthew's[40]. Nel listened and was moved to smile. To smile at the sheer loveliness that pressed in from the windows and touched his grief, making it a pleasure to behold.

Although it was she alone who saw this magic, she did not wonder at it. She knew it was all due to Sula's return to the Bottom. It was like getting the use of an eye back, having a cataract removed[41]. Her old friend had come home. Sula. Who made her laugh, who made her see old things with new eyes, in whose presence she felt clever, gentle and a little raunchy. Sula, Whose past she had lived through and with whom the present was a constant sharing of perceptions. Talking to Sula had always been a conversation with herself. Was there anyone else before whom she could never be foolish[42]? In whose view inadequacy was mere idiosyncrasy, a character trait rather than a deficiency[43]? Anyone who left behind[44] that aura of fun and complicity? Sula never competed; she simply helped others define themselves. Other people seemed to turn their volume on and up when Sula was in the room[45]. More than any other thing, humor returned. She could listen to the crunch of sugar underfoot that the children had spilled without reaching for the

40 his silhouette... : 마태오 성당의 하얀 벽에 드리워진, 슬픔으로 힘없이 늘어진 그림자

41 백내장이 제거되어 시력을 되찾은 것 같았다.

42 자신이 어리석지 않다는 느낌을 다른 누구와 함께 있을 때 가질 수 있겠는가. 즉, 술라와 함께 있으면 자신이 어리석지 않다고 느꼈다는 뜻임.

43 술라 함께 있으면 미련함도 결점도, 모두 개성이 되었다.

44 앞지르다.

45 술라와 함께 있으면 사람들은 목소리를 크게 높였다. 즉, 자기주장이 강해졌다는 뜻임.

switch[46]; and she forgot the tear in the living-room window shade[47]. Even Nel's love for Jude, which over the years had spun a steady gray web around her heart,[48] became a bright and easy affection, a playfulness that was reflected in their lovemaking.

Sula would come by of an afternoon[49], walking along with her fluid stride[50], wearing a plain yellow dress the same way her mother, Hannah, had worn those too-big house dresses[51] — with a distance, an absence of a relationship to clothes which emphasized everything the fabric covered[52]. When she scratched the screen door, as in the old days, and stepped inside, the dishes piled in the sink looked as though they belonged there; the dust on the lamps sparkled; the hair brush lying on the "good" sofa in the living room did not have to be apologetically retrieved, and Nel's grimy intractable children looked like three wild things happily insouciant[53] in the May shine.

"Hey, girl." The rose mark over Sula's eye gave her glance a suggestion of startled pleasure. It was darker than Nel remembered.

"Hey yourself. Come on in here."

"How you doin'?" Sula moved a pile of ironed diapers from a

---

46 불을 켜지도 않고 아이들이 흘린 설탕이 발 밑에서 바스락거리는 소리를 술라는 들을 수 있었다.

47 넬은 거실 창문 커튼이 해진 것도 잊어 버렸다.

48 수년동안 천천히 회색의 거미줄이 쳐졌던 사랑. 사랑이 습관적이고 그 뜨거움이 식었다는 뜻.

49 오후에. 대체로 습관적인 경우에 많이 쓰임.

50 나긋나긋한 걸음걸이

51 엄마 한나가 헐렁하게 큰 일상복을 입던 방식으로.

52 멀리서 보면, 옷감에 감춰진 몸을 강조하면서도, 옷과 술라는 아무런 상관없는 것 같다.

53 무심한.

chair and sat down.

"Oh, I ain't strangled nobody yet so I guess I'm all right[54]."

"Well, if you change your mind call me[55]."

"Somebody need killin'?"

"Half this town need it."

"And the other half?"

"A drawn-out disease[56]."

"Oh, come on. Is Medallion that bad?"

"Didn't nobody tell you?"

"You been gone too long, Sula."

"No too long, but maybe too far."

"What's that supposed to mean?" Nel dipped her fingers into the bowl of water and sprinkled a diaper[57].

"Oh, I don't know."

"Want some cool tea?"

"Mmmm. Lots of ice, I'm burnin' up."

"Iceman don't come yet, but it's good and cold."

"That's fine."

"Hope I didn't speak too soon. Kids run in and out of here so much." Nel bent to open the icebox.

"You puttin' it on, Nel. Jude must be wore out[58]."

"*Jude* must be wore out? You don't care nothin' 'bout my back, do you?[59]"

"Is that where it's at, in your back?[60]"

---

54 아직 누구도 목 졸라 죽이지 않았으니 잘 지낸다고 할 수 있겠지.

55 네 마음이 변하면 말해 줘. 즉, 누군가를 죽일 맘이 생기면 알려 달라는 뜻임.

56 만성 질병에 결려있지.

57 물그릇에 손가락으로 물을 찍어 헝겊 기저귀에 뿌린다.

58 살이 찌고 있구나. 쥬드가 이젠 지쳐버린 모양이지?

59 넌 내 허리가 어떨지 상관도 않는구나.

60 바로 거기가 성감대란 말이니? 네 허리가?

"Hah! Jude thinks it's everywhere."

"He's right, it is everywhere. Just be glad he found it, wherever it is. Remember John L.?"

"When Shirley said he got her down by the well and tried to stick it[61] in her hip?" Nel giggled at the remembrance of that teen-time tale. "she should have been grateful. Have you seen her since you been back?"

"Mmm. Like a ox[62]."

"That was one dumb nigger, John L."

"Maybe. Maybe he was just sanitary[63]."

"Sanitary?"

"Well. Think about it. Suppose Shirley was all splayed out in front of you[64]? Wouldn't you go for the hipbone instead?"

Nel lowered her head onto crossed arms while tears of laughter dripped into the warm diapers. Laughter that weakened her knees and pressed her bladder into action. Her rapid soprano and Sula's dark sleepy chuckle made a duet that frightened the cat and made the children run in from the back yard, puzzled at first by the wild free sounds, then delighted to see their mother stumbling merrily toward the bathroom, holding on to her stomach, fairly singing through the laughter: "Aw. Aw. Lord. Sula. Stop." And the other one, the one with the scary black thing over her eye[65], laughing softly and egging their mother on[66]: "Neatness counts[67]. You know what cleanliness is

61 여기서 it는 성기를 의미함.

62 황소처럼 등뒤에서 성교하려 했다는 뜻임.

63 그가 위생을 고려했기 때문인지도 모르지.

64 네 앞에 셜리가 몸을 쭉 벌리고 있다면 어떨까.

65 눈위에 반점이 있는 술라를 가리킴.

66 egg on: 부추기다.

67 깨끗한 것은 중요하지.

next to..."

"Hush." Nel's plea was clipped off[68] by the slam of the bathroom door.

"What y'all laughing at?"

"Old time-y stuff. Long gone, old time-y stuff."

"Tell us."

"Tell *you*?" The black mark leaped.

"Uh huh. Tell us."

"What tickles us wouldn't tickle you[69]."

"Uh huh, it would."

"Well, we was talking about some people we used to know when we was little."

"Was my mamma little?"

"Of course."

"What happened?"

"Well, some old boy we knew name John L. and a girl name..."

Damp-faced, Nel stepped back into the kitchen. She felt new, soft and new. It had been the longest time since she had had a rib-scraping laugh[70]. She had forgotten how deep and down it could be. So different from the miscellaneous giggles and smiles she had learned to be content with these past few years.

"O Lord, Sula. You haven't changed none." She wiped her eyes. "What was all that about, anyway? All that scramblin we did trying to do it and not do it at the same time[71]?"

"Beats me[72]. Such a simple thing."

68 clip off: 멈추다.

69 어른들에게 우스운 것이 꼬마들에게도 재미있진 않아.

70 배가 잡고 웃는 웃음.

71 we did 다음에 쉼표를 넣으면 해석이 용이함. 즉, 우리가 행했던 모든 짓거리들, 하려고도 애쓰고, 동시에 하지 않으려고 애썼던 일들...

"But we sure made a lot out of it[73], and the boys were dumber than we were."

"Couldn't nobody be dumber than I was."

"Stop lying. All of 'em liked you best."

"Yeah? Where are they?"

"They still here. You the one went off[74]."

"Didn't I, though?"

"Tell me about it. The big city."

"Big is all it is[75]. A big Medallion."

"No. I mean the life. The nightclubs, and parties..."

"I was in college, Nellie. No nightclubs on campus."

"Campus? That what they call it? Well. You wasn't in no college for — what — ten years now? and you didn't write to nobody. How come you never wrote?"

"You never did either."

"Where was I going to write to? All I knew was that you was in Nashville. I asked Miss Peace about you once or twice."

"What did *she* say?"

"I couldn't make much sense out of her[76]. You know she been gettin' stranger and stranger after she come out the hospital. How is she anyway?"

"same, I guess. Not so hot[77]."

"No? Laura, I know, was doing her cooking and things. Is she still?"

"No. I put her out."

---

72 그 때문에 난 손 들었어.

73 우린 많은 것을 배웠지.

74 떠난 사람은 바로 너야.

75 그저 크다는 것이 전부야.

76 할머니가 무슨 말을 하는지 이해할 수 없었어.

77 그리 혈기왕성하진 않아.

"Put her out? What for?"

"She made me nervous."

"But she was doing it for nothing, Sula."

"That's what you think. She was stealing right and left[78]."

"Since when did you get froggy[79] about folks' stealing?"

Sula smiled. "OK. I lied. You wanted a reason."

"Well, give me the real one."

"I don't know the real one. She just didn't belong in that house. Digging around in the cupboards, picking up pots and ice picks..."

"You sure have changed. That house was always full of people digging in cupboards and carrying on."

"That's the reason, then."

"Sula. Come on, now."

"You've changed too. I didn't used to have to explain everything to you."

Nel blushed. "Who's feeding the deweys and Tar Baby? You?"

"Sure me. Anyway Tar Baby don't eat and the deweys still crazy."

"I heard one of 'em's mamma came to take him back but didn't know which was hern.[80]"

"Don't nobody know."

"And Eva? You doing the work for her too?"

"Well, since you haven't heard it, let me tell you. Eva's real sick. I had her put where she could be watched and taken care of."

"Where would that be?"

78 이런 저런 방식으로 집안 물건을 훔쳐내고 있었지.

79 미국속어로, "불만스러운"의 뜻.

80 학교 문법에 맞게 문장을 고치면, "I heard one of their mamas came to take him back but didn't know which was hers."

"Out by Beechnut."

"You mean that home the white church run[81]? Sula! That ain't no place for Eva. All them women is dirt poor with no people at all[82]. Mrs. Wilkens and them. They got dropsy and can't hold their water[83] — crazy as loons, Eva's odd, but she got sense. I don't think that's right, Sula."

"I'm scared of her, Nellie. That's why. . ."

"Scared? Of Eva?"

"You don't know her. Did you know she burnt Plum?"

"Oh, I heard that years ago. But nobody put no stock in it[84]."

"They should have. It's true. I saw it. And when I got back here she was planning to do it to me too."

"Eva? I can't hardly believe that. She almost died trying to get to your mother."

Sula leaned forward, her elbows on the table. "You ever known me to lie to you?"

"No. But you could be mistaken. Why would Eva. . ."

"All I know is I'm scared. And there's no place else for me to go. We all that's left, Eva and me. I guess I should have stayed gone[85]. I didn't know what else to do. Maybe I should have talked to you about it first. You always had better sense than me. Whenever I was scared before, you knew just what to do."

The closed place in the water spread before them[86]. Nel put

---

81 백인 교회가 운영하는 양로원.

82 그 양로원에 있는 노인들은 모두 더럽고 가난하고 그리고 돌볼 사람이 없는 노인들이야.

83 그들은 전신부종에다가 오줌도 가릴 수 없는 사람들이야.

84 그러나 그것을 믿는 사람은 없어.

85 멀리 떠난 채 돌아오지 말았어야 할 것을.

86 강물에 치킨 리틀이 떨어져 죽은 것을 회상한다. "The closed place in the water"란 소년이 빠진 강물을 의미하고, "spread before them"은 그 장면이 그들 앞에 펼쳐진다는 의미다.

the iron on the stove. The situation was clear to her now. Sula, like always, was incapable of making any but the most trivial decisions. When it came to matters of grave importance, she behaved emotionally and irresponsibly and left it to others to straighten out[87]. And when fear struck her, she did unbelievable things. Like that time with her finger[88]. Whatever those hunkies did, it wouldn't have been as bad as what she did to herself. But Sula was so scared she had mutilated herself, to protect herself.

"What should I do, Nellie? Take her back and sleep with my door locked again?"

"No. I guess it's too late anyway. But let's work out a plan for taking care of her. So she won't be messed over[89]."

"Anything you say[90]."

"What about money? She got any?"

Sula shrugged. "The checks come still. It's not much, like it used to be. Should I have them made over to me[91]?"

"Can you? Do it, then. We can arrange for her to have special comforts. That place is a mess, you know. A doctor don't never set foot in there. I ain't figured out yet how they stay alive in there as long as they do."

"Why don't I have the checks made over to you, Nellie? You better at this than I am."

"Oh no. People will say I'm scheming[92]. You the one to do it. Was there insurance from Hannah?"

---

87 straight out: 해결하다.

88 술라가 손가락을 자해한 사건처럼.

89 그래서 이바가 그 곳에서 엉망이 되지 않도록.

90 네가 말하는 것이면 뭐든 할게.

91 수표(연금)를 내 이름으로 발급 받도록 해볼까?

92 내가 돈을 갈취하려고 술수를 쓰고 있다고 사람들이 생각할지도 몰라.

"Yes. Plum too. He had all that army insurance."

"Any of it left?"

"Well I went to college on some. Eva banked the rest. I'll look into it, though."

". . . and explain it all to the bank people."

"Will you go down with me?"

"Sure. It's going to be all right."

"I'm glad I talked to you 'bout this. It's been bothering me."

"Well, tongues will wag[93], but so long as we know the truth, it don't matter."

Just at that moment the children ran in announcing the entrance of their father. Jude opened the back door and walked into the kitchen. He was still a very good-looking man, and the only difference Sula could see was the thin pencil mustache under his nose, and a part in his hair.

"Hey, Jude. What you know good?[94]"

"White man running it — nothing good[95]."

Sula laughed while Nel, high-tuned to his moods[96], ignored her husband's smile saying, "Bad day, honey?"

"Same old stuff," he replied and told them a brief tale of some personal insult done him by a customer and his boss — a whiney[97] tale that peaked somewhere between anger and a lapping[98] desire for comfort. He ended it with the observation that a Negro man had a hard row to hoe in this world[99]. He

93 혀가 나불거리다. 즉, 사람들의 말이 많을 거라는 뜻임.

94 인사말. 잘 지냈나요?

95 백인이 운영하고 있으니 좋은 일이 없지요.

96 high-tuned to his moods: 남편의 기분에 민감하여.

97 투덜대는

98 게걸스러운

99 흑인들은 이 세상에서 고생할 수밖에 없다는 결론으로 자신의 이야기를 끝

expected his story to dovetail into milkwarm commiseration[1], but before Nel could excrete it, Sula said she didn't know about that—it looked like a pretty good life to her.

"Say what?" Jude's temper flared just a bit[2] as he looked at this friend of his wife's, this slight woman, not exactly plain, but not fine either, with a copperhead over her eye. As far as he could tell, she looked like a woman roaming the country trying to find some man to burden down with a lot of lip and a lot of mouths.

Sula was smiling. "I mean, I don't know what the fuss is about[3]. I mean, everything in the world loves you. White men love you. They spend so much time worrying about your penis they forget their own[4]. The only thing they want to do is cut off a nigger's privates[5]. And if that ain't love and respect I don't know what is. And white women? They chase you all to every corner of the earth, feel for you under every bed. I knew a white woman wouldn't leave the house after 6 o'clock for fear one of you would snatch her. Now ain't that love? They think rape soon's they see you[6], and if they don't get the rape they looking for, they scream it anyway just so the search won't be in vain. Colored women worry themselves into bad health just trying to hang on to your cuffs[7]. Even little

맺었다.

1 자신의 이야기가 따뜻한 동정을 이끌어 내리라 기대했다.

2 쥬드는 약간 부르르 떨며 화를 냈다.

3 웬 소란인지 알 수가 없어.

4 자신의 것이 되지 못한 당신 흑인 남자들의 성기를 부러워하면서 백인들은 시간을 보내지요.

5 성기

6 당신들이 백인여자를 보자마자 그들은 강간을 생각하게 되지요. soon's는 as soon as 로 보면 됨.

children — white and black, boys and girls — spend all their childhood eating their hearts out[8] 'cause they think you don't love them. And if that ain't enough, you love yourselves. Nothing in this world loves a black man more than another black man. You hear of solitary white men, but niggers? Can't stay away from one another a whole day. So. It looks to me like you the envy of the world[9]."

Jude and Nel were laughing, he saying, "Well, if that's the only way they got to show it[10] — cut off my balls[11] and throw me in jail — I'd just as soon they left me alone[12]." But thinking that Sula had an odd way of looking at things and that her wide smile took some of the sting from that rattlesnake over her eye[13]. A funny woman, he thought, not that bad-looking. But he could see why she wasn't married; she stirred a man's mind maybe, but not his body.

* * *

He left his tie. The one with the scriggly[14] yellow lines running lopsided across the dark-blue field[15]. It hung over the top of

---

7 흑인 여자들은 당신네들 바지자락에 매달리면서 걱정으로 건강을 해치고 있지요.

8 eating their hearts out: 애간장을 태운다.

9 그러하니, 당신이야말로 이 세상의 부러움인 것 같아요. you와 the envy 사이에 "are"가 생략된 것으로 보면 됨.

10 그들이 부러워할 만한 것이 내 성기 밖에 없다면. 여기서 it는 "부러움"이란 뜻임.

11 balls: 속어로 남자의 성기를 의미함.

12 그러면 당장에 나를 내버려두겠지요.

13 her wide smile...: 술라의 환한 웃음이 눈 위의 방울뱀 반점이 주는 험상궂은 인상을 좀 완화시켰다. 여기서 sting은 방울뱀의 독침이란 뜻인데, 결국 험상궂은 인상을 의미한다.

14 꿈틀거리는: wriggly 혹은 scrawly의 뜻임.

the closet door pointing steadily downward while it waited with every confidence for Jude to return.

Could he be gone if his tie is still here? He will remember it and come back and then she would. . . uh. Then she could. . . tell him. Sit down quietly and tell him. "But Jude," she would say, "You *knew* me. All those days and years, Jude, you *knew* me. My ways and my hands and how my stomach folded and how we tried to get Mickey to nurse and how about that time when the landlord said. . . but you said. . . and I cried, Jude. You knew me and had listened to the things I said in the night, and heard me in the bathroom and laughed at my raggedy girdle and I laughed too because I knew you too, Jude. So how could you leave me when you knew me?"

But they had been down on all fours naked, not touching except their lips right down there on the floor where the tie is pointing to, on all fours like (uh huh, go on, say it) like dogs. Nibbling at each other, not even touching, not even looking at each other, just their lips[16], and when I opened the door they didn't even look for a minute and I thought the reason they are not looking up is because they are not doing that. So it's all right. I am just standing here. They are not doing that. I am just standing here and seeing it, but they are not really doing it. But then they did look up. Or you did. You did, Jude. And if only you had not looked at me the way the soldiers did on the train, the way you look at the children when they come in while you are listening to Gabriel Heatter[17] and break your train of thought — not

15 넥타이 문양을 묘사한 것으로, "검푸른 바탕에 노란색 사선이 꿈틀거리는 모양으로 그려진 넥타이."

16 입술을 제외하고는 서로 만지지도 쳐다보지도 않은 채, 서로를 조금씩 물어뜯으면서.

focusing exactly but giving them an instant, a piece of time, to remember what they are doing, what they are interrupting, and to go on back to wherever they were and let you listen to Gabriel Heatter[18]. And I did not know how to move my feet or fix my eyes or what. I just stood there seeing it and smiling, because maybe there was some explanation, something important that I did not know about that would have made it all right[19]. I waited for Sula to look up at me any minute and say one of those lovely college words like *aesthetic* or *rapport*, which I never understood but which I loved because they sounded so comfortable and firm. And finally you just got up and started putting on your clothes and your privates were hanging down, so soft, and you buckled your pants belt but forgot to button the fly[20] and she was sitting on the bed not even bothering to put on her clothes because actually she didn't need to because somehow she didn't look naked to me, only you did. Her chin was in her hand and she sat like a visitor from out of town waiting for the hosts to get some quarreling done and over with so the card game could continue and me wanting her to leave so I could tell you privately that you had forgotten to button your fly because I didn't want to say it in front of her, Jude. And even when you began to talk, I couldn't hear because I was worried about you not knowing that your fly was open and

17 1930년대와 40년대 미국의 유명한 라디오 프로그램 "We the People"을 방송했던 인물.

18 아이들이 하는 말에 집중하지 않고, 그저 잠시 아이들이 지금 하고 있는 일, 즉, 아이들이 자신을 방해하고 있음을 기억할 수 있도록 잠시 시간을 내주고, 다시 아이들이 제자리로 돌아가서 자신을 라디오방송을 들을 수 있도록 짧은 시간만 (건성으로) 내줄 뿐이었다.

19 내가 알지 못하는 뭔가 중요한 것, 그것을 알면 오해가 풀려 모든 일이 괜찮아질지도 모르는 어떤 것.

20 바지섶

scared too because your eyes looked like the soldiers' that time on the train when my mother turned to custard[21].

Remember how big that bedroom was? Jude? How when we moved here we said, Well, at least we got us a real big bedroom, but it was small then, Jude, and so shambly, and maybe it was that way all along[22] but it would have been better if I had gotten the dust out from under the bed because I was ashamed of it in that small room. And then you walked past me saying, "I'll be back for my things." And you did but you left your tie.

The clock was ticking. Nel looked at it and realized that it was two thirty, only forty-five minutes before the children would be home and she hadn't even felt anything right or sensible and now there was no time or wouldn't be until nighttime when they were asleep and she could get into bed and maybe she could do it then. Think. But who could think in that bed where *they*[23] had been and where *they*[24] also had been and where only she was now?

She looked around for a place to be. A small place. The closet? No. Too dark. Small enough to contain her grief. Bright enough to throw into relief the dark things that cluttered her. Once inside, she sank to the tile floor next to the toilet. On her knees, her hand on the cold rim of the bathtub, she waited for

21 custard란 우유, 달걀, 설탕을 넣어 만든 빵이나 과자를 말하는데, 엄마가 이러한 빵으로 변했다는 말은 매우 복합적인 의미를 띤다. 즉, 한 개체로서 당당하게 대접받지 못하고 빵처럼 흔한 먹거리, 혹은 욕망의 대상이 되었다는 의미와 동시에, 어머니의 검은 피부색이 담황색을 띠었다는 의미로, 욕망의 대상이 되었다는 사실에 대한 분노와 수치심의 빛깔을 의미하기도 한다.

22 it was that way all along: 처음부터 늘 침실은 좁았다.

23 여기서의 they는 넬과 쥬드를 의미한다.

24 술라와 쥬드

something to happen. . . inside. There was stirring, a movement of mud and dead leaves. She thought of the women at Chicken Little's funeral. The women who shrieked over the bier and at the lip of the open grave. What she had regarded since as unbecoming behavior seemed fitting to her now; they were screaming at the neck of God, his giant nape, the vast back-of-head that he had turned on them in death[25]. But it seemed to her now that it was not a fist-shaking grief they were keening[26] but rather a simple obligation to say something, do something, feel something about the dead. They could not let that heart-smashing event pass[27] unrecorded, unidentified. It was poisonous, unnatural to let the dead go with a mere whimpering, a slight murmur, a rose bouquet of good taste. Good taste was out of place in the company of death, death itself was the essence of bad taste[28]. And there must be much rage and saliva in its presence. The body must move and throw itself about, the eyes must roll, the hands should have no peace, and the throat should release all the yearning, despair and outrage that accompany the stupidity of loss.

"The real hell of Hell is that it is forever[29]." Sula said that. She said doing anything forever and ever was hell. Nel didn't understand it then, but now in the bathroom, trying to feel, she thought, "If I could be sure that I could stay here in this small white room with the dirty tile and water gurgling in the

25 they were screaming...: 그들은 신의 목, 그 거대한 목덜미, 죽음에서야 그들에게 보여준 신의 거대한 뒤통수에 대고 소리치고 있었다.

26 그들이 통곡하는 것은 주먹을 휘두르는 식의 원망에 가까운 슬픔은 아니었던 것 같다.

27 heart-smashing event: 가슴을 치며 통곡할 사건, 죽음을 의미함.

28 죽음이 있는 곳엔 훌륭한 매너 따위는 어울리지 않았다.

29 지옥이 지옥인 것은 그것이 영원하기 때문이야.

pipes and my head on the cool rim of this bathtub and never have to go out the door, I would be happy. If I could be certain that I never had to get up and flush the toilet, go in the kitchen, watch my children grow up and die, see my food chewed on my plate. . . Sula was wrong. Hell ain't things lasting forever. Hell is change[30]." Not only did men leave and children grow up and die, but even the misery didn't last[31]. One day she wouldn't even have that. This very grief that had twisted her into a curve on the floor and flayed her would be gone[32]. She would lose that too.

"Why, even in hate here I am thinking of what Sula said[33]."

Hunched down in the small bright room Nel waited. Waited for the oldest cry. A scream not for others, not in sympathy for a burnt child, or a dead father, but a deeply personal cry for one's own pain. A loud, strident: "Why me?" She waited. The mud shifted, the leaves stirred, the smell of overripe green things enveloped her and announced the beginnings of her very own howl[34].

But it did not come.

The odor evaporated; the leaves were still, the mud settled. And finally there was nothing, just a flake of something dry and nasty in her throat. She stood up frightened. There was something just to the right of her, in the air, just out of view. She could not see it, but she knew exactly what it looked like. A

30 지옥은 영원히 지속되기 때문은 아니야. 변화하는 것이 바로 지옥이야.

31 남편이 떠나고 아이들이 자라서 죽을 뿐 아니라, 슬픔 그 자체도 지속하는 것은 아니었다.

32 화장실 바닥에 웅크려 그녀의 기슴을 뜯는 이 슬픔도 없어져 버릴 것이다.

33 여기서 증오에 사로잡혀 있으면서도 난 술라가 한 말을 생각하고 있군.

34 진흙이 움직이고, 나뭇잎이 바스락거리고, 너무 익어버린 푸성귀냄새가 이제 막 터져 나오는 울부짖음을 에워쌌다.

gray ball hovering just there. Just there. To the right. Quiet, gray, dirty. A ball of muddy strings, but without weight, fluffy but terrible in its malevolence. She knew she could not look, so she closed her eyes and crept past it out of the bathroom, shutting the door behind her. Sweating with fear, she stepped to the kitchen door and onto the back porch. The lilac bushes preened at the railing[35], there were no lilacs yet. Wasn't it time? Surely it was time. She looked over the fence to Mrs. Rayford's yard. Hers were not in bloom either. Was it too late? She fastened on this question with enthusiasm, all the time aware of something she was not thinking[36]. It was the only way she could get her mind off the flake in her throat[37].

She spent a whole summer with the gray ball, the little ball of fur and string and hair always floating in the light near her but which she did not see because she never looked. But that was the terrible part, the effort it took not to look. But it was there anyhow, just to the right of her head and maybe further down by her shoulder, so when the children went to a monster movie at the Elmera Theater and came home and said, "Mamma, can you sleep with us tonight?" she said all right and got into bed with the two boys, who loved it, but the girl did not. For a long time she could not stop getting in the bed with her children and told herself each time that they might dream a dream about dragons and would need her to comfort them. It was so nice to think about their scary dreams and not about a ball of fur. She even hoped their dreams would rub off on her[38] and give her

35 난간에 잘 다듬어진 라일락 덤불.

36 그녀가 (의식적으로) 생각하지 않는 것을 늘 의식하면서, 열정적으로 이 문제에 몰두했다.

37 그녀의 목에 낀 조각을 마음속에서 떨쳐버리는 유일한 방법이었다.

the wonderful relief of a nightmare so she could stop going around scared to turn her head this way or that lest she see it. That was the scary part—seeing it. It was not coming at her; it never did that, or tried to pounce on her. It just floated there for the seeing, if she wanted to, and O my God for the touching if she wanted to. But she didn't want to see it, ever, for if she saw it, who could tell but what she might actually touch it, or want to, and then what would happen if she actually reached out her hand and touched it? Die probably, but no worse than that. Dying was OK because it was sleep and there Wasn't no gray ball in death, was there? Was there? She would have to ask somebody about that, somebody she could confide in and who knew a lot of things, like Sula, for Sula would know or if she didn't she would say something funny that would make it all right. Ooo no, not Sula. Here she was in the midst of it, hating, scared of it, and again she thought of Sula as though they were still friends and talked things over. That was too much. To lose Jude and not have Sula to talk to about it because it was Sula that he had left her for.

Now her thighs were really empty. And it was then that what those women said about never looking at another man made some sense to her, for the real point, the heart of what they said, was the word *looked*[39]. Not to promise never to make love to another man, not to refuse to marry another man[40], but to promise and know that she could never afford to look again, to see and accept the way in which their heads cut the air or see moons and tree limbs framed by their necks and shoulders. . .

38 아이들이 꿈이 그녀에게 전이되어.

39 정말 중요한 것은, 그들이 하는 말의 핵심은 바로 "보았다"라는 말에 있었다.

40 다른 남자와 성관계를 갖지 않겠다고 약속하거나 혹은 다른 남자와의 결혼을 거부하지 않고.

never to look, for now she could not risk looking—and anyway, so what? For now her thighs were truly empty and dead too, and it was Sula who had taken the life from them and Jude who smashed her heart and the both of them who left her with no thighs and no heart just her brain raveling away[41].

And what am I supposed to do with these old thighs now, just walk up and down these rooms? What good are they, Jesus? They will never give me the peace I need to get from sunup to sundown, what good are they, are you trying to tell me that I am going to have to go all the way through these days all the way, O my god, to that box with four handles[42] with never nobody settling down between my legs even if I sew up those old pillow cases and rinse down the porch and feed my children and beat the rugs and haul the coal up out of the bin even then nobody, O Jesus, I could be a mule or plow the furrows with my hands if need be or hold these rickety walls up with my back if need be if I knew that somewhere in this world in the pocket of some night I could open my legs to some cowboy lean hips but you are trying to tell me no and O my sweet Jesus what kind of cross[43] is that?

41 both of them...: 두 사람은 그녀에게서 성적 욕망도 열정도 남겨 놓지 않았고, 단지 그녀의 머리 속만 혼란하게 만들어 놓았다.

42 that box with four handles: 관을 의미함.

43 형벌

1939

When the word got out about Eva being put in Sunnydale, the people in the Bottom shook their heads and said Sula was a roach. Later, when they saw how she took Jude, then ditched him for others, and heard how he bought a bus ticket to Detroit (where he bought but never mailed birthday cards to his sons), they forgot all about Hannah's easy ways (or their own) and said she was a bitch. Everybody remembered the plague of robins that announced her return, and the tale about her watching Hannah burn was stirred up again.

But it was the men who gave her the final label, who fingerprinted her for all time[1]. They were the ones who said she was guilty of the unforgivable thing — the thing for which there was no understanding, no excuse, no compassion. The route from which there was no way back, the dirt that could not ever be washed away. They said that Sula slept with white men. It may not have been true, but it certainly could have been. She was obviously capable of it. In any case, all minds were closed to her[2] when that word was passed around. It made the old women draw their lips together[3]; made small children look away from her in shame; made young men fantasize elaborate torture for her[4] — just to get the saliva back in their mouths when they

1 술라의 지문처럼 항상 따라다니는 그녀의 최종 이름을 지워준 것은 바로 남자들이었다.

2 모든 사람들이 그녀에게 등을 돌렸다.

3 여자들은 입을 삐죽 내밀었다.

4 젊은이들은 그녀를 교묘하게 고문하는 상상을 즐겼다.

saw her.

Every one of them imagined the scene, each according to his own predilections — Sula underneath some white man — and it filled them with choking disgust. There was nothing lower she could do, nothing filthier. The fact that their own skin color was proof that it had happened in their own families was no deterrent to their bile[5]. Nor was the willingness of black men to lie in the beds of white women a consideration that might lead them toward tolerance[6]. They insisted that all unions between white men and black women be rape; for a black woman to be willing was literally unthinkable. In that way, they regarded integration with precisely the same venom that white people did[7].

So they laid broomsticks across their doors at night and sprinkled salt on porch steps[8]. But aside from one or two unsuccessful efforts to collect the dust from her footsteps[9], they did nothing to harm her. As always the black people looked at evil stony-eyed and let it run.

Sula acknowledged none of their attempts at counter-conjure[10] or their gossip and seemed to need the services of nobody. So they watched her far more closely than they watched any other roach or bitch in the town, and their alertness was gratified[11].

---

5 자신의 검은 피부를 보면서 그런 일들이 모두 자신의 집안, 즉 종족 안에서 일어났다고 하는 사실조차 술라에 대한 미움을 저지하지는 못했다.

6 흑인 남자들은 흔쾌히 백인 여자와 관계를 갖는다는 사실이 (흑인 여자를) 너그럽게 용납하게 만들지도 못했다.

7 백인들과 마찬가지로 흑인들도, 각 인종이 서로 융화되는 것을 극도로 싫어했다.

8 빗자루를 문에 가위표로 붙여놓고 현관에 소금을 뿌렸다. 모두 악귀를 쫓는 행위임.

9 문설주에 먼지를 털음으로써 심판날에 가혹한 심판을 받는다는 성경을 따라 하는 행위.

10 악귀를 쫓기 위한 여러 조치.

11 열심히 경계한 보람이 있었다.

Things began to happen.

First off, Teapot knocked on her door to see if she had any bottles. He was the five-year-old son of an indifferent mother, all of whose interests sat around the door of the Time and a Half Pool Hall. Her name was Betty but she was called Teapot's Mamma because being his mamma was precisely her major failure. When Sula said no, the boy turned around and fell down the steps. He couldn't get up right away and Sula went to help him. His mother, just then tripping home, saw Sula bending over her son's pained face. She flew into a fit of concerned, if drunken, motherhood[12], and dragged Teapot home. She told everybody that Sula had pushed him, and talked so strongly about it she was forced to abide by the advice of her friends and take him to the county hospital. The two dollars she hated to release turned out to be well spent[13], for Teapot did have a fracture, although the doctor said poor diet had contributed substantially to the daintiness[14] of his bones.

Teapot's Mamma got a lot of attention anyway and immersed herself in a role she had shown no inclination for: motherhood[15]. The very idea of a grown woman hurting her boy kept her teeth on edge[16]. She became the most devoted mother: sober, clean and industrious. No more nickels for Teapot to go to Dick's for a breakfast of Mr. Goodbars and soda pop: no more long hours of him alone or wandering the roads while she was otherwise

12 취기인지, 아니면 갑작스레 발작처럼 발동한 모성의 관심인지, 티폿의 엄마가 달려갔다.

13 억지로 쓴 돈 2달러는 결국 쓰기를 잘한 셈이었다.

14 daintiness: 절되기 쉬운 뼈를 말함.

15 티폿의 엄마는 많은 사람들의 주의를 끌게 되었고, 그간 전혀 관심을 보이지 않았던 엄마역할에 이제 충실하게 되었다.

16 keep one's teeth on edge: 불쾌감을 갖다. 역겹게 하다.

engaged. Her change was a distinct improvement, although little Teapot did miss those quiet times at Dick's.

Other things happened. Mr. Finley sat on his porch sucking chicken bones, as he had done for thirteen years, looked up, saw Sula, choked on a bone and died on the spot. That incident, and Teapot's Mamma, cleared up for everybody the meaning of the birthmark over her eye[17]; it was not a stemmed rose, or a snake, it was Hannah's ashes marking her from the very beginning[18].

She came to their church suppers without underwear, bought their steaming platters of food and merely picked at it[19] — relishing nothing, exclaiming over no one's ribs or cobbler[20]. They believed that she was laughing at their God.

And the fury she created in the women of the town was incredible — for she would lay their husbands once and then no more. Hannah had been a nuisance, but she was complimenting the women, in a way, by wanting their husbands. Sula was trying them out and discarding them without any excuse the men could swallow[21]. So the women, to justify their own judgment, cherished their men more, soothed the pride and vanity Sula had bruised.

Among the weighty evidence piling up was the fact that Sula did not look her age[22]. She was near thirty and, unlike them,

17 이 사건과 티폿엄마가 변화한 사건은 모든 사람들에게 술라 반점의 의미를 분명하게 만들었다.

18 it was Hannah's ashes...: 처음부터 술라에게 표시된 한나의 재였던 것이다.

19 pick at: 들쑤시며 조금만 먹다.

20 어느 음식도 맛있게 먹는 법이 없고, 어떤 고기나 과일파이도 먹고는 맛있다는 감탄을 해본 적이 없다.

21 하룻밤 자보고는 남자들을 버렸다. 남자들이 삼킬만한(모욕적이지만 그런대로 참아줄 만한) 이유도 대지 않은 채.

had lost no teeth, suffered no bruises, developed no ring of fat at the waist or pocket at the back of her neck[23]. It was rumored that she had had no childhood diseases, was never known to have chicken pox[24], croup[25] or even a runny nos e[26]. She had played rough as a child — where were the scar s[27]? Except for a funny-shaped finger and that evil birthmark, she was free of any normal signs of vulnerability[28]. Some of the men, who as boys had dated her, remembered that on picnics neither gnats nor mosquitoes would settle on her. Patsy, Hannah's one-time friend, agreed and said not only that, but she had witnessed the fact that when Sula drank beer she never belched[29].

The most damning evidence, however, came from Dessie, who was a big Daughter Elk and knew things. At one of the social meetings she revealed something to her friends.

"Yeh, well I noticed something long time ago. ain't said nothing 'bout it 'cause I Wasn't sure what it meant. Well. . . I did mention it to Ivy but not nobody else. I disremember how long ago. 'bout a month or two I guess 'cause I hadn't put down my new linoleum yet. Did you see it, Cora? It's that kind we saw in the catalogue."

---

22 Sula did not look her age: 제 나이대로 보이지 않았다.

23 no ring of fat...: 허리에 두루뭉실한 군살이나 뒷목에 주머니처럼 접혀진 군살.

24 수두

25 위막성 후두염

26 코감기

27 어릴 적 술라는 매우 험하게 노는 아이였다. 그런데 상처는 어디에 있는가? (상처가 없다는 뜻임.)

28 이상하게 생긴 손가락이나 사악한 반점을 제외하고는, 흔히 볼 수 있는 약점 같은 것은 찾아볼 수 없었다.

29 belch: 트림하다.

"Naw."

"Get on with it, Dessie[30]."

"Well, Cora was with me when we looked in the catalogue. . ."

"We all know 'bout your linoleum. What we don't know is. . ."

"OK. Let me tell it, will you? Just before the linoleum come I was out front and seed[31] Shadrack carryin' on[32] as usual. . . up by the well. . . walkin' 'round it salutin' and carryin' on. You know how he does. . . hollerin' commands and. . ."

"Will you get on with it?"

"Who's tellin' this? Me or you?"

"You."

"Well, let me tell it then. Like I say, he was just cuttin' up[33] as usual when Miss Sula Mae walks by on the other side of the road. And quick as that"—she snapped her fingers —"he stopped and cut on[34] over 'cross the road, steppin' over to her like a tall turkey in short corn[35]. and guess what? He tips his hat[36]."

"Shadrack don't wear no hat."

"I know that but he tipped it anyway. You know what I mean. He acted like he had a hat and reached up for it and tipped it at her. Now you know Shadrack ain't civil to nobody!"

"Sure ain't."

"Even when you buyin' his fish he's cussin'. If you ain't got the right change he cussin' you. If you act like a fish ain't too

---

30 빨리 본론으로 들어가란 말이야.

31 seed: saw

32 carry on: 분별 없는 짓을 하다.

33 cut up: 까불다. 익살떨다.

34 cut on: 급히 나아가다.

35 like a tall turkey...: 키가 작은 옥수수 밭에 있는 키 큰 칠면조처럼.

36 모자챙에 손을 대며 인사한다.

fresh he snatch it out of your hand like he doin' you the favor."

"Well, everybody know he a reprobate[37]."

"Yeh, so how come he tip his hat to Sula? How come he don't cuss her?"

"Two devils."

"Exactly!"

"What'd she do when he tipped it? Smile and give him a curtsey?"

"No, and that was the other thing. It was the first time I see her look anything but hateful. Like she smellin' you with her eyes and don't like your soap. When he tipped his hat she put her hand on her throat for a minute and *cut* out[38]. Went runnin' on up the road to home. And him still standin' there tippin' away. And — this the point I was comin' to — when I went back in the house a big sty[39] come on my eye. And I ain't never had no sty before. Never!"

"That's 'cause you saw it."

"Exactly."

"Devil all right."

"No two ways about it[40]," Dessie said, and she popped the rubber band off the deck of cards to settle them down[41] for a nice long game of bid whist[42].

Their conviction of Sula's evil changed them in accountable yet mysterious ways. Once the source of their personal misfortune

---

37 reprobate: 무뢰한

38 cut out: 급히 도망가다.

39 sty: 다래끼

40 사악하기는 모두 마찬가지지.

41 카드를 묶은 고무줄을 풀어서 내려놓았다.

42 bid whist: 카드놀이의 일종.

was identified, they had leave[43] to protect and love one another. They began to cherish their husbands and wives, protect their children, repair their homes and in general band together against the devil in their midst[44]. In their world, aberrations were as much a part of nature as grace. It was not for them to expel or annihilate it. They would no more run Sula out of town than they would kill the robins that brought her back[45], for in their secret awareness of Him, He was not the God of three faces they sang about[46]. They knew quite well that He had four[47], and that the fourth explained Sula. They had lived with various forms of evil all their days, and it Wasn't that they believed God would take care of them. It was rather that they knew God had a brother and that brother hadn't spared God's son, so why should he spare them[48]?

There was no creature so ungodly as to make them destroy it[49]. They could kill easily if provoked to anger, but not by design, which explained why they could not "Mob kill" anyone[50]. To do

43 leave: 허락

44 in general band...: 대체로, 그들 가운데 있는 악마에 대하여 연합하여 대항하고 있었다.

45 술라를 돌아오게 만든 로빈새를 죽이지 않았던 것처럼 마을 사람들은 술라를 쫓아내지 않았다.

46 그들이 개인적으로 인식하는 신이란, 그들이 교회에서 노래부르는 삼위일체의 신이 아니었다.

47 그들의 신은 삼위(三位)에서 하나가 추가되어 사위(四位)를 지닌 신이었다.

48 신은 형제가 하나 있었는데, 그 형제는 신의 아들을 가만 내버려두지 않은 것이다. 그럴진대, 그 형제가 왜 우리는 가만 내버려두겠는가? 즉, 우리를 해치는 것은 당연하다는 뜻임.

49 그들 가운데 있는 악을 없애버릴 만큼 불경한 사람은 없었다.

50 그들은 화가 나서 (우발적으로) 사람을 죽이기는 쉬워도, 계획적으로 살인하지는 않았다. 그것을 보면, 왜 그들이 군중심리로 사람을 살해할 수 없는지를 이해할 수 있다.

so was not only unnatural, it was undignified. The presence of evil was something to be first recognized, then dealt with, survived, outwitted[51], triumphed over.

Their evidence against Sula was contrived[52], but their conclusions about her were not. Sula was distinctly different. Eva's arrogance and Hannah's self-indulgence merged in her and, with a twist that was all her own imagination, she lived out her days exploring her own thoughts and emotions, giving them full reign, feeling no obligation to please anybody unless their pleasure pleased her. As willing to feel pain as to give pain, to feel pleasure as to give pleasure, hers was an experimental life — ever since her mother's remarks sent her flying up those stairs, ever since her one major feeling of responsibility had been exorcised on the bank of a river with a closed place in the middle. The first experience taught her there was no other that you could count on; the second that there was no self to count on either. She had no center, no speck around which to grow. In the midst of a pleasant conversation with someone she might say, "Why do you chew with your mouth open?[53]" not because the answer interested her but because she wanted to see the person's face change rapidly. She was completely free of ambition, with no affection for money, property or things, no greed, no desire to command attention or compliments — no ego. For that reason she felt no compulsion to verify herself — be consistent with herself.

She had clung to Nel as the closest thing to both an other and a self, only to discover that she and Nel were not one and the same thing. She had no thought at all of causing Nel pain

51 outwit: 선수치다.

52 술라의 악평에 대한 증거는 일부러 도모된 것이었다.

53 왜 입을 벌리고 껌을 씹지? 무례하고 상대방을 당황하게 하는 말임.

when she bedded down with Jude. They had always shared the affection of other people: compared how a boy kissed, what line he used with one and then the other. Marriage, apparently, had changed all that, but having had no intimate knowledge of marriage, having lived in a house with women who thought all men available, and selected from among them with a care only for their tastes, she was ill prepared for the possessiveness of the one person she felt close to[54]. She knew well enough what other women said and felt, or said they felt. But she and Nel had always seen through[55] them. They both knew that those women were not jealous of other women; that they were only afraid of losing their jobs. Afraid their husbands would discover that no uniqueness lay between their legs.

Nel was the one person who had wanted nothing from her, who had accepted all aspects of her. Now she wanted everything, and all because of *that*[56]. Nel was the first person who had been real to her, whose name she knew, who had seen as she had the slant of life that made it possible to stretch it to its limits[57]. Now Nel was one of *them*. One of the spiders whose

54 but...: 결혼이 무엇인지 술라는 직접적인 경험을 할 수 있는 기회가 없었고, 또 모든 남자들, 혹은 자신의 취향에 맞는 남자를 골라 언제든지 침실로 끌어들일 수 있는 여자들(이바와 한나)과 함께 살아온 터이라, 술라는 자신이 친밀하게 느끼는 한 사람을 소유한다는 것에 거의 준비되지 않은 상태였다.

55 see through: 꿰뚫어보다. 간파하다.

56 all because of that: 넬은 이제 모든 것을 원하기 때문에 바로 모든 일(둘 사이가 소원해 진 것)이 일어난 것이다.

57 who had seen as she had the slant of life...: 삶을 극한으로 몰아가는 것을 가능케 하는, 삶에 대한 관점을 지닐 수 있었기 때문에 술라를 이해해 주었던 첫 번째 사람이 넬이었다. 즉, 그냥 어정쩡하게 다른 사람들의 눈치를 보며 사는 것이 아니라, 삶의 모든 가능성을 타진해보는 것에 대해서 긍정적으로 이해해 줄만한 사람이 바로 넬이었다는 뜻이다.

only thought was the next rung of the web, who dangled in dark dry places suspended by their own spittle, more terrified of the free fall than the snake's breath below[58]. Their eyes so intent on the wayward stranger who trips into their net, they were blind to the cobalt on their own backs, the moonshine fighting to pierce their corners. If they were touched by the snake's breath, however fatal, they were merely victims and knew how to behave in that role (just as Nel knew how to behave as the wronged wife). But the free fall, oh no, that required—demanded—invention[59]: a thing to do with the wings, a way of holding the legs and most of all a full surrender to the downward flight[60] if they wished to taste their tongues or stay alive. But alive was what they, and now Nel, did not want to be. Too dangerous. Now Nel belonged to the town and all of its ways. She had given herself over to them, and the flick of their tongues[61] would drive her back into her little dry corner where she would cling to her spittle high above the breath of the snake and the fall.

It had surprised her a little and saddened her a good deal when Nel behaved the way the others would have. Nel was one of the reasons she had drifted back to Medallion, that and the boredom[62] she found in Nashville, Detroit, New Orleans, New

58 아래에 있는 뱀의 숨결보다도 자유낙하를 더욱 두려워하면서, 어둡고 메마른 공간에서 자신의 침에 의지해 매달려 오로지 다음 단계의 거미줄 엮을 일만을 생각하는 거미들 중의 하나일 뿐이었다.

59 여기서 invention은 창의력을 의미함.

60 a thing to do with the wings....: 창의력(invention)이 무엇을 의미하는지 부연 설명하고 있음. 날개(자유)와 관련된 것, 다리는 붙들고, 밑으로 떨어지는 힘에 완전히 자신을 떠맡기는 것.

61 마을 사람들이 몇 마디 휘둘러대면.

62 that and the boredom: that은 앞서 말한, 고향으로 다시 돌아온 이유가 넬때문이고, 또 다른 도시들이 모두 시시했기 때문이라고 설명한다. boredom은

York, Philadelphia, Macon and San Diego. All those cities held the same people, working the same mouths, sweating the same sweat. The men who took her to one or another of those places had merged into one large personality: the same language of love, the same entertainments of love, the same cooling of love. Whenever she introduced her private thoughts into their rubbings or goings, they hooded their eyes[63]. They taught her nothing but love tricks, shared nothing but worry, gave nothing but money. She had been looking all along for a friend, and it took her a while to discover that a lover was not a comrade and could never be — for a woman. And that no one would ever be that version of herself which she sought to reach out to and touch with an ungloved hand[64]. There was only her own mood and whim, and if that was all there was, she decided to turn the naked hand toward it[65], discover it and let others become as intimate with their own selves as she was[66].

In a way, her strangeness, her naiveté, her craving for the other half of her equation was the consequence of an idle imagination. Had she paints, or clay, or knew the discipline of the dance, or strings; had she anything to engage her tremendous curiosity and her gift for metaphor, she might

다시 뒤에서 수식받고 있다.

63 자신의 은밀한 생각을 남자가 안달하거나 떠날 때 슬쩍 말하면, 그들은 눈을 덮어버렸다. 즉, 술라의 남자들의 속 깊은 얘기를 나눌 수 있는 대상이 아니었다는 뜻임.

64 touch with ungloved hand: 장갑 끼지 않은 손으로 만지다. 즉, 거짓이나 가장 없이 상대방에게 다가가다.

65 it는 her own mood and whim을 말함.

66 다른 사람과 친밀한 관계를 맺을 수는 없고, 오로지 그때그때 생기는 자신의 기분에만 충실하리라고 술라는 결심한다. 또한 다른 사람들도 자신처럼 그렇게 스스로의 기분에 충실할 수 있게 만들려고 했다는 뜻이다.

have exchanged the restlessness and preoccupation with whim for an activity that provided her with all she yearned for. And like any artist with no art form, she became dangerous[67].

She had lied only once in her life — to Nel about the reason for putting Eva out, and she could lie to her only because she cared about her. When she had come back home, social conversation was impossible for her because she could not lie. She could not say to those old acquaintances, "Hey, girl, you looking good," when she saw how the years had dusted their bronze with ash[68], the eyes that had once opened wide to the moon bent into grimy sickles of concern[69]. The narrower their lives, the wider their hips. Those with husbands had folded themselves into starched coffins[70], their sides bursting with other people's skinned dreams and bony regrets[71]. Those without men were like sour-tipped needles featuring one constant empty eye[72]. Those with men had had the sweetness sucked from their breath by ovens and steam kettles[73]. Their children were like distant but exposed wounds whose aches were no less intimate because separate from their flesh[74]. They had looked at the world and back at their children,

---

67 형상화할 수 있는 예술의 형태를 찾지 못한 술라는 위험한 존재가 되었다.

68 when she saw how the years...: 세월에 재처럼 푸석푸석해진 그들의 갈색피부를 보면서

69 한때 달빛을 바라보던 커다란 눈망울이 이제 근심으로 더러워진 낫 모양으로 변해버렸는지 보면서.

70 결혼한 친구들은 풀먹인 듯 딱딱한 관속으로 자신들을 접어 넣어 버렸다. 즉 살아 있으면서도 죽은 듯한 삶을 살고 있었다는 뜻이다.

71 분사구문. 그들의 옆구리는 다른 이들의 빼앗긴 꿈과 앙상한 회한으로 가득 차 터져 버릴 것 같다.

72 실 꿰는 구멍은 늘 빈 채로, 끝이 못쓰게 된 바늘과도 같았다.

73 남자가 있는 여자들은 오븐과 증기솥이 그들의 달콤한 입김을 모두 빨아내 버렸다.

back at the world and back again at their children, and Sula knew that one clear young eye was all that kept the knife away from the throat's curve[75].

She was pariah, then, and knew it. Knew that they despised her and believed that they framed their hatred as disgust for the easy way she lay with men[76]. Which was true. She went to bed with men as frequently as she could. It was the only place where she could find what she was looking for: misery and the ability to feel deep sorrow. She had not always been aware that it was sadness that she yearned for. Lovemaking seemed to her, at first, the creation of a special kind of joy. She thought she liked the sootiness of sex and its comedy; she laughed a great deal during the raucous beginnings, and rejected those lovers who regarded sex as healthy or beautiful. Sexual aesthetics bored her. Although she did not regard sex as ugly (ugliness was boring also), she liked to think of it as wicked. But as her experiences multiplied she realized that not only was it not wicked, it was not necessary for her to conjure up the idea of wickedness in order to participate fully. During the lovemaking she found and needed to find the cutting edge[77]. When she left off cooperating with her body and began to assert herself in the act[78], particles of strength

74 어린 아이들은 몸이 분리되어 있다 해서 결코 덜 아프지 않은, 멀리 있으나 노출된 상처와도 같았다.

75 아이들의 순수한 눈망울 때문에 여자들은 목을 칼을 대고 죽을 수 없었다.

76 believed that they framed...: 남자들과 쉽게 잠자리를 함께 한다는 사실 때문에 술라를 미워한다고 사람들은 믿었다.

77 cutting edge: 날카로운 가장자리를 의미하는데 매우 함축적이다. 여기서 가장자리란 성관계시 상대방과 진정한 결합을 이루지 못하고 가장자리만 겨우 맞대고 있다는 의미이고, 그 느낌은 언제나 통렬하고 날카로움 슬픔으로 다가옴을 의미한다.

78 자신의 몸과 협력하는 것을 멈추었을 때, 다시 말해서, 여성의 생물학적 충

gathered in her like steel shavings drawn to a spacious magnetic center[79], forming a tight cluster that nothing, it seemed, could break. And there was utmost irony and outrage in lying under someone, in a position of surrender, feeling her own abiding strength and limitless power[80]. But the cluster did break, fall apart, and in her panic to hold it together she leaped from the edge into soundlessness and went down howling, howling in a stinging awareness of the endings of things[81]: an eye of sorrow in the midst of all that hurricane rage of joy. There, in the center of that silence was not eternity but the death of time and a loneliness so profound the word itself had no meaning. For loneliness assumed the absence of other people, and the solitude she found in that desperate terrain had never admitted the possibility of other people. She wept then. Tears for the deaths of the littlest things: the castaway shoes of children; broken stems of marsh grass battered and browned by the sea; prom[82] photographs of dead women she never knew: wedding rings in pawnshop[83] windows; the tidy bodies of Cornish hens in a nest of rice[84].

When her partner disengaged himself[85], she looked up at

동, 즉 수동적인 행위에서 벗어나 좀더 적극적으로 변했을 때.

79 steel shavings...: 철가루가 넓은 자기장의 중심으로 빨려 들어가는 것처럼.

80 자신 속에 내재하는 힘과 끝없는 권력을 느끼면서도 굴욕적인 자세로 누군가의 아래에 깔려 누워있다는 사실은 매우 아이러니칼하고 분한 일이었다.

81 모리슨 특유의 역설적인 아름다움과 풍부한 함축성이 돋보이는 문장이다. 자석으로 몰려든 철가루가 깨져 흩어져 버렸다. 깜짝 놀라 다시 주워 모으려고 그녀는 가장자리에서 침묵으로 펄쩍 뛰어 옮겼다. 그리고 모든 것의 끝, 그 끝을 날카롭게 인식하고 울부짖으며 밑으로 내려갔다.

82 고등학교 졸업파티.

83 전당포.

84 볏짚으로 만든 둥지에 가지런히 죽어있는 콘월 지방의 암탉.

85 성관계가 끝나고 났을 때.

him in wonder trying to recall his name; and he looked down at her, smiling with tender understanding of the state of tearful gratitude to which he believed he had brought her. She waiting impatiently for him to turn away and settle into a wet skim of satisfaction and light disgust, leaving her to the post-coital privateness in which she met herself, welcomed herself, and joined herself in matchless harmony.

At twenty-nine she knew it would be no other way for her, but she had not counted on the footsteps on the porch, and the beautiful black face that stared at her through the blue-glass window. Ajax.

Looking for all the world[86] as he had seventeen years ago when he had called her pig meat. He was twenty-one then, she twelve. A universe of time between them[87]. Now she was twenty- nine, he thirty-eight, and the lemon-yellow haunches[88] seemed not so far away after all.

She opened the heavy door and saw him standing on the other side of the screen door[89] with two quarts of milk tucked into his arms[90] like marble statues. He smiled and said, "I been lookin' all over for you."

"Why?" she asked.

"To give you these," and he nodded toward one of the quarts of milk.

"I don't like milk," she said.

"But you like bottles don't you?" He held one up. "ain't that pretty?"

---

86 He was 가 문두에 생략되어 있음.
87 그 당시 그들의 나이 차이는 매우 큰 차이였다.
88 레몬색의 엉덩이와 뒷다리.
89 screen door: 방충망으로 된 덧문.
90 양팔에 두개의 우유병을 끼고.

And indeed it was. Hanging from his fingers, framed by a slick blue sky, it looked precious and clean and permanent. She had the distinct impression that he had done something dangerous to get them.

Sula ran her fingernails over the screen thoughtfully for a second and then, laughing, she opened the screen door.

Ajax came in and headed straight for the kitchen. Sula followed slowly. By the time she got to the door he had undone the complicated wire cap[91] and was letting the cold milk run into his mouth.

Sula watched him — or rather the rhythm in his throat — with growing interest. When he had had enough, he poured the rest into the sink, rinsed the bottle out and presented it to her. She took the bottle with one hand and his wrist with the other and pulled him into the pantry. There was no need to go there, for not a soul was in the house, but the gesture came to Hannah's daughter naturally. There in the pantry, empty now of flour sacks, void of row upon row of canned goods, free forever of strings of tiny green peppers, holding the wet milk bottle right in her arm she stood wide-legged against the wall and pulled from his track-lean hips all the pleasure her thighs could hold.

He came regularly then, bearing gifts: clusters of black berries still on their branches, four meal-fried porgies[92] wrapped in a salmon-colored sheet of the Pittsburgh *Courier*,[93] handful of jacks[94], two boxes of lime Jell-Well[95], a hunk of ice-wagon

---

91 복잡하게 철사로 만든 우유뚜껑을 따다.

92 옥수수 가루를 입혀 튀긴 네 마리의 도미.

93 연어색 피츠버그 신문지에 둘둘 싸서.

94 과자 한 움큼.

ice, a can of Old Dutch Cleanser[96] with the bonneted woman chasing dirt with her stick; a page of Tillie the Toiler comics, and more gleaming white bottles of milk.

Contrary to what anybody would have suspected from just seeing him lounging around the pool hall, or shooting at Mr. Finley for beating his own dog[97], or calling filthy compliments to passing women, Ajax was very nice to women. His women, of course, knew it, and it provoked them into murderous battles over him in the streets, brawling thick-thighed women with knives disturbed many a Friday night with their bloodletting and attracted whooping crowds[98]. On such occasions Ajax stood, along with the crowd, and viewed the fighters with the same golden-eyed indifference with which he watched old men playing checkers. Other than[99] his mother, who sat in her shack with six younger sons working roots[1], he had never met an interesting woman in his life.

His kindness to them in general was not due to a ritual of seduction (he had no need for it) but rather to the habit he acquired in dealing with his mother, who inspired thoughtfulness and generosity in all her sons.

She was an evil conjure woman[2], blessed with seven ador-

95 lime은 레몬과 비슷한 과일이고, Jell-Well은 라임으로 만든 음식 혹은 과자의 고유명사인 듯함.

96 비누의 종류.

97 shooting at...: 핀리 자신의 개를 때린 것에 분노하여 에이젝스가 핀리를 공격한 것

98 brawling thick-thighed women...: 다리가 굵직한 여자들이 칼을 가지고 피를 흘리는 싸움은 수많은 금요일을 혼란스럽게 만들었고, 사람들이 우르르 몰려들었다.

99 Other than: 제외하고는.

1 나무뿌리를 캐서 다듬는 일을 하는 여섯 명의 아들.

2 사악한 마술사.

ing children whose joy it was to bring her the plants, hair, under- clothing, fingernail parings[3], white hens, blood, camphor[4], pictures, kerosene and footstep dust that she needed, as well as to order Van Van, High John the Conqueror, Little John to Chew, Devil's Shoe String, Chinese Wash, Mustard Seed and the Nine Herbs from Cincinnati. She knew about the weather, omens, the living, the dead, dreams and all illnesses and made a modest living with her skills. Had she any teeth or ever straightened her back, she would have been the most gorgeous thing alive, worthy of her sons' worship for her beauty alone, if not for the absolute freedom she allowed them (known in some quarters as neglect) and the weight of her hoary knowledge.

This woman Ajax loved, and after her — airplanes[5]. There was nothing in between[6]. And when he was not sitting enchanted listening to his mother's words, he thought of airplanes, and pilots, and the deep sky that held them both. People thought that those long trips he took to large cities in the state were for some sophisticated good times they could not imagine but only envy; actually he was leaning against the barbed wire[7] of airports, or nosing around hangars just to hear the talk of the men who were fortunate enough to be in the trade[8]. The rest of the time, the time he was not watching his mother's magic or thinking of airplanes, he

3 깎아낸 손톱.

4 장뇌.

5 그 여인이 에이젝스가 사랑하는 사람이고, 그 다음으로 사랑하는 것은 비행기였다.

6 엄마와 비행기, 그 외에는 아무것도 사랑하지 않았다.

7 barbed wire: 울타리.

8 비행과 관련된 직업.

spent in the idle pursuits of bachelors without work in small towns. He had heard all the stories about Sula, and they aroused his curiosity. Her elusiveness and indifference to established habits of behavior reminded him of his mother, who was as stubborn in her pursuits of the occult as the women of Greater Saint Matthew's were in the search for redeeming grace. So when his curiosity was high enough he picked two bottles of milk off the porch of some white family[9] and went to see her, suspecting that this was perhaps the only other woman he knew whose life was her own, who could deal with life efficiently, and who was not interested in nailing him.

Sula, too, was curious. She knew nothing about him except the word he had called out to her years ago and the feeling he had excited in her then. She had grown quite accustomed to the clichés of other people's lives as well as her own increasing dissatisfaction with Medallion. If she could have thought of a place to go, she probably would have left, but that was before Ajax looked at her through the blue glass and held the milk aloft like a trophy.

But it was not the presents that made her wrap him up in her thighs[10]. They were charming, of course (especially the jar of butterflies he let loose in the bedroom), but her real pleasure was the fact that he talked to her. They had genuine conversations. He did not speak down to her or at her[11], nor content himself with puerile questions about her life or monologues of his own activities. Thinking she was possibly

9 어느 백인 가정의 현관 앞에 놓은 우유병을 집어 들었다.

10 강조 용법의 문장. 그녀의 다리로 그를 감싸게 된 것은 (즉, 잠자리를 함께 한 것은) 선물 때문은 아니었다.

11 speak down: 무시하며 말하다.

brilliant, like his mother, he seemed to expect brilliance from her, and she delivered. And in all of it, he listened more than he spoke. His clear comfort at being in her presence, his lazy willingness to tell her all about fixes[12] and the powers of plants, his refusal to baby[13] or protect her, his assumption that she was both tough and wise — all of that coupled with a wide generosity of spirit only occasionally erupting into vengeance sustained Sula's interest and enthusiasm[14].

His idea of bliss (on earth as opposed to bliss in the sky) was a long bath in piping-hot[15] water — his head on the cool white rim, his eyes closed in reverie.

"Soaking in hot water give you a bad back." Sula stood in the doorway looking at his knees glistening just at the surface of the soap-gray water.

"Soaking in Sula give me a bad back."

"Worth it?"

"Don't know yet. Go 'way."

"Airplanes?"

"Lindbergh[16] know about you?"

"Go 'way."

She went and waiting for him in Eva's high bed, her head turned to the boarded-up window. She was smiling, thinking how like Jude's was his craving to do the white man's work[17],

---

12 약제를 만드는 법.

13 baby: 어린애 취급하다.

14 all of that...: 이러한 모든 것 때문에, 가끔씩 복수심으로 솟구치는 해도 넓은 포용력 때문에 술라는 관심과 열정을 유지할 수 있었다.

15 piping hot: 아주 뜨거운

16 1927년 최초로 대서양을 횡단한 미국인 비행사.

17 thinking how like Jude's was...: 보통 백인들이 하는 일을 하고 싶어 하는 면에서 에이젝스도 얼마나 쥬드를 닮았는지 생각하면서.

when two deweys came in with their beautiful teeth and said, "We sick."

Sula turned her head slowly and murmured, "Gget well."

"We need some medicine."

"Look in the bathroom."

"Aajax in there."

"Then wait."

"We sick now."

Sula leaned over the bed, picked up a shoe and threw in at them.

"Ccocksucker[18]!" they screamed, and she leaped out of the bed naked as a yard dog. She caught the redheaded dewey by his shirt and held him by the heels over the banister until he wet his pants[19]. The other dewey was joined by the third[20], and they delved into their pockets for stones[21], which they threw at her. Sula, ducking and tottering with laughter[22], carried the wet dewey to the bedroom and when the other two followed her, deprived of all weapons except their teeth, Sula had dropped the first dewey on the bed and was fishing in her purse. She gave each of them a dollar bill which they snatched and then scooted off down the stairs to Dick's to buy the catarrh[23] remedy they loved to drink.

Ajax came sopping wet[24] into the room and lay down on

---

18 치사한 놈.

19 술라는 빨강머리 듀이의 옷을 잡고는, 그가 바지를 적실 때 까지 계단의 난간에 거꾸로 들고 있었다.

20 나머지 두 명의 듀이가 합세하여.

21 주머니에서 돌맹이를 꺼내어.

22 몸을 홱 구부렸다가는 비틀거리고 웃어대면서.

23 카타르. 콧물감기.

24 sopping wet: 흠뻑 젖은 채로.

the bed to let the air dry him. They were both still for a long time until he reached out and touched her arm.

He liked for her to mount him so he could see her towering above him and call soft obscenities up into her face. As she rocked there, swayed there, like a Georgia pine on its knees, high above the slipping, falling smile, high above the golden eyes and the velvet helmet of hair, rocking, swaying, she focused her thoughts to bar[25] the creeping disorder that was flooding her hips. She looked down, down from what seemed an awful height at the head of the man whose lemon-yellow gabardines[26] had been the first sexual excitement she'd known. Letting her thoughts dwell on his face in order to confine, for just a while longer, the drift of her flesh toward the high silence of orgasm.

If I take a chamois[27] and rub real hard on the bone, right on the ledge[28] of your cheek bone, some of the black will disappear. It will flake[29] away into the chamois and underneath there will be gold leaf. I can see it shining through the black. I know it is there. . .

How high she was over his wand-lean body[30], how slippery was his sliding sliding smile[31].

And if I take a nail file[32] or even Eva's old paring knife — that

25 bar: 가로막다.
26 개버딘 바지.
27 갈색 쎄무 가죽.
28 ledge: 쑥 내민 곳.
29 flake: 벗겨지다.
30 wand-lean body: 막대기처럼 군살 없이 마른 몸.
31 미끄러지는 듯한 웃음이 얼마나 미끌미끌한지. 모두가 성행위를 묘사하고 있음.
32 nail file: 손톱 다듬는 줄.

will do[33] *— and scrape away at the gold, it will fall away and there will be alabaster. The alabaster is what gives your face its planes, its curves*[34]*. That is why your mouth smiling does not reach your eyes. Alabaster is giving it a gravity that resists a total smile*[35]*.*

The height and the swaying dizzied her, so she bent down and let her breasts graze his chest.

Then I can take a chisel and small tap hammer and tap away at the alabaster. It will crack then like ice under the pick, and through the breaks I will see the loam, fertile, free of pebbles and twigs. For it is the loam that is giving you that smell.

She slipped her hands under his armpits, for it seemed as though she would not be able to dam the spread of weakness she felt under her skin without holding on to something.

I will put my hand deep into your soil, lift it, sift it with my fingers, feel its warm surface and dewy chill below.

She put her head under his chin with no hope in the world of keeping anything at all at bay[36].

I will water your soil, keep it rich and moist. But how much? How much water to keep the loam moist[37]*? And how much loam will I need to keep my water still*[38]*? And when do the two make mud?*

He swallowed her mouth just as her thighs had swallowed

33 that will do: 그것이면 될 것이다.

34 alabaster는 본래 석고를 의미하는데, 여기서는 뼈를 의미한다. "석고야말로 얼굴의 윤곽을 잡아주는 것이지."

35 이 석고야말로 얼굴전체가 웃는 것을 막도록 지탱하는 것이다.

36 keep something at bay: 저지하다. 여기서의 뜻은, "철저하게 차단된 세계에서 아무런 희망도 없이 그의 턱밑에 자신의 머리를 놓았다."

37 흙을 촉촉하게 하려면 물을 얼마나 주어야 하지?

38 내 물이 출렁거리지 않으려면 또 흙은 양은 얼마나 되어야 하지?

his genitals, and the house was very, very quiet.

* * *

Sula began to discover what possession was. Not love, perhaps, but possession or at least the desire for it. She was astounded by so new and alien a feeling. First there was the morning of the night before when she actually wondered if Ajax would come by that day. Then there was an afternoon when she stood before the mirror finger-tracing the laugh lines around her mouth and trying to decide whether she was good-looking or not[39]. She ended this deep perusal by tying a green ribbon in her hair. The green silk made a rippling whisper[40] as she slid it into her hair — a whisper that could easily have been Hannah's chuckle, a soft slow nasal hiss she used to emit when something amused her. Like women sitting for two hours under the marcelling irons[41] only to wonder two days later how soon they would need another appointment[42]. The ribbon-tying was followed by other activity, and when Ajax came that evening, bringing her a reed whistle he had carved that morning, not only was the green ribbon still in her hair, but the bathroom was gleaming, the bed was made, and the table was set for two.

He gave her the reed whistle, unlaced his shoes and sat in the rocking chair in the kitchen.

---

39 거울 앞에 서서 웃을 때 생기는 입 주변의 주름을 손으로 만져보면서 자신이 잘 생겼을까, 의아해하는 오후도 있었다.

40 비단이 스치는 소리.

41 물결모양의 웨이브를 만드는 기계.

42 미장원에서 2시간이나 웨이브 기계를 머리에 얹고 있다가 겨우 이틀이 지나다 풀려버려 다시 미장원에서 가야하는 여자처럼.

Sula walked toward him and kissed his mouth. He ran his fingers along the nape of her neck.

"I bet you ain't even missed Tar Baby, have you[43]?" he asked.

"Missed? No. Where is he?"

Ajax smiled at her delicious indifference. "Jail."

"Since when?"

"Last Saturday."

"Picked up for drunk[44]?"

"Little bit more than that," he answered and went ahead to tell her about his own involvement in another of Tar Baby's misfortunes.

On Saturday afternoon Tar Baby had stumbled drunk into traffic[45] on the New River Road. A woman driver swerved to avoid him and hit another car. When the police came, they recognized the woman as the mayor's niece and arrested Tar Baby. Later, after the word got out, Ajax and two other men went to the station[46] to see about him. At first they wouldn't let them in. But they relented[47] after Ajax and the other two just stood around for one hour and a half and repeated their request at regular intervals[48]. When they finally got permission to go in and looked in at him in the cell, he was twisted up in a corner badly beaten and dressed in nothing but extremely soiled underwear[49]. Ajax and the other men

43 타르 베이비가 없어진 줄도 당신은 모르고 있겠지?

44 술 때문에 경찰에 잡혔나요?

45 술에 취해 도로에 넘어져 교통을 막고 있었다.

46 police station: 경찰서

47 relent: 마음이 누그러지다.

48 at regular intervals: 일정한 시간 간격을 두고.

49 똥오줌이 범벅이 된 팬티 하나만 걸치고 흠씬 얻어맞은 채, 감옥의 한 구석에

asked the officer why Tar Baby couldn't have back his clothes. "It ain't right," they said, "To let a grown man lay around in his own shit."

The policeman, obviously in agreement with Eva, who had always maintained that Tar Baby was white, said that if the prisoner didn't like to live in shit, he should come down out of those hills, and live like a decent white man.

More words were exchanged, hot words and dark[50], and the whole thing ended with the arraignment of the three black men, and an appointment to appear in civil court Thursday next[51].

Ajax didn't seem too bothered by any of it[52]. More annoyed and inconvenienced than anything else[53]. He had had several messes with the police, mostly in gambling raids[54], and regarded them as the natural hazards of Negro life[55].

But Sula, the green ribbon shining in her hair, was flooded with an awareness of the impact of the outside world on Ajax. She stood up and arranged herself on the arm of the rocking chair[56]. Putting her fingers deep into the velvet of his hair, she murmured, "Come on. Lean on me."

Ajax blinked. Then he looked swiftly into her face. In her

꼬부라져 누워있었다.

50 hot words and dark: 욕설과 폭언을 의미함.

51 세 흑인의 죄를 물어 법정에 소환하기로 결정하여, 다음 목요일에 민간법정에 출두하기로 약속하고 모든 일은 마무리되었다.

52 에이젝스은 그런 일들(경찰과 논쟁하고 법정에 출두하는 일)을 특별히 귀찮아하는 것 같지 않았다.

53 오히려 다른 어떤 일보다도 그런 일에 더욱 분노하고 마음이 불편한 것 같았다.

54 gambling raids: 도박에 대한 경찰에 불시 단속.

55 경찰을 흑인 삶의 천적으로 간주했다.

56 흔들의자의 팔걸이에 걸쳐 앉았다.

words, in her voice, was a sound he knew well. For the first time he saw the green ribbon. He looked around and saw the gleaming kitchen and the table set for two and detected the scent of the nest. Every hackle on his body rose, and he knew that very soon she would, like all of her sisters before her, put to him the death-knell question "Where you been?" His eyes dimmed with a mild and momentary regret.

He stood and mounted the stairs with her and entered the spotless bathroom where the dust had been swept from underneath the claw-foot tub[57]. He was trying to remember the date of the air show in Dayton. As he came into the bedroom, he saw Sula lying on fresh white sheets, wrapped in the deadly odor of freshly applied cologne.

He dragged her under him and made love to her with the steadiness and the intensity of a man about to leave for Dayton.

Every now and then she looked around for tangible evidence of his having ever been there. Where were the butterflies? the blueberries? the whistling reed? She could find nothing, for he had left nothing but his stunning absence. An absence so decorative, so ornate, it was difficult for her to understand how she had ever endured, without falling dead or being consumed, his magnificent presence.

The mirror by the door was not a mirror by the door, it was an altar where he stood for only a moment to put on his cap before going out. The red rocking chair was a rocking of his own hips as he sat in the kitchen. Still, there was nothing of his —his own—that she could find. It was as if she were afraid she had hallucinated him and needed proof to the contrary[58]. His

57 발톱 모양으로 밑이 뾰족한 욕조.

58 그의 존재가 그녀가 창조한 망상에 불과한 것이 아닌지 두려워서 실제로 존

absence was everywhere, stinging everything, giving the furnishings primary colors, sharp outlines to the corners of rooms and gold light to the dust collecting on table tops. When he was there he pulled everything toward himself. Not only her eyes and all her senses but also inanimate things seemed to exist because of him, backdrops to his presence[59]. Now that he had gone, these things, so long subdued by his presence, were glamorized in his wake[60].

Then one day, burrowing[61] in a dresser drawer, she found what she had been looking for: proof that he had been there, his driver's license. It contained just what she needed for verification—his vital statistics: Born 1901, height 5'11", weight 152 lbs., eyes brown, hair black, color black. Oh yes, skin black. Very black. So black that only a steady careful rubbing with steel wool would remove it, and as it was removed there was the glint of gold leaf and under the gold leaf the cold alabaster and deep, deep down under the cold alabaster more black only this time the black of warm loam.

But what was this? Albert Jacks? His name was Albert Jacks? A. Jacks. She had thought it was Ajax. All those years. Even from the time she walked by the pool hall and looked away from him sitting astride a wooden chair, looked away to keep from seeing the wide space of intolerable orderliness[62] between his

---

재했다는 증거를 필요로 하는 듯했다.

59 눈과 그녀의 전 감각뿐 아니라, 물건들조차 모두 그로 인해 존재하고 있는 듯했다. 오로지 그의 존재에 대한 배경으로서만 존재했다.

60 이제 그가 떠나가고, 오랜 동안 그의 존재에 의해 잠잠하던 물건들이 그를 닮아서 매혹적으로 빛나고 있었다.

61 burrow: 뒤적거리다.

62 looked away...: 다리 사이의 성기가 아무런 성적 흥분도 보이지 않는다는 사실을 모욕적으로 느끼고, 보지 않으려고 일부러 고개를 돌렸다.

legs; the openness[63] that held no sign, no sign at all, of the animal that lurked in his trousers; looked away from the insolent nostrils and the smile that kept slipping and falling, falling, falling so she wanted to reach out with her hand to catch it[64] before it fell to the pavement and was sullied by the cigarette butts and bottle caps and spittle at his feet and the feet of other men who sat or stood around outside the pool hall, calling, singing out to her and Nel and grown women too with lyrics[65] like *pig meat* and *brown sugar*[66] and *jailbait*[67] and *O Lord, what have I done to deserve the wrath,* and *Take me, Jesus, I have seen the promised land,* and *Do, Lord, remember me* in voices mellowed by hopeless passion into gentleness. Even then, when she and Nel were trying hard not to dream of him and not to think of him when they touched the softness in their underwear or undid their braids as soon as they left home to let the hair bump and wave[68] around their ears, or wrapped the cotton binding around their chests so the nipples would not break through their blouses and give him cause to smile his slipping, falling smile, which brought the blood rushing to their skin. And even later, when for the first time in her life she had lain in bed with a man and said his name involuntarily or said it truly meaning *him,* the name she was screaming and saying was not his at all.

63 openness: 본래 "개방상태," "관용"을 의미하지만, 여기서는 앞 문장과 마찬가지로, 성적 흥분이 전혀 없는 "無私," 즉, 집착이 없는 마음상태를 의미한다.

64 it: 웃음을 의미함.

65 노래 가사처럼 지나가는 여자들을 부르는 말들.

66 brown sugar: sweet heart처럼 애인을 부르는 애칭.

67 jailbait: 매우 매력적인 여자.

68 bump and wave: (머리카락을) 구부려 물결치는 모양으로 만든다.

Sula stood with a worn slip of paper in her fingers and said aloud to no one, "I didn't even know his name. And if I didn't know his name, then there is nothing I did know and I have known nothing ever at all since the one thing I wanted was to know his name so how could he help but leave me since he was making love to a woman who didn't even know his name.

"When I was a little girl the heads of my paper dolls came off, and it was a long time before I discovered that my own head would not fall off if I bent my neck[69]. I used to walk around holding it very stiff because I thought a strong wind or a heavy push would snap my neck. Nel was the one who told me the truth. But she was wrong. I did not hold my head stiff enough when I met him and so I lost it just like the dolls.

"It's just as well he left[70]. Soon I would have torn the flesh from his face just to see if I was right about the gold and nobody would have understood that kind of curiosity. They would have believed that I wanted to hurt him just like the little boy who fell down the steps and broke his leg and the people think I pushed him just because I looked at it."

Holding the driver's license she crawled into bed and fell into a sleep full of dreams of cobalt blue.

When she awoke, there was a melody in her head she could not identify or recall ever hearing before. "Perhaps I made it up," she thought. Then it came to her — the name of the song and all its lyrics just as she had heard it many times before. She sat on the edge of the bed thinking, "There aren't any more new songs and I have sung all the ones there are. I have sung them all. I have sung all the songs there are.[71]" She lay down again

69 it was a long time...: 오랜 시간이 지나서야 비로소 내 머리는 구부려도 부러지지 않는다는 사실을 알았다.

70 그가 떠난 것은 당연한 일이다.

on the bed and sang a little wandering tune made up of the words *I have sung all the songs all the songs I have sung all the songs there are* until, touched by her own lullaby, she grew drowsy, and in the hollow of near-sleep she tasted the acridness of gold, left the chill of alabaster and smelled the dark, sweet stench of loam.

71 해 아래 새로운 것이 없다는 전도서의 말처럼, 이제 실험적 삶의 모든 실험을 끝내고 허망함이 진하게 느껴지는 부분이다.

1940

"I heard you was sick. Anything I can do for you?"

She had practiced not just the words but the tone, the pitch of her voice. It should be calm, matter-of-fact, but strong in sympathy — for the illness though, not for the patient.

The sound of her voice as she heard it in her head betrayed[1] no curiosity, no pride, just the inflection of any good woman come to see about a sick person who, incidentally, had such visits from nobody else[2].

For the first time in three years she would be looking at the stemmed rose that hung over the eye of her enemy. Moreover, she would be doing it with the taste of Jude's exit in her mouth[3], with the resentment and shame that even yet pressed for release in her stomach. She would be facing the black rose that Jude had kissed and looking at the nostrils of the woman who had twisted her love for her own children into something so thick and monstrous she was afraid to show it lest it break loose and smother them with its heavy paw. A cumbersome bear-love that, given any rein, would suck their breath away in its crying need for honey[4].

Because Jude's leaving was so complete, the full responsibility of the household was Nel's. There were no more fifty dollars in

---

1 betray: 내보이다.

2 woman과 come 사이에 관계대명사 who를 넣으면 해석이 매끄러움.

3 with the taste of Jude's exit in her mouth: 쥬드가 자신을 버리고 떠났기 때문에, 그에 대한 씁쓸한 기분을 가지고 술라를 방문했다는 뜻임.

4 고삐를 매도 꿀을 찾아 숨을 헐떡거리는 곰의 성가신 꿀 사랑처럼.

brown envelopes to count on[5], so she took to cleaning rather than fret away[6] the tiny seaman's pension her parents lived on. And just this past year she got a better job working as a chambermaid in the same hotel Jude had worked in. The tips were only fair, but the hours were good — she was home when the children got out of school.

At thirty her hot brown eyes had turned to agate[7], and her skin had taken on the sheen of maple struck down, split and sanded at the height of its green[8]. Virtue, bleak and drawn[9], was her only mooring. It brought her to Number 7 Carpenter's Road and the door with the blue glass; it helped her to resist scratching the screen as in days gone by[10]; it[11] hid from her the true motives for her charity, and, finally, it gave her voice the timbre she wanted it to have: free of delight or a lip-smacking "I told you so" with which the news of Sula's illness had been received up in the Bottom[12] — free of the least hint of retribution.

Now she stood in Eva's old bedroom, looking down at that dark rose, aware of the knife-thin arms sliding back and forth over the quilt and the board-up window Eva had jumped out of.

Sula looked up and without a second's pause followed Nel's

---

5 count on: 의지하다.

6 fret away: 야금야금 써버리다.

7 agate: 마노. 즉, 붉은 빛을 의미함.

8 her skin had taken on the sheen...: 그녀의 피부는 한참 푸른 시절에 베어져 모래에 파묻혀 죽은 단풍나무의 빛깔로 변해버렸다.

9 bleak and drawn: 황량하고 고립되어 있지만.

10 파란색 유리창 덕에, 과거에 그랬듯이 (분노로) 방범창을 손으로 긁는 행위를 하지 않게 되었다.

11 it: Virtue를 의미함.

12 free of delight...: 술라가 아프다는 소식이 바텀 마을에 떠돌았을 때, 기쁨으로 혀를 차며 "거봐. 내가 뭐랬어"라고 말하지 않을 수 있었다.

example of leaving out the greeting when she spoke.

"As a matter of fact, there is. I got a prescription. Nathan usually goes for me but he. . . school don't let out till three. Could you run it over to the drugstore[13]?

"Where is it?" Nel was glad to have a concrete errand. Conversation would be difficult. (Trust Sula to pick up a relationship exactly where it lay[14].)

"Look in my bag. No. Over there."

Nel walked to the dresser and opened the purse with the beaded clasp. She saw only a watch and the folded prescription down inside. No wallet, no change purse. She turned to Sula: "Where's your. . .[15]"

But Sula was looking at the boarded-up window. Something in her eye right there in the corner stopped Nel from completing her question. That and the slight flare of the nostrils[16] — a shadow of a snarl. Nel took the piece of paper and picked up her own purse, saying, "OK. I'll be right back."

As soon as the door was shut, Sula breathed through her mouth. While Nel was in the room the pain had increased. Now that this new pain killer, the one she had been holding in reserve, was on the way her misery was manageable. She let a piece of her mind lay on Nel[17]. It was funny, sending Nel off to that drugstore right away like that, after she had not seen her to speak to for years. The drugstore was where Edna Finch's

---

13 처방전을 가지고 약국에 가서 약을 좀 지어다 줄래?

14 넬이 속으로 하는 말임. 즉, "술라는 분명히 우리 관계를 예전처럼 만들 수 있을 거야." 그런데, 이 말은 술라를 정말 신뢰하는 말이라기 보다는, 술라의 관계회복 능력에 대한 빈정거림이 섞여 있음.

15 약을 살 돈이 어디 있느냐고 물으려 함.

16 the slight flare of the nostrils: 콧구멍을 살짝 벌름거림.

17 넬에 대해서 조금 생각할 시간을 할애했다.

Mellow House used to be years back when they were girls. Where they used to go, the two of them, hand in hand, for the 18-cent ice-cream sundaes, past the Time and a Half Pool Hall, where the sprawling men said "Pig meat," and they sat in that cool room with the marble-top tables and ate the first ice-cream sundaes of their lives. Now Nel was going back there alone and Sula was waiting for the medicine the doctor said not to take until the pain got really bad. And she supposed "really bad" was now. Although you could never tell. She wondered for an instant what Nellie wanted; why she had come. Did she want to gloat[18]? Make up[19]? Following this line of thought required more concentration than she could muster. Pain was greedy; it demanded all of her attention. But it was good that this new medicine, the reserve, would be brought to her by her old friend. Nel, she remembered, always thrived on a crisis[20]. The closed place in the water; Hannah's funeral. Nel was the best. When Sula imitated her, or tried to, those long years ago, it always ended up in some action noteworthy not for its coolness but mostly for its being bizarre. The one time she tried to protect Nel, she had cut off her own finger tip and earned not Nel's gratitude but her disgust. From then on she had let her emotions dictate her behavior.

She could hear Nel's footsteps long before she opened the door and put the medicine on the table near the bed.

As Sula poured the liquid into a sticky spoon, Nel began the sickroom conversation[21].

"You look fine, Sula."

18 gloat: 고소한 듯 바라보다.

19 Make up: 보복하다.

20 넬은 위기대처 능력이 뛰어났다.

21 sickroom conversation: 병문안할 때 통상 이루어지는 대화.

"You lying, Nellie. I look bad." She gulped the medicine.

"No. I haven't seen you for a long time, but you look. . ."

"You don't have to do that, Nellie. It's going to be all right."

"What ails you? Have they said?"

Sula licked the corners of her lips. "You want to talk about that?"

Nel smiled, slightly, at the bluntness she had forgotten. "No. No, I don't, but you sure you should be staying up here alone?"

"Nathan comes by. The deweys sometimes, and Tar Baby. . ."

"That ain't help, Sula. You need to be with somebody grown. Somebody who can. . ."

"I'd rather be here, Nellie."

"You know you don't have to be proud with me[22]."

"Proud?" Sula's laughter broke through the phlegm. "What you talking about? I like my own dirt, Nellie. I'm not proud. You sure have forgotten me."

"Maybe. Maybe not. But you a woman and you alone."

"And you? ain't you alone?"

"I'm not sick. I work."

"Yes. Of course you do. Work's good for you, Nellie. It don't do nothing for me."

"You never *had* to."

"I never would."

"There's something to say for it, Sula. 'Specially if you don't want people to have to do for you."

"Neither one, Nellie. Neither one."

"You can't have it all, Sula." Nel was getting exasperated with her arrogance, with her lying at death's door still smart-talking.

"Why? I can do it all, why can't I have it all?"

22 내 앞에서 잘난 척 할 필요 없어.

"You can't do it all. You a woman and a colored woman at that. You can't act like a man. You can't be walking around all independent-like, doing whatever you like, taking what you want, leaving what you don't."

"You repeating yourself[23]."

"How repeating myself?"

"You say I'm a woman and colored. ain't that the same as being a man?"

"I don't think so and you wouldn't either if you had children[24]."

"Then I really would act like what you call a man. Every man I ever knew left his children."

"Some were taken."

"Wrong, Nellie. The word is 'left.'"

"You still going to know everything, ain't you?"

"I don't know everything, I just do everything."

"Well, you don't do what I do."

"You think I don't know what your life is like just because I ain't living it? I know what every colored woman in this country is doing."

"What's that?"

"Dying. Just like me. But the difference is they dying like a stump[25]. Me, I'm going down like one of those redwoods. I sure did live in this world."

"Really? What have you got to show for it?[26]"

"Show? To who? Girl, I got my mind. And what goes on

---

23 중언부언 쓸데없는 말을 되풀이하고 있구나.

24 애들이 있다면 넌 남자와 같을 수 없어.

25 다른 여자들은 잘려지고 남겨진 밑동처럼 죽어가지만, 난 삼나무처럼 죽어가지. 삼나무는 곧고 나무질이 좋아서 목재로 쓰여지는 것처럼, 술라도 쓰임받는 목재가 되리라는 뜻임.

26 네 말을 증명하기 위해서 보여줄 만한 것이 뭐가 있지?

in it. Which is to say, I got me."

"Lonely, ain't it?"

"Yes. But, my lonely is mine. Now your lonely is somebody else's. Made by somebody else and handed to you. ain't that something? A secondhand lonely."

Nel sat back on the little wooden chair. Anger skipped[27] but she realized that Sula was probably just showing off. No telling what shape she was really in[28], but there was no point in saying anything other than what was the truth[29]. "I always understood how you could take a man. Now I understand why you can't keep none."

"Is that what I'm supposed to do? Spend my life keeping a man?"

"They worth keeping, Sula."

"They ain't worth more than me. And besides, I never loved no man because he was worth it. Worth didn't have nothing to do with it."

"What did?"

"My mind did. That's all."

"Well I guess That's it. You own the world and the rest of us is renting. You ride the pony and we shovel the shit[30]. I didn't come up here for this kind of talk, Sula. . ."

"No?"

"No. I come to see about you. But now that you opened it up, I may as well close it." Nel's fingers closed around the brass rail of the bed. Now she would ask her. "How come you did it, Sula?"

There was a silence but Nel felt no obligation to fill it.

---

27 화가 치밀었다.

28 그녀가 정말 어떤 상태에 있는지 알 길이 없다.

29 그러나 진실이 아닌 다른 것을 말하는 것은 아무런 의미가 없다.

30 너는 말을 타고, 우리는 말똥이나 치우는 사람들이지. 빈정대는 말임.

Sula stirred a little under the covers. She looked bored as she sucked her teeth. "Well, there was this space in front of me, behind me, in my head. Some space. And Jude filled it up. That's all. He just filled up the space."

"You mean you didn't even love him?" The feel of the brass was in Nel's mouth[31]. "It Wasn't even loving him?"

Sula looked toward the boarded-up window again. Her eyes fluttered as if she were about to fall off into sleep.

"But. . ." Nel held her stomach in. "But what about me? What about me? Why didn't you think about me? didn't I count? I never hurt you. What did you take him for if you didn't love him and why didn't you think about me?" And then, "I was good to you, Sula, why don't that matter?"

Sula turned her head away from the boarded window. Her voice was quiet and the stemmed rose over her eye was very dark. "It matters, Nel, but only to you. Not to anybody else. Being good to somebody is just like being mean to somebody. Risky. You don't get nothing for it."

Nel took her hands from the brass railing. She was annoyed with herself. Finally when she had gotten the nerve to ask the question, the right question, it made no difference. Sula couldn't give her a sensible answer because she didn't know. Would be, in fact, the last to know[32]. Talking to her about right and wrong was like talking to the deweys. She picked at the fringe on Sula's bedspread[33] and said softly, "We were friends."

"Oh, yes. Good friends," Sula said.

"And you didn't love me enough to leave him alone. To let him love me. You had to take him away."

31 쇠맛이 느껴졌다. 즉, 불쾌한 감정을 뜻함.

32 술라는 절대로 이해하지 못할 것이다.

33 침대 커버의 가장자리를 당겼다.

"What you mean take him away? I didn't kill him, I just fucked him. If we were such good friends, how come you couldn't get over it?"

"You laying there in that bed without a dime or a friend to your name[34] having done all the dirt you did in this town and you still expect folks to love you?"

Sula raised herself up on her elbows. Her face glistened with the dew of fever. She opened her mouth as though to say something, then fell back on the pillows and sighed. "Oh, they'll love me all right. It will take time, but they'll love me." The sound of her voice was as soft and distant as the look in her eyes. "After all the old women have lain with the teen-agers; when all the young girls have slept with their old drunken uncles; after all the black men fuck all the white ones; when all the white women kiss all the black ones; when the guards have raped all the jailbirds and after all the whores make love to their grannies; after all the faggots get their mothers' trim[35]; when Lindbergh[36] sleeps with Bessie Smith[37] and Norma Shearer[38] makes it with Stepin Fetchit[39]; after all the dogs have fucked all the cats and every weathervane[40] on every barn flies off the roof to mount the hogs. . . then there'll be a little love left over for

34 without a dime...: 네 소유의 돈 한 푼, 친구하나 없이.

35 모든 남성동성연애자들이 자신의 어머니께 머리를 깎아달라고 할 때. 일어나기 힘든 일을 열거하고 있음.

36 찰스 린드버그. 대서양을 최초로 횡단한 백인 남성.

37 미국의 흑인 여가수.

38 미국의 백인 여배우.

39 미국의 흑인 남자 배우.

40 weathervane: 지붕 위에 설치하는 수탉모양의 바람개비. 지붕 위에서 늘 고고하게 꽂힌 바람개비가 비천한 돼지 위에 떨어진다는 뜻임. After all 로 시작하는, 이 단락의 모든 문장은 전혀 상반되는 것들이 금기를 깨고 서로 화합하게 되는 시점을 의미한다.

me. And I know just what it will feel like."

She closed her eyes then and thought of the wind pressing her dress between her legs as she ran up the bank of the river to four leaf-locked trees and the digging of holes in the earth.

Embarrassed, irritable and a little bit ashamed, Nel rose to go. "goodbye, Sula. I don't reckon I'll be back."

She opened the door and heard Sula's low whisper. "Hey, girl." Nel paused and turned her head but not enough to see her.

"How you know?" Sula asked.

"Know what?" Nel still wouldn't look at her.

"About who was good. How you know it was you?"

"What you mean?"

"I mean maybe it Wasn't you. Maybe it was me."

Nel took two steps out the door and closed it behind her. She walked down the hall and down the four flights of steps[41]. The house billowed around her light then dark, full of presences without sounds[42]. The deweys, Tar Baby, the newly married couples, Mr. Buckland Reed, Patsy, Valentine, and beautiful Hannah Peace. Where were they? Eva out at the old folks' home, and deweys living anywhere, Tar Baby steeped in wine, and Sula upstairs in Eva's bed with a boarded-up window and an empty pocketbook on the dresser.

* * *

When Nel closed the door, Sula reached for more medicine. Then she turned the pillow over to its cool side and thought

41 down the four flights of steps: 계단을 4칸씩 뛰어내려 감.

42 술라의 집은 소리 없는 존재들로 가득 차서, 밝음과 어두움이 교차하며 그녀의 주변에 일렁거렸다.

about her old friend. "so she will walk on down that road, her back so straight in that old green coat, the strap of her handbag pushed back all the way to the elbow, thinking how much I have cost her[43] and never remember the days when we were two throats and one eye and we had no price[44]."

Pictures drifted through her head as lightly as dandelion spores[45]: the blue eagle that swallowed the E of the Sherman's Mellowe wine that Tar Baby drank[46]; the pink underlid of Hannah's eye as she probed for a fleck of coal dust or a lash. She thought of looking out of the windows of all those trains and buses, looking at the feet and backs of all those people. Nothing was ever different. They were all the same. All of the words and all of the smiles, every tear and every gag just something to do.

"That's the same sun I looked at when I was twelve, the same pear trees. If I live a hundred years my urine will flow the same way, my armpits and breath will smell the same. My hair will grow from the same holes. I didn't mean anything. I never meant anything. I stood there watching her burn and was thrilled. I wanted her to keep on jerking like that, to keep on dancing."

Then she had the dream again. The Clabber Girl Baking Powder lady[47] was smiling and beckoning to her, one hand

43 how much I have cost her: 자신이 넬에게 얼마나 값비싼 대가를 치르게 했는지.

44 we had no price: 대가 없이 뭐든 나눌 수 있었다.

45 as lightly...: 민들레 포자처럼 가볍게.

46 술라의 머리속에 떠오르는 그림들: 타르 베이비가 마셨던 포도주병의 E자를 삼키는 푸른 독수리.

47 Clabber Girl Baking Power는 베이킹파우더 고유 상표이고, lady는 상표에 그려져 있는 부인을 의미함.

under her apron. When Sula came near she disintegrated into white dust, which Sula was hurriedly trying to stuff into the pockets of her blue-flannel house-coat. The disintegration was awful to see, but worse was the feel of the powder — its starchy slipperiness[48] as she tried to collect it by handfuls. The more she scooped, the more it billowed. At last it covered her, filled her eyes, her nose, her throat, and she woke gagging and overwhelmed with the smell of smoke.

Pain took hold. First a fluttering as of doves in her stomach, then a kind of burning, followed by a spread of thin wires to other parts of her body[49]. Once the wires of liquid pain were in place, they jelled and began to throb[50]. She tried concentrating on the throbs, identifying them as waves, hammer strokes, razor edges or small explosions. Soon even the variety of the pain bored her and there was nothing to do, for it was joined by fatigue so great she could not make a fist or fight the taste of oil at the back of her tongue.

Several times she tried to cry out, but the fatigue barely let her open her lips, let alone take the deep breath necessary to scream. So she lay there wondering how soon she would gather enough strength to lift her arm and push the rough quilt away from her chin and whether she should turn her cheek to the cooler side of the pillow now or wait till her face was thoroughly soaked and the move would be more refreshing. But she was reluctant to move her face for another reason. If she turned her head, she would not be able to see the boarded-up window Eva

48 끈적거리고 미끈거림.

49 위장에 비둘기가 팔딱거리는 듯 하다가, 일종의 타는 듯한 느낌으로, 그리고는 가는 철사가 온몸으로 퍼지는 것처럼 아팠다.

50 철사 같은 고통의 흐름이 자리를 잡자, 이제 흐름은 굳어지면서 욱신거리기 시작했다.

jumped out of. And looking at those four wooden planks with the steel rod slanting across them was the only peace she had. The sealed window soothed her with its sturdy termination, its unassailable finality. It was as though for the first time she was completely alone — where she had always wanted to be — free of the possibility of distraction. It would be here, only here, held by this blind window high above the elm tree, that she might draw her legs up to her chest, close her eyes, put her thumb in her mouth and float over and down the tunnels, just missing the dark walls[51], down, down until she met a rain scent and would know the water was near, and she would curl into its heavy softness and it would envelop her, carry her, and wash her tired flesh always. Always. Who said that? She tried hard to think. Who was it that had promised her a sleep of water always? The effort to recall was too great; it loosened a knot in her chest that turned her thoughts again to the pain.

While in this state of weary anticipation, she noticed that she was not breathing, that her heart had stopped completely. A crease of fear touched her breast, for any second there was sure to be a violent explosion in her brain, a gasping for breath. Then she realized, or rather she sensed, that there was not going to be any pain. She was not breathing because she didn't have to. Her body did not need oxygen. She was dead.

Sula felt her face smiling. "Well, I'll be damned[52]," she thought, "it didn't even hurt. Wait'll I tell Nel[53]."

---

51 just missing: 어두운 벽에 가까스로 부딪히지 않고.

52 엄청난 일이군.

53 기다렸다가 넬에게 말해야지.

1941

The death of Sula Peace was the best news folks up in the Bottom had had since the promise of work at the tunnel. Of[1] the few who were not afraid to witness the burial of a witch and who had gone to the cemetery, some had come just to verify her being put away but stayed to sing "shall We Gather at the River" for politeness' sake[2], quite unaware of the bleak promise of their song. Others came to see that nothing went awry[3], that the shallow-minded and small-hearted kept their meanness at bay, and that the entire event be characterized by that abiding gentleness of spirit to which they themselves had arrived by the simple determination not to let anything—anything at all: not failed crops, not rednecks[4], lost jobs, sick children, rotten potatoes, broken pipes, bug-ridden flour[5], third-class coal, educated social workers, thieving insurance men[6], garlic-ridden hunkies[7], corrupt Catholics, racist Protestants, cowardly Jews, slaveholding Moslem, jackleg nigger preachers[8], squeamish Chinamen[9], cholera, dropsy[10] or the Black Plague, let alone a

---

1 of: 중에서.

2 for politeness' sake: 마음엔 없지만 예의상.

3 go awry: 실패하다.

4 redneck: 가난한 백인 노동자.

5 bug-ridden flour: 벌레가 득실대는 밀가루.

6 thieving insurance men: 사기치는 보험판매인.

7 garlic-riddden hunkies: 마늘 냄새 퐁퐁 나는 외국태생 노동자들.

8 jackleg nigger preachers: 엉터리 흑인 목사들.

9 squeamish Chinamen: 괴팍한 중국인들.

strange woman — keep them from their God[11].

In any case, both the raw-spirited[12] and the gentle who came — not to the white funeral parlor but to the colored part of the Beechnut Cemetery — felt that either *because* Sula was dead or just *after* she was dead a brighter day was dawning. There were signs. The rumor that the tunnel spanning the river[13] would use Negro workers became an announcement. Planned, abandoned and replanned for years, this project had finally begun in 1937. For three years there were rumors that blacks would work it, and hope was high in spite of the fact that the River Road leading to the tunnel had encouraged similar hopes in 1927 but had ended up being built entirely by white labor — hillbillies[14] and immigrants taking even the lowest jobs. But the tunnel itself was another matter. The craft work[15] — no, they would not get that[16]. But it was a major job, and the government seemed to favor opening up employment to black workers. It meant black men would not have to sweep Medallion to eat, or leave the town altogether for the steel mills in Akron and along Lake Erie.

The second sign was the construction begun on an old people's home[17]. True, it was more renovation than construction[18], but

---

10 dropsy: 수종.

11 simple determination not to let anything... keep them from their God: (열거한 어떤 비천한 사람들도) 하나님의 은혜를 받아야 한다는 단순한 믿음.

12 the raw-spirited: 비열한 마음을 가진 사람들.

13 tunnel spanning the river: 강을 가로지르는 터널.

14 hillbillies: 두메산골 시골뜨기.

15 터널을 뚫는 작업은 기술을 요한다.

16 그들도 그런 기술은 이해하지 못할 것이다.

17 old people's home: 양로원.

18 새로 짓는 다기보다는 개조하는 것이었다.

the blacks were free, or so it was said, to occupy it. Some said that the very transfer of Eva from the ramshackle house that passed for[19] a colored women's nursing home to the bright new one was a clear sign of the mystery of God's ways, His mighty thumb having been seen at Sula's throat[20].

So it was with a strong sense of hope that the people in the Bottom watched October close.

Then Medallion turned silver. It seemed sudden, but actually there had been days and days of no snow[21] — just frost — when, late one afternoon, a rain fell and froze. Way down Carperter's Road, where the concrete sidewalks started, children hurried to the sliding places before shopkeepers and old women sprin-gled stove ashes, like ancient onyx,[22] onto the new-minted silver[23]. They hugged trees simply to hold for a moment all that life and largeness stilled in glass[24], and gazed at the sun pressed against the gray sky like a worn doubloon[25], wondering all the while if the world were coming to an end. Grass stood blade by blade, shocked into separateness by an ice that held for days[26]. Late-harvesting things were ruined, of course, and

19 pass for: ...로 통하다.

20 His mighty thumb...: 분사구문으로, '신의 심판이 술라에게 이른 것에 반해'로 해석함이 적절함. 즉, 마을 사람들의 생각에 사악한 술라는 신의 심판을 받아 죽은 반면에, 술라의 희생자인 이바는 좋은 양로원으로 옮겨진 것이 신의 오묘한 섭리라고 믿고 있다.

21 며칠 동안 전혀 눈이 오지 않았다.

22 ancient onyx: 고대의 얼룩마노.

23 new-minted silver: 새로 주조된 은, 즉 꽝꽝 얼어붙은 길을 의미함.

24 얼음 속에 멈춰진 생명과 그 큰 부피를 잠시라도 움켜쥐려는 듯이, 그들은 나무를 껴안았다.

25 worn doubloon: 닳아빠진 금화

26 며칠 안 녹지 않는 얼음으로, 놀란 듯 빳빳하게, 풀잎은 제각각 날서 있

fowl died of both chill and rage. Cider turned to ice and split the jugs, forcing the men to drink their cane liquor too soon. It was better down the valley, since, as always, the hills protected it, but up in the Bottom black folks suffered heavily in their thin houses[27] and thinner clothes. The ice-cold wind bled what little heat they had through windowpanes and ill-fitting doors[28]. For days on end[29] they were virtually housebound, venturing out only to coal-bins or right next door for the trading of vital foodstuffs[30]. Never to the stores. No deliveries were being made anyway, and when they were, the items were saved for better-paying white customers[31]. Women could not make it down the icy slopes and therefore missed days of wages they sorely needed.

The consequence of all that ice was a wretched Thanksgiving of tiny tough birds, heavy pork cakes, and pithy sweet potatoes. By the time the ice began to melt and the first barge was seen shuddering through the ice skim on the river, everybody under fifteen had croup[32], or scarlet fever[33], and those over had chilblains[34], rheumatism, pleurisy[35], earaches and a world of

---

었다.

27 thin houses: 난방이 잘 안 되는 부실한 집.

28 차가운 바람은 그나마 창문과 잘 맞지 않는 문으로 보존한 열기조차 날려 버렸다.

29 여러 날 계속해서.

30 석탄창고에 가거나, 이웃집에 식량을 바꿔 먹으러 갈 때를 제외하고는 말 그대로 집 안에 꼭꼭 틀어박혀 있었다.

31 when they were, the items...: 배달 물건이 있을 때는, 더 좋은 가격을 지불할 수 있는 백인 고객을 위해서 비축되었다.

32 croup: 위막성 후두염.

33 scarlet fever: 성홍열.

34 chilblains: 동상.

35 pleurisy: 늑막염.

other ailments.

Still it was not those illnesses or even the ice that marked the beginning of the trouble, that self-fulfilled prophecy that Shadrack carried on his tongue[36]. As soon as the silvering began, long before the cider cracked the jugs, there was something wrong. A falling away, a dislocation[37] was taking place. Hard on the heels of the general relief that Sula's death brought[38] a restless irritability took hold. Teapot, for example, went into the kitchen and asked his mother for some sugar-butter-bread. She got up to fix it and found that she had no butter, only oleomargarine[39]. Too tired to mix the saffron-colored powder into the hard cake of oleo[40], she simply smeared the white stuff on the bread and sprinkled the sugar over it. Teapot tasted the difference and refused to eat it. This keenest of insults that a mother can feel, the rejection by a child of her food, bent her into fury and she beat him as she had not done since Sula knocked him down the steps. She was not alone. Other mothers who had defended their children from Sula's malevolence (or who had defended their positions as mothers from Sula's scorn for the role) now had nothing to rub up against[41]. The tension was gone and so was the reason for the effort they had made. Without her mockery, affection for others sank into flaccid disrepair. Daughters who had complained bitterly about the responsibilities of taking care of

36 the self-fulfilled ...: 쉐드랙이 입에 달고 다녔던, 실현된 예언.

37 dislocation: 혼란.

38 Hard on the heel...: 술라의 죽음이 가져온 일반적인 안도감에 곧 뒤이어.

39 oleomargarine: 인조버터.

40 너무 피곤하여, 딱딱한 인조버터에 사프란색 (샛노랑) 가루를 섞을 수가 없어서.

41 자신을 추스르기 위하여 비교할 만한 대상이 없어졌다.

their aged mothers-in-law had altered when Sula locked Eva away, and they began cleaning those old women's spittoons[42] without a murmur. Now that Sula was dead and done with, they returned to a steeping resentment of the burdens of old people. Wives uncoddled[43] their husbands; there seemed no further need to reinforce their vanity. And even those negroes who had moved down from Canada to Medallion, who remarked every chance they got that they had never been slaves, felt a loosening of the reactionary compassion for Southern-born blacks Sula had inspired in them. They returned to their original claims of superiority.

The normal meanness that the winter brought was compounded by the small-spiritedness[44] that hunger and scarlet fever produced. Even a definite and witnessed interview of four colored men (and the promise of more in the spring) at the tunnel site could not break the cold vise of that lean and bitter year's end.

Christmas came one morning and haggled[45] everybody's nerves like a dull ax — too shabby to cut clean but too heavy to ignore. The children lay wall-eyed on creaking beds or pallets near the stove, sucking peppermint and oranges in between coughs while their mothers stomped the floors in rage at the cakes that did not rise because the stove fire had been so stingy; at the curled bodies of men who chose to sleep the day away rather than face the silence made by the absence of Lionel trains, drums, crybaby dolls and rocking horses. Teen-agers sneaked into the Elmira Theater in the afternoon and let Tex

---

42 가래나 침을 뱉도록 마련한 그릇. 즉, 타구.

43 uncoddle: 홀대하다.

44 small-spiritedness: 마음의 편협함.

45 haggle: 괴롭히다.

Ritter[46] free them from the recollection of their fathers' shoes, yawning in impotence under the bed. Some of them had a bottle of wine, which they drank at the feet of the glittering Mr. Ritter, making such a ruckus the manager had to put them out. The white people who came with Christmas bags of rock candy and old clothes were hard put to get a *Yes'm, thank you*, out of those sullen mouths.

Just as the ice lingered in October, so did the phlegm of December — which explained the enormous relief brought on by the first three days of 1941. It was as though the season had exhausted itself, for on January first the temperature shot up to sixty-one degrees and slushed the whiteness overnight. On January second drab patches of grass could be seen in the fields. On January third the sun came out — and so did Shadrack with his rope, his bell and his childish dirge.

He had spent the night before watching a tiny moon. The people, the voices that kept him company, were with him less and less. Now there were long periods when he heard nothing except the wind in the trees and the plop of buckeyes on the earth[47]. In the winter, when the fish were too hard to get to, he did picking-up jobs[48] for small businessmen (nobody would have him in or even near their homes), and thereby continued to have enough money for liquor. Yet the drunk times were becoming deeper but more seldom. It was as though he no longer needed to drink to forget whatever it was he could not remember. Now he could not remember that he had ever

46 Tex Ritter: 미국 컨트리 음악 가수

47 except the wind in ...: 나무를 스치는 바람이나 칠엽수가 땅위에 쿵하고 쓰러지는 소리 이외엔.

48 심부름 같은 허드렛일.

forgotten anything. Perhaps that was why for the first time after that cold day in France he was beginning to miss the presence of other people. Shadrack had improved enough to feel lonely. If he was lonely before, he didn't know it because the noise he kept up, the roaring, the busyness, protected him from knowing it. Now the compulsion to activity, to filling up the time when he was not happily fishing on the riverbank, had dwindled[49]. He sometimes fell asleep before he got drunk; sometimes spent whole days looking at the river and the sky; and more and more he relinquished the military habits of cleanliness in his shack. Once a bird flew into his door — one of the robins during the time there was a plague of them. It stayed, looking for an exit, for the better part of an hour[50]. When the bird found the window and flew away, Shadrack was grieved and actually waited and watched for its return. During those days of waiting, he did not make his bed, or sweep, or shake out the little rag-braid rug[51], and almost forgot to slash with his fish knife the passing day on his calendar[52]. When he did return to housekeeping, it was not with the precision he had always insisted upon. The messier his house got, the lonelier he felt, and it was harder and harder to conjure up sergeants, and orderlies, and invading armies; harder and harder to hear the gunfire and keep the platoon marching in time. More frequently now he looked at and fondled the one piece of evidence[53] that

49 강둑에서 행복하게 낚시질하는 시간 이외에 시간을 매꾼다던지 뭔가 해야겠다는 충동이 줄어들었다.

50 for the better part of an hour: 한 시간 가까이.

51 rag-braided rug: 걸레조각을 꼬아서 만든 깔개.

52 almost forgot to...: 달력에 하루가 지날 때마다 낚시용 칼로 줄을 긋는 것도 거의 잊곤 했다.

he once had a visitor in his house: a child's purple-and-white belt. The one the little girl left behind when she came to see him. Shadrack remembered the scene clearly. He had stepped into the door and there was a tear-stained face turning, turning toward him; eyes hurt and wondering; mouth parted in an effort to ask a question. She had wanted something — from him. Not fish not work, but something only he could give. She had a tadpole over her eye (that was how he knew she was a friend — she had the mark of the fish he loved), and one of her braids had come undone. But when he looked at her face he had seen also the skull beneath, and thinking she saw it too — knew it was there and was afraid — he tried to think of something to say to comfort her, something to stop the hurt from spilling out of her eyes. So he had said "always," so she would not have to be afraid of the change — the falling away of skin, the drip and slide of blood, and the exposure of bone underneath. He had said "always" to convince her, assure her, of permanency.

It worked[54], for when he said it her face lit up and the hurt did leave. She ran then, carrying his knowledge, but her belt fell off and he kept it as a memento. It hung on a nail near his bed — unfrayed, unsullied[55] after all those years, with only the permanent bend in the fabric made by its long life on a nail[56]. It was pleasant living with that sign of a visitor, his only one. And after a while he was able to connect the belt with the face, the tadpole-over-the-eye-face that he sometimes saw up in the Bottom. His visitor, his company, his guest, his social life, his woman, his daughter, his friend — they all hung there on a nail

53 fondled...: 한 가지 분명한 사실만 만지작거리듯 기억하고 있었다.
54 그 말은 효과가 있었다.
55 unfrayed or unsullied: 닳거나 더러워지지 않은 채.
56 못에 오랫동안 걸려있던 탓에 허리띠는 영원히 구부러진 채로.

near his bed.

Now he stared at the tiny moon floating high over the ice-choked river[57]. His loneliness had dropped down somewhere around his ankles. Some other feeling possessed him. A feeling that touched his eyes and made him blink. He had seen her again months? weeks? ago. Raking leaves for Mr. Hodges, he had gone into the cellar for two bushel baskets to put them in. In the hallway he passed an open door leading to a small room. She lay on a table there. It was surely the same one. The same little-girl face, same tadpole over the eye. So he had been wrong. Terribly wrong. No "always" at all. Another dying away of someone whose face he knew[58].

It was then he began to suspect that all those years of rope hauling and bell ringing were never going to do any good. He might as well sit forever on his riverbank and stare out of the window at the moon.

By his day-slashed calendar he knew that tomorrow was the day. And for the first time he did not want to go. He wanted to stay with the purple-and-white belt. Not go. Not go.

Still, when the day broke in an incredible splash of sun, he gathered his things. In the early part of the afternoon, drenched in sunlight and certain that this would be the last time he would invite them to end their lives neatly and sweetly, he walked over the rickety bridge and on into the Bottom. But it was not heartfelt this time, not loving this time, for he no longer cared whether he helped them or not. His rope was improperly tied; his bell had a tinny unimpassioned sound. His visitor was dead and would come no more.

---

57 ice-choked river: 꽝꽝 얼어붙은 강.

58 그가 아는 또 한 사람의 죽음.

Years later people would quarrel about who had been the first to go. Most folks said it was the deweys, but one or two knew better, knew that Dessie and Ivy had been first. Said that Dessie had opened her door first and stood there shielding her eyes from the sun while watching Shadrack coming down the road. She laughed.

Maybe the sun; maybe the clots[59] of green showing in the hills promising so much; maybe the contrast between Shadrack's doomy, gloomy bell glinting in all that sweet sunshine. Maybe just a brief moment, for once, of not feeling fear, of looking at death in the sunshine and being unafraid[60]. She laughed.

Upstairs, Ivy heard her and looked to see what caused the thick music that rocked her neighbor's breasts[61]. Then Ivy laughed too. Like the scarlet fever that had touched everybody and worn them down to gristle[62], their laughter infected Carpenter's Road. Soon children were jumping about giggling and men came to the porches to chuckle. By the time Shadrack reached the first house, he was facing a line of delighted faces.

Never before had they laughed. Always they had shut their doors, pulled down the shades and called their children out of the road. It frightened him, this glee, but he stuck to his habit — singing his song, ringing his bell and holding fast to his rope. The deweys with their magnificent teeth ran out from Number 7 and danced a little jig[63] around the befuddled Shadrack, then

59 clots: 응고된 덩어리.

60 두려움을 느끼지 않는, 햇빛에서 죽음을 대면하고도 잠시 잠깐 두려워하지 않게 된 탓인지도 모른다.

61 윗 층에 있던 아이비는 데씨의 웃음소리를 듣고, 데씨의 가슴을 감동시키는 진한 음악이 어디에서 나오는지 보려고 나아갔다.

62 worn them down to gristle: 뼈 속까지 사람들을 지치게 만들다.

cut into a wild aping of his walk[64], his song and his bell-ringing. By now women were holding their stomachs, and the men were slapping their knees. It was Mrs. Jackson, who ate ice, who tripped down off her porch and marched — actually marched — along behind him. The scene was so comic the people walked into the road to make sure they saw it all. In that way the parade started.

Everybody, Dessie, Tar Baby, Patsy, Mr. Buckland Reed, Teapot's Mamma, Valentine, the deweys, Mrs. Jackson, Irene, the proprietor of the Palace of Cosmetology, Reba, the Herrod brothers and flocks of teen-agers got into the mood and, laughing, dancing, calling to one another, formed a pied piper's band[65] behind Shadrack. As the initial group of about twenty people passed more houses, they called to the people standing in doors and leaning out of windows to join them; to help them open further this slit in the veil, this respite from anxiety, from dignity, from gravity, from the weight of that very adult pain that had undergirded them all those years before. Called to them to come out and play in the sunshine — as though the sunshine would last, as though there really was hope. The same hope that kept them picking beans for other farmers; kept them from finally leaving as they talked of doing[66]; kept them knee-deep in other people's dirt[67]; kept them excited about other people's wars[68]; kept

63 jig: 속도가 빠르고 변화가 많은 춤.

64 cut into a wild aping of his walk: 쉐드랙이 걷는 모양을 무턱대고 흉내내기 시작했다.

65 formed a pied piper's band: 얼룩덜룩한 피리밴드를 형성했다.

66 항상 떠난다고 말하지만 결국 떠나지 못하게 하는 것, 그 희망.

67 다른 사람의 오물에 무릎까지 발을 담글 수 있게 하는 희망. 즉, 굴욕을 참아내게 하는 희망.

68 희망 때문에 다른 사람들의 싸움에 (무관심하지 않고) 흥분할 수 있었다.

them solicitous of white people's children[69]; kept them convinced that some magic "government" was going to lift them up, out and away from that dirt, those beans, those wars.

Some, of course, like Helene Wright, would not go. She watched the ruckus with characteristic scorn. Others, who understood the SpirIt's touch which made them dance[70], who understood whole families bending their backs in a field while singing as from one throat[71], who understood the ecstasy of river baptisms under suns just like this one, did not understand this curious disorder, this headless display and so refused also to go.

Nevertheless, the sun splashed on a larger and larger crowd that strutted, skipped, marched, and shuffled down the road. When they got down to where the sidewalk started, some of them stopped and decided to turn back, too embarrassed to enter the white part of town whooping like banshees. But except for three or four, the fainthearted were put to shame by the more aggressive and abandoned, and the parade danced down Main Street past Woolworth's and the old poultry house, turned right and moved on down the New River Road.

At the mouth of the tunnel excavation, in a fever pitch of excitement and joy[72], they saw the timber, the bricks, the steel ribs and the tacky wire gate that glittered under ice struck to diamond in the sun[73]. It dazzled them, at first, and they were

69 희망 때문에 그들은 백인 아이들에 대해서도 염려할 수 있었다.

70 앞의 단락에서 쉐드랙이 이끄는 행렬에서 구원을 희망하는 사람들과는 달리, 헬렌과 같은 인물은 이들의 희망을 조소하고, 또한 기독교도들 역시 행렬에 참여하지 않는다.

71 한 목소리로 노래 부르며 밭에서 허리 굽혀 일하는 가족을 이해하는 사람들. 즉, 쉐드랙의 행렬에 참가하는 대다수의 사람들이 공동체로부터 유리된 사람들인 반면, 참여하지 않는 사람들은 나름대로 종교적 신앙이나, 공동체적 결속을 갖고 있는 사람들이다.

72 in a fever pitch of excitement and joy: 흥분과 기쁨의 열기 속에서.

suddenly quiet. Their hooded eyes[74] swept over the place where their hope had lain since 1927. There was the promise: leaf-dead[75]. The teeth unrepaired, the coal credit cut off[76], the chest pains unattended, the school shoes unbought, the rushstuffed mattresses[77], the broken toilets, the leaning porches[78], the slurred remarks[79] and the staggering childish malevolence of their employers. All there in blazing sunlit ice rapidly becoming water.

Like antelopes they leaped over the little gate — a wire barricade that was never intended to bar anything but dogs, rabbits and stray children — and led by the tough, the enraged and the young they picked up the lengths of timber and thin steel ribs and smashed the bricks they would never fire in yawning kilns[80], split the sacks of limestone they had not mixed or even been allowed to haul; tore the wire mesh, tipped over wheelbarrows and rolled forepoles down the bank, where they sailed far out on the icebound river.

Old and young, women and children, lame and hearty[81], they killed, as best they could, the tunnel they were forbidden to

---

73 that glittered under ice struck to...: 다이아몬드처럼 변한 얼음 밑에서 햇살을 받아 빛나고 있는.

74 덮개가 씌워진 눈. 여기서는 "흐릿한" 눈으로 해석함이 적절함.

75 leaf-dead: 희망을 leaf에 비유하여 잎이 맥없이 죽는 모습처럼 희망이 사그라지는 것을 말함.

76 the coal credit cut off: 석탄을 외상으로 살 수 액수가 줄어듬. 아마도 지속되는 가난으로 인하여 빚을 갚을 수 없으므로 신용한도가 줄어드는 것을 의미한다.

77 골풀을 넣은 침대 매트리스.

78 leaning porches: 부서져 기울어진 현관.

79 slurred remarks: 비방하는 말.

80 yawning kilns: (입이) 크게 벌어진 가마솥.

81 lame and hearty: 시원치 않거나, 혹은 튼튼한 사람이나.

build.

They didn't mean to go in, to actually go down into the lip of the tunnel, but in their need to kill it all, all of it, to wipe from the face of the earth the work of the thin-armed Virginia boys, the bull-necked Greeks and the knife-faced men who waved the leaf-dead promise, they went too deep, too far. . .

A lot of them died there. The earth, now warm, shifted; the first forepole slipped[82]; loose rock fell from the face of the tunnel and caused a shield to give way[83]. They found themselves in a chamber of water, deprived of the sun that had brought them there. With the first crack and whoosh of water[84], the clamber to get out was so fierce[85] that others who were trying to help were pulled to their deaths. Pressed up against steel ribs and timber blocks young boys strangled when the oxygen left them to join the water. Outside, others watched in terror as ice split and earth shook beneath their feet. Mrs. Jackson, weighing less than 100 pounds, slid down the bank and met with an open mouth the ice she had craved all her life. Tar Baby, Dessie, Ivy, Valentine, the Herrod boys, some of Ajax's younger brothers and the deweys (at least it was supposed; their bodies were never found) — all died there. Mr. Buckland Reed escaped, so did Patsy and her two boys, as well as some fifteen or twenty who had not gotten close enough to fall, or whose timidity would not let them enter an unfinished tunnel.

And all the while Shadrack stood there. Having forgotten his song and his rope, he just stood there high up on the bank ringing, ringing his bell.

82 터널의 첫 번째 기둥이 삐끗했다.

83 바위가 터널 바닥으로 떨어지고 받침대가 쓰러졌다.

84 터널이 처음 와지끈 붕괴되고 물이 휩쓸려 들어오자.

85 밖으로 빠져나오려고 사람들이 너무 난폭하게 기어오르는 바람에.

1965

Things were so much better in 1965. Or so it seemed. You could go downtown and see colored people working in the dime store[1] behind the counters, even handling money with cash- register keys around their necks. And a colored man taught mathematics at the junior high school. The young people had a look about them that everybody said was new but which reminded Nel of the deweys, whom nobody had ever found. Maybe, she thought, they had gone off and seeded the land and growed up in these young people in the dime store with the cash-register keys around their necks.

They were so different, these young people. So different from the way she remembered them forty years ago.

Jesus, there were some beautiful boys in 1921! Look like the whole world was bursting at the seams with them[2]. Thirteen, fourteen, fifteen years old. Jesus, they were fine. L. P., Paul Freeman and his brother Jake, Mrs. Scott's twins — and Ajax had a whole flock of younger brothers. They hung out of attic windows, rode on car fenders, delivered the coal, moved into Medallion and moved out, visited cousins, plowed, hoisted, lounged on the church steps, careened[3] on the school playground. The sun heated them and the moon slid down their backs. God, the world was *full* of beautiful boys in 1921.

---

1 dime store: 싸구려 물건을 파는 가게.

2 세상이 온통 아름다운 청년으로 넘쳐나고 있었던 것 같다.

3 careen: 기울어지며 질주하다.

Nothing like these kids. Everything had changed. Even the whores were better then: tough, fat, laughing women with burns on their cheeks and wit married to their meanness[4]: or widows couched in small houses in the woods with eight children to feed and no man. These modern-day whores were pale and dull before those women. These little clothes-crazy things were always embarrassed. Nasty but shamed. They didn't know what shameless was. They should have known those silvery widows in the woods who would get up from the dinner table and walk into the trees with a customer with as much embarrassment as a calving mare.

Lord, how time flies. She hardly recognized anybody in the town any more. Now there was another old people's home. Look like this town just kept on building homes for old people. Every time they built a road they built a old folks' home. You'd think folks was living longer, but the fact of it was, they was just being put out faster[5].

Nel hadn't seen the insides of this most recent one yet, but it was her turn in Circle Number 5[6] to visit some of the old women there. The pastor visited them regularly, but the circle thought private visits were nice too. There were just nine colored women out there, the same nine that had been in the other one. But a lot of white ones[7]. White people didn't fret about putting their old ones away[8]. It took a lot for black people to let them

---

4 tough, fat, laughing women ...: 거칠고 뚱뚱하고 얼굴이 벌개지도록, 비열함과 재치를 함께 섞어 웃어대는 여자들.

5 but the fact of it...: 사실은 노인들은 집에서 더 빨리 쫓겨나고 있는 것이었다.

6 Circle Number 5: 교회에서 양로원을 방문하는 조 중, 다섯 번째 조.

7 백인을 위한 양로원도 많다.

8 백인들은 자신의 부모를 양로원으로 보내는데 그다지 죄책감을 갖지 않

go[9] and even if somebody was old and alone, others did the dropping by, the floor washing, the cooking[10]. Only when they got crazy and unmanageable were they let go. Unless it was somebody like Sula, who put Eva away out of meanness. It was true that Eva was foolish in the head, but not so bad as to need locking up.

Nel was more than a little curious to see her. She had been really active in church only a year or less, and that was because the children were grown now and took up less time and less space in her mind. For over twenty-five years since Jude walked out she had pinned herself into a tiny life[11]. She spent a little time trying to marry again, but nobody wanted to take her on with three children, and she simply couldn't manage the business of keeping boyfriends. During the war she had had a rather long relationship with a sergeant stationed at the camp twenty miles down river from Medallion, but then he got called away and everything was reduced to a few letters — then nothing. Then there was a bartender at the hotel. But she was fifty-five and hard put to remember what all that had been about.

It didn't take long, after Jude left, for her to see what the future would be. She had looked at her children and knew in her heart that that would be all. That they were all she would ever know of love[12]. But it was a love that, like a pan of syrup kept too long on the stove, had cooked out, leaving only its odor

---

았다.

9 흑인들의 경우는 부모를 양로원으로 보내기를 꺼려했다.

10 누군가 늙고 혼자 살게 되면, (양로원에 보내는 대신) 다른 사람들이 찾아와서 청소도 하고 음식도 만들어 주었다.

11 좁은 생활 속에 자신 스스로를 고정시켰다.

12 사랑에 관한 한, 아이들에 대한 사랑이 전부라는 것을 알고 있었다.

and a hard, sweet sludge, impossible to scrape off[13]. For the mouths of her children quickly forgot the taste of her nipples, and years ago they had begun to look past her face into the nearest stretch of sky.

In the meantime the Bottom had collapsed. Everybody who had made money during the war moved as close as they could to the valley, and the white people were buying down river, cross river, stretching Medallion like two strings on the banks. Nobody colored lived much up in the Bottom any more. White people were building towers for television stations up there and there was a rumor about a golf course or something. Anyway, hill land was more valuable now, and those black people who had moved down right after the war and in the fifties couldn't afford to come back even if they wanted to. Except for the few blacks still huddled by the river bend, and some undemolished houses on Carpenter's Road, only rich white folks were building homes in the hills. Just like that, they had changed their minds and instead of keeping the valley floor to themselves, now they wanted a hilltop house with a river view and a ring of elms. The black people, for all their new look[14], seemed awfully anxious to get to the valley, or leave town, and abandon the hills to whoever was interested. It was sad, because the Bottom had been a real place. These young ones kept talking about the community, but they left the hills to the poor, the old, the stubborn—and the rich white folks. Maybe it hadn't been a community, but it had been a place. Now there weren't any places left, just separate houses with separate televisions and

13 그러나 사랑이란, 스토브 위에 장시간 놓여있던 시럽처럼, 익을 대로 익은 후 남은 것이라곤 오직 향내와 딱딱하고 달콤한 찌꺼기라서 도저히 긁어낼 수 없는 것이다.

14 for all their new look: 그들의 새로운 전망에도 불구하고.

separate telephones and less and less dropping by.

These were the same thoughts she always had when she walked down into the town. One of the last true pedestrians, Nel walked the shoulder road[15] while cars slipped by. Laughed at by her children, she still walked wherever she wanted to go, allowing herself to accept rides only when the weather required it.

Now she went straight through the town and turned left at its farthest end, along a tree-lined walk that turned into a country road farther on and passed the cemetery, Beechnut Park.

When she got to Sunnydale, the home for the aged, it was already four o'clock and turning chill. She would be glad to sit down with those old birds and rest her feet.

A red-haired lady at the desk gave her a pass card and pointed to a door that opened onto a corridor of smaller doors. It looked like what she imagined a college dormitory to be. The lobby was luxurious — modern — but the rooms she peeped into were sterile green cages. There was too much light everywhere; it needed some shadows. The third door, down the hall, had a little name tag over it that read EVA PEACE. Nel twisted the knob and rapped[16] a little on the door at the same time, then listened a moment before she opened it.

At first she couldn't believed it. She seemed so small, sitting at that table in a black-vinyl chair. All the heaviness had gone and the height. Her once beautiful leg had no stocking and the foot was in a slipper. Nel wanted to cry — not for Eva's milk-dull eyes or her floppy lips, but for the once proud foot accustomed for over a half century to a fine well-laced shoe, now stuffed gracelessly into a pink terrycloth slipper[17].

15 shoulder road: 갓길.

16 rap: 톡톡 두드리다.

"Good evening, Miss Peace. I'm Nel Greene come to pay a call on you. You remember me, don't you?"

Eva was ironing and dreaming of stairwells. She had neither iron nor clothes but did not stop her fastidious lining up of pleats or pressing out of wrinkles even when she acknowledged Nel's greeting[18].

"Howdy. Sit down."

"Thank you." Nel sat on the edge of the little bed. "You've got a pretty room, a real pretty room, Miss Peace."

"You eat something funny today?"[19]

"Ma'am?"

"Some chop suey[20]? Think back."

"No, Ma'am."

"No? Well, you gone be sick later on[21]."

"But I didn't have no chop suey."

"You think I come all the way over here for you to tell me that[22]? I can't make visits too often. You should have some respect for old people."

"But Miss Peace, I'm visiting *you*. This is *your* room." Nel smiled.

"What you say your name was?"

"Nel Greene."

"Wiley Wright's girl?"

---

17 but for the once proud foot ...: 50년이 넘게 예쁘게 레이스 달린 신발에 익숙했던 한때 오만했던 그 발이 아무렇게나 테리천의 슬리퍼에 신겨진 모습 때문에.

18 그녀는 다리미도 옷도 없으면서, 넬의 인사를 받을 때조차, 까다롭게 옷의 주름을 잡고 구김을 펴서 다림질하는 일을 멈추지 않았다.

19 뭘 잘못 먹은 것 아니냐?

20 chop suey: 잡채 (미국식 중국요리)

21 후에 좀 아프게 될게다.

22 너의 그런 말이나 듣기 위해 내가 여기까지 온 줄 아니?

"Uh huh. You do remember. That makes me feel good, Miss Peace. You remember me and my father."

"Tell me how you killed that little boy."

"What? What little boy?"

"The one you threw in the water. I got oranges. How did you get him to go in the water?"

"I didn't throw no little boy in the river. That was Sula."

"You. Sula. What's the difference? You was there. You watched, didn't you? Me, I never would've watched."

"You're confused, Miss Peace. I'm Nel. Sula's dead."

"It's awful cold in the water. Fire is warm. How did you get him in?" Eva wet her forefinger and tested the iron's heat.

"Who told you all these lies? Miss Peace? Who told you? Why are you telling lies on me?"

"I got oranges. I don't drink they[23] old orange juice. They puts something in it[24]."

"Why are you trying to make out like I did it?"[25]

Eva stopped ironing and looked at Nel. For the first time her eyes looked sane.

"You think I'm guilty?" Nel was whispering.

Eva whispered back, "Who would know that better than you?"

"I want to know who you been talking to." Nel forced herself to speak normally.

"Plum. Sweet Plum. He tells me things." Eva laughed a light, tinkly giggle — girlish.

"I'll be going now, Miss Peace." Nel stood.

---

23 they: their의 뜻임.

24 누군가가 쥬스에 독약을 넣는다는 과대 망상에 사로잡혀 있음. 자신의 아들을 불에 태워 죽이고, 딸인 한나가 사고로 불에 타서 죽은 사실에 대한 죄의식의 표현인 듯함.

25 내가 마치 한 일처럼 꾸며대는 이유가 뭐지요?

"You ain't answered me yet."

"I don't know what you're talking about."

"Just alike. Both of you. Never was no difference between you. Want some oranges? It's better for you than chop suey. Sula? I got oranges."

Nel walked hurriedly down the hall, Eva calling after her, "Sula?" Nel couldn't see the other women today. That woman had upset her. She handed her pass[26] back to the lady, avoiding her look of surprise.

Outside she fastened her coat against her rising wind. The top button was missing so she covered her throat with her hand. A bright space opened in her head and memory seeped into it[27].

Standing on the riverbank in a purple-and-white dress, Sula swinging Chicken Little around and around. His laughter before the hand-slip and the water closing quickly over the place. What had she felt then, watching Sula going around and around and then the little boy swinging out over the water? Sula had cried and cried when she came back from Shadrack's house. But Nel had remained calm.

"*Shouldn't we tell?*"

"*Did he see?*"

"*I don't know. No.*"

"*Let's go. We can't bring him back.*"

What did old Eva mean by *you watched*? How could she help seeing it[28]? She was right there. But Eva didn't say *see*, she said *watched*. "I did not watch it. I just saw it." But it was there anyway, as it had always been, the old feeling and the old question. The good feeling she had had when Chicken's hands

26 pass: 출입증.

27 머리속에 밝은 공간이 열리고, 그곳에서 옛 기억이 서서히 살아났다.

28 어떻게 그 광경을 보지 않을 수 있었겠는가.

slipped. She hadn't wondered about that in years. "Why didn't I feel bad when it happened? How come it felt so good to see him fall?"

All these years she had been secretly proud of her calm, controlled behavior when Sula was uncontrollable, her compassion for Sula's frightened and shamed eyes. Now it seemed that what she had thought was maturity, serenity and compassion was only the tranquillity that follows a joyful stimulation. Just as the water closed peacefully over the turbulence of Chicken Little's body, so had contentment washed over her enjoyment.

She was walking too fast. Not watching where she placed her feet[29], she got into the weeds by the side of the road. Running almost, she approached Beechnut Park. Just over there was the colored part[30] of the cemetery. She went in. Sula was buried there along with Plum, Hannah and now Pearl. With the same disregard for name changes by marriage that the black people of Medallion always showed[31], each flat slab had one word carved on it[32]. Together they read like a chant: PEACE 1895-1921, PEACE 1890-1923, PEACE 1910-1940, PEACE 1892-1959.

They were not dead people. They were words. Not even words. Wishes, longings.

All these years she had been harboring good feelings about Eva; sharing, she believed, her loneliness and unloved state as no one else could or did. She, after all, was the only one who

---

29 발이 어딜 딛는지도 알지 못한 채.

30 colored part: 흑인을 위한 묘지구역.

31 메달리온의 흑인들이 늘 그러하듯이, 결혼 후에 바뀌는 이름에 대해서는 아랑곳하지 않고.

32 납작한 석판에는 각각 한 글자만 새겨져 있었다.

really understood why Eva refused to attend Sula's funeral. The others thought they knew; thought the grandmother's reasons were the same as their own — that to pay respect to someone who had caused them so much pain was beneath them[33]. Nel, who did go, believed Eva's refusal was not due to pride or vengeance but to a plain unwillingness to see the swallowing of her own flesh into the dirt, a determination not to let the eyes see what the heart could not hold.

Now, however, after the way Eva had just treated her, accused her, she wondered if the townspeople hadn't been right the first time[34]. Eva *was* mean. Sula had even said so. There was no good reason for her to speak so. Feebleminded or not. Whatever. Eva knew what she was doing. Always had. She had stayed away from Sula's funeral and accused Nel of drowning Chicken Little for spite. The same spite that galloped all over the Bottom. That made every gesture an offense, every off-center smile a threat, so that even the bubbles of relief that broke in the chest of practically everybody when Sula died did not soften their spite and allow them to go to Mr. Hodges' funeral parlor or send flowers from the church or bake a yellow cake.

She thought about Nathan opening the bedroom door the day she had visited her, and finding the body. He said he knew she was dead right away not because her eyes were open but because her mouth was. It looked to him like a giant yawn that she never got to finish. He had run across the street to Teapot's Mamma, who, when she heard the news, said, "Ho!" like the

33 that to pay...: that 이하는 thought의 목적절임. 즉, 그렇게 많은 고통을 안겨준 사람(술라)에게 경의를 표하는 일은 그들답지 않은 일이었다.

34 (이바가 손녀의 장례식에 참석하지 않은 이유가 술라의 사악함 때문이라고 생각했던) 마을 사람들의 짐작이 처음부터 옳지 않았는지 넬은 생각하게 되었다.

conductor on the train when it was about to take off except louder, and then did a little dance. None of the women left their quilt patches in disarray to run to the house[35]. Nobody left the clothes halfway through the wringer to run to the house[36]. Even the men just said "Uhn," when they heard. The day passed and no one came. The night slipped into another day and the body was still lying in Eva's bed gazing at the ceiling trying to complete a yawn. It was very strange, this stubbornness about Sula. For even when China, the most rambunctious whore in the town, died (whose black son and white son said, when they heard she was dying, "She ain't dead yet?"), even then everybody stopped what they were doing and turned out in numbers to put the fallen sister away.

It was Nel who finally called the hospital, then the mortuary, then the police, who were the ones to come. So the white people took over. They came in a police van and carried the body down the steps past the four pear trees and into the van for all the world as with Hannah. When the police asked questions nobody gave them any information. It took them hours to find out the dead woman's first name. The call was for a Miss Peace at 7 Carpenter's Road. So they left with that: a body, a name and an address. The white people had to wash her, dress her, prepare her and finally lower her. It was all done elegantly, for it was discovered that she had a substantial death policy[37]. Nel went to the funeral parlor, but was so shocked by the closed coffin she stayed only a few minutes.

35 어느 누구도 이불 조각을 늘어놓은 채 술라의 집으로 달려가는 사람은 없었다.

36 어느 누구도 빨래를 반쯤 짜다 말고 술라의 집으로 달려가는 사람은 없었다.

37 she had a substantial death policy: 상당한 양의 사망 보험금이 있었다.

The following day Nel walked to the burying and found herself the only black person there, steeling her mind to the roses and pulleys[38]. It was only when she turned to leave that she saw the cluster of black folk at the lip of the cemetery. Not coming in, not dressed for mourning, but there waiting. Not until the white folks left[39] — the gravediggers, Mr. and Mrs. Hodges, and their young son who assisted them — did those black people from up in the Bottom enter with hooded hearts and filed eyes[40] to sing "shall We Gather at the River? over the curved earth that cut them off from the most magnificent hatred they had ever known. Their question clotted the October air, Shall We Gather at the River? The beautiful, the beautiful river? Perhaps Sula answered them even then, for it began to rain, and the women ran in tiny leaps through the grass[41] for fear their straightened hair would beat them home[42].

Sadly, heavily, Nel left the colored part of the cemetery. Further along the road Shadrack passed her by. A little shaggier, a little older, still energetically mad, he looked at the woman hurrying along the road with the sunset in her face.

He stopped. Trying to remember where he had seen her before. The effort of recollection was too much for him and he moved on. He had to haul some trash out at Sunnydale and it would be good and dark before he got home[43]. He hadn't sold

---

38 steeling her mind to ...: 장미와 도르레 등(장례식에서 쓰이는 물품)에 대해 마음을 고정시키면서.

39 백인들이 떠나서야 비로소.

40 with hooded hearts and filed eyes: 두건 쓴 가슴과 다듬어진 눈으로, 즉 경건한 마음으로.

41 the women ran in tiny leaps...: 여자들은 종종걸음 치며 초원을 달렸다.

42 펴진 머리가 집으로 먼저 달아날까봐. 즉 공들여 편 머리카락이 비를 맞아 금방 구불거릴까봐 얼른 집으로 가는 모양을 묘사함.

fish in a long time now. The river had killed them all. No more silver-gray flashes, no more flat, wide, unhurried look. No more slowing down of gills. No more tremor on the line.

Shadrack and Nel moved in opposite directions, each thinking separate thoughts about the past. The distance between them increased as they both remembered gone things.

Suddenly Nel stopped. Her eye twitched and burned a little.

"Sula?" she whispered, gazing at the tops of trees. "Sula?"

Leaves stirred; mud shifted; there was the smell of over-ripe green things. A soft ball of fur[44] broke and scattered like dandelion spores in the breeze.

"All that time, all that time, I thought I was missing Jude." And the loss pressed down on her chest and came up into her throat. "We was girls together," she said as though explaining something. "O Lord, Sula," she cried, "girl, girl, girlgirlgirl."

It was a fine cry — loud and long — but it had no bottom and it had no top, just circles and circles of sorrow.

---

43 it would be good and dark...: 쓰레기의 양은 꽤 많아서 집에 도착하기 전에 어두워질 참이었다.

44 술라로 인하여 쥬드를 잃고 깊은 슬픔에 잠겼을 때, 넬의 머리 주변을 맴돌던 재색의 덩어리.

CRITICAL ESSAYS

Experimental Lives: Meaning and Self in *Sula**

It is in Morrison's second novel, *Sula*(1973), and specifically in her treatment and characterization of its two central characters, Sula and Shadrack, that the archetypal, authentic heroic personalities of her canon are first explored. Unlike the static lives of the Breedloves in *The Bluest Eye*, the lives of these characters are rich and experimental, for neither conforms to the prevailing social standards and values. Both fit Morrison's description of what she calls salt tasters who "express either an effort of the will or a freedom of the will," which,, as Claudia Taste noted, makes them "free people, the dangerously free people."

Unlike Pecola, who is driven by a desire for acceptance, Shadrack and Sula are risk takers who reflect "an abrogation of society with its constricting values," according to Naana Banyiwa-Horne. Sula, the critic writes, "Protects herself against the mean world with a meanness which bristles against the hostility of the world. Independent, adventurous, inquisitive, strong-willed and self-centered, Sula offers a welcome, if uncanny foil to Pecola's unquestioned acceptance and futile pursuit of those values which lead to her destruction.

* From *Toni Morrison* by Wilfred D. Samuels and Cleonora Hudson- Weems. Wilfred D. Samuels and Cleonora Hudson-Weems. *Toni Morrison*. Boston: Twayne Publishers, 1990.

On the surface, *Sula* is about the experiences of the citizens of the Bottom, a Black community in Medallion, a fictional midwestern town. Its central focus, however, is on Shadrack and Sula, the preoccupation of the Medallionites, who wonder "What Shadrack was all about [and] what that little girl Sula who grew into woman in their town was all about" (6).

Residing with her mother, Hannah, in the house of her grandmother, Eva Peace, Sula initially draws her world view from both women. However, her inability to find meaning in the prescribed domestic roles of the women of the Bottom, coupled with her desire to be "distinctly different" (118), leaves Sula spiritually and physically alienated. "she had no center, no speck around which to grow" (103). Similarly, Shadrack is socially ostracized in the Bottom. Fragmented by his war experience, his life is a continual struggle for consistency and wholeness in the midst of isolation. In spite of this, however, both Shadrack and Sula shatter Pearl K. Bell's assertion that "The pursuit of authentic self is the last thing one expects in a novel by Toni Morrison."

This central concern is muddled by the ironies, ambiguities, and inconsistencies that are endemic to the text. *Sula*'s complexity is visible, for example, in the name of the setting, for although Medallion's Blacks live in the Bottom, their community is actually located at the top of a hill, as a result, the narrator tells us, of a "Nigger joke"; of "The kind white folks tell when the mill closes down and they're looking for a little comfort somewhere" (4). Located "High up in the hill," the Bottom had been given to a former slave in place of the promised fertile valley land he was to have received for performing "some very difficult chores," the dishonest white farmer falsely explained that the hilly land was at the bottom of heaven, "Best land there is" (5).

There is irony as well in the structure, For example, chapter Two bears the title "1919," yet much of the action takes place before the end of World War I; very little takes place in this particular year. The most significant irony, however, evolves around Sula's and Shadrack's characterizations; although both are considered evil and psychologically unbalanced, they are, in fact, closer to being actualized individuals than anyone else in the novel.

Sula's Status in the Bottom

Sula is a pariah whose values are often the polar opposites of those adopted by her provincial society. Unlike Pecola, Sula lives out of her own fantasies, creates her own realities, and sets her own personal objectives. She is motivated by a firm sense of her "Me-ness." Morrison uses Sula to question "The tendency to blindly accept existence as a given, rather than something which can be challenged," wrote Odette A. Martin. To best explore Sula's quest for authentic existence, Morrison develops her character much as she developed Pecola's: through the community; the Peace women (Sula's mother and grandmother); and through Nel Wright, her best friend, that we note Sula's vigilance against the destruction of the self — that we find her fortressing her "Me-ness."

Morrison describes her intention for the Bottom community in an interview with Robert Stepto: "When I wrote *Sula*, I was interested in making the town, the community, the neighborhood, as strong a character as I could . . . because the most extraordinary thing about any group, and particularly our group, is the fantastic variety of people and things and behavior and so on." Morrison's pronouncements here substantiate her premise that there are no boring black people; for above all she seems interested not only in exploring the significance of place but "The fantastic variety of [black] people," because they are never dull. Contrary to Addison Gayle's criticism of what for him is the stereotypical image of the blacks of the Bottom as "Primitives," Morrison is reclaiming and, by extension, recreating a lost community. The novel begins, "In that place, where they tore the nightstand and blackberry patches from their roots to make room for the Medallion City Golf Course, there was once a neighborhood" (3).

Although "Terminated and dramatically obliterated," as Susan Willis notes, the Bottom "refers to the past, the rural South the reservoir of culture that has been uprooted — like the blackberry bushes — to make way for modernization." It necessarily refers as well to the mythology, one honed in an environment of caring, that is also lost. The Bottom is different from Medallion, an "amorphous institutionalized power . . . which suggests neither nature nor people," for in it responsibility is no longer central to communal life but is instead a part of the legal system. Thus Sula's interaction with the community, her neighborhood, from which she is alienated, is of paramount importance.

Sula's status as outsider manifests itself symbolically in a mysterious birthmark that runs from the middle of the lid toward the eyebrow of her right eye. It marks her as evil to most Bottomites, who blame her for unpleasant occurrences. For example, when Teapot knocks on Sula's door to ask for empty bottles, he falls off the porch while leaving. His mother accuses Sula of pushing him. When Mr. Finley dies, Sula is blamed. He was sitting on his porch sucking chicken bones, as he had done for thirteen years, when he saw Sula and choked.

Her peripheral life makes Sula a scapegoat for the Bottom's citizens. Philip Royster contends, "The folk create the scapegoat by identifying Sula sa the cause of the misery, which they identify as evil, in their lives. It is undoubtedly easier for the folk to anthropomorphize their misery than to examine the generation of that misery by their relation to the environment. The folk produced good in their lives, that is, loving and caring for one another, by reacting to their own conception of evil, Sula, who they considered a witch." From the outset, Sula's role as scapegoat is clearly established. The community's "conviction of Sula's evil changed them in accountable yet mysterious ways. Once the source of their personal misfortune was identified, they had to leave to protect and love one another. They began to cherish their husbands and wives, protect children, repair their homes and in general band together against the devil in their midst." (117-18).

What Banyiwa-Horne suggests is of paramount importance. Sula, she argues, "Becomes a pariah precisely because she rejects those values that aim at uniformity and stifle the self." Her willingness to reject them makes her "evil" to those in the community who never express their own "freedom of the will." Sula is "evil" because she, unlike Nel for example, does not live "Totally by the law" nor surrender "completely to it without questioning anything sometimes"; she is "Perfectly willing to think the unthinkable."

Directly speaking, Sula's rebelliousness manifests itself in several ways. Unlike other Medallion women, including Nel, Sula refuses to marry, settle down, and raise a family. Moreover, as insult to them she attends their church functions underwearless, buys and picks over their food, and "Tries out" and discards their husbands. She feels no obligation to please anyone unless she in turn gains pleasure. As she once confessed to Nel: "I got my mind. And what goes on in it" (43). Her determination to achieve self-fulfillment allows her to "Live in the world" (43), but not be caught up in the spiderweb-like life of the Bottom where she would be called upon to conform, to "dangle in dry places suspended by [her] own spittle more terrified of the free fall than the snake's breath below" (103-104).

At issue is the whole question of "good and evil," for if Nel Wright is positive (her names suggest as much), then Sula is the opposite. Yet Morrison does not assess this age-old concern in strictly religious, particularly Christian, terms. In Morrisonian discourse, evil is not a sin against God, per se. Conceptually, it is inverted to become a sin against oneself; it is one's failure to act existentially. Though Sula is viewed as evil, in the final analysis it is the Bottom's women, who do not "Protest God's will but acknowledge it and confirm . . . their conviction that the only way to avoid the Hand of God is to get in it" (66), who emerge as less attractive. They sit passively during the eulogy for Chicken Little with unfolded hands, "Like pairs of raven's wings" (65), suggesting a sense of total helplessness. What is significant, however, is that the Bottom community does not move to destroy or eradicate Sula from its midst. It tolerates her. Morrison explains that for blacks, "Evil is not an alien force; It's just a different force." In spite of her nonconformist behavior, Sula is tolerated until she commits the unpardonable sin of putting her grandmother in an old folks home. This is out of sync with the notion of "Neighborhood" — the extended compound where people care for and look after one another.

Paradoxically, for many critics, Morrison falls victim to traditional stereotypes in her treatment of Sula and the blacks of the Bottom. As noted earlier, Gayle sees her characters as "Primitives." While Odette Martin believes *Sula* "Breathes new life" into traditional Black stereotypes — with Eva as "The folk woman." Hannah as the "Primitive," Cecile Sabat as the "Tragic mulatto," and Sula sa the "exotic" — he associates these images with the romanticism of a "*Negritude* tradition," which he believes Morrison sets out to criticize. Martin concludes: "It is difficult to perceive that repeating images, even for critical purposes, is to provide them with certain legitimacy."

In the end what might be true, however, is suggested by Barbara Lounsberry and Grace Ann Hovet, who argue that Morrison is more interested in showing " the constriction and ultimate futility of any single ordering vision [traditional institutions such as church, family, state] within the black community." A desire to transcend the sterile soil of the Bottom, coupled with her need for independedce, lead Sula away from it. After years of traveling and pursuing an education, she returns, having discovered that the Bottom and Medallion are microcosmic of the world at large. They are thus as appropriate as any where else for her pursuit of self.

The Peace Women

The verbal exchange Sula has with her grandmother Eva upon returning to Medallion evolves around the impact the Peace women have on their progeny in her quest for authentic existence. In the midst of the conversation Eve asks

> "When you gone to get married? You need to have babies. It'll

settle you."

"I don't want to make somebody else. I want to make myself."

"selfish. ain't no woman got no business floatin' around without no man." (79-80)

On the one hand, Sula's existential pronouncement — "I want to make myself" — is in character, because it is the adult voice, the voice of Sula-as-woman, that we hear. Eva's defense of the traditional roles of women, on the other hand, might seem out of place at first, especially because her name suggests that she is at one (at peace) with herself and because her sense of wholeness does not center on traditional views of women as only wives and mothers. Thus, as Martin notes, "Sula is to be taken as opposed to telling culture to do so, especially since its definitions are negative ones."

During Sula's childhood, it appears that neither Eva nor Hannab served as a positive role model who enforced or exhibited a lifestyle of domestic tranquility or security. In fact, just the opposite appears true, for neither woman provided Sula with an "Intimate knowledge of marriage" (103). In the Peace house the women behaved like "all men [were] available," and so they "selected from among them with a care only for their taste" (103). Contrary to Chikwenye Okonjo Ogunyemi, however, they are not whores, like the prostitutes in *The Bluest Eye*. Their interest in men has to do with pleasure, not economics and pure hate. In fact, Eva and Hannah conformed to convention by marrying and raising families.

Their traditional behavior ends there, however. For example, although she was once married, Hannah never bothers to remarry after being left a widow. She gives Sula an unconventional image of womanhood and motherhood through her "sooty" lifestyle. "Hannah simply refused to live without the attentions of a man, after Rekus's death she had a steady sequence of lovers, mostly the husbands of her friends and neighbors" (36). Moreover, in her mother/daughter role, Hannah, who had not found Eva to be a loving mother, comes up short on the nurturing yardstick. She damages Sula's childhood by confessing that although she had the obligatory love of a parent for her child, she "Just, don't like her" (49). From her mother Sula would learn that "sex was pleasant and frequent, but otherwise unremarkable" (37-38). Consequently, Sula's lack of desire for domestic ties seems a natural legacy, for like the other Peace women, she "simply loved maleness, for its own sake" (41). Hannah's remark, however, will have the most lasting impact and lead Sula to the independence she strives for with her "experimental life" (102). Indirectly, Hannah has taught Sula that "There was no other [than self] that [one] could count on" (102).

That Sula has no feelings of self-disparagement must be attributed in part to her grandmother, Eva, as well. It is Eva's influence on the young Sula that leads her to accept the code of ethics practiced in the Peace home, disallowing any guilt over licentiousness or hint of inferiority, even though the community on the whole regards the Peace women as not merely unethical but socially unacceptable. Bottomites, such as Helene Wright, expected Sula to have her "Mother's slackness" (29); they are surprised to discover that she does not. When she meets Sula for the first time, "Helene's curdled scorn turned to butter" (29). Consequently, as Martin asserts, "While Sula's relationships function as an explicit criticism of Black values and patterns of behavior, they are also a vehicle for grasping Sula's real identity. She is neither evil nor a fixed, unchanging Absolute. Rather, as the sensual and the experimental, she represents potential: the raw energy of Life and the creative impulse of Art."

Such assesssment does not take into account the question of account-ability, which is Cynthia Dubin Edelberg's central argument when she questions the assertions Morrison makes relating to formal education, the work ethic, and the Bible through the untrammelled characters in her "Brutal fictional world." According to Edelberg, "The narrator in Morrison's novels does not permit the characters to succeed through channels generally thought to be useful and reliable." Specifically, in *Sula*, Edelberg maintains, "formal education is derided, characters with Biblical names live their namesakes' lives in reverse, and the omniscient narrator will not allow the all pervasive suffering to come to rest."

Edelberg offers a purely literal reading of Sula, making it a "grotesque though essentially realistic novel." Consequently, she overlooks the central ironies and contradictions of the text, as well as Morrison's propensity to topsy-turvy the norm for the sake of emphasis and exploraion. Although it is true that Sula "ridicules" education as one of the conventional ways that blacks have transcended their otherwise circum-scribed lives, she does take the pain to achieve formal training by going to college. Moreover, Morrison is an academic who, no matter what her connection with the world of letters as a writer or editor, continues to teach, lecture, visit, and assume residencies on college and university campuses across the United States, suggesting not only a belief in the value of these institutions and the educational process but, perhaps most important, a commitment to them. Her children, too, are being formally educated. Above all, however, it would be most contradictory for Morrison to create someone interested in her "Me-ness" and have that character defer self to a process that is often either restrictive or alienating. Consequently, Sula's rejection of formal education is in character. she is not about saving the race but herself.

More important, Edelberg overlooks the fact that Eva and Hannah provide the community of women that nurtures. Su1a, directly and indirectly, allowing her to see the alternatives available to her, as woman, wife, and mother. Although she questions traditional use (and misuse) of Christianty, Morrison seems more interested in examining the full implications of her characters' biblical names rather then in revealing the Bible as "The wrong book," as Edelberg also suggests.

Eva (Eve) provides the ideal, for she is the archetypal "great Mother." She is the numinous woman who embodies the feminine principle and, consequently, fulfills rather than mocks her name, as Edelberg suggests. Abandoned without a means of support by her husband, Boy Boy, Eva is forced to become self-sufficient and provide for herself and three children. Destitution forces her to leave them in a neighbor's care for eighteen months. When she returns, she has only one leg, but she has the economic wherewithal to support her family. Isolating herself in a room on the top of her home, Eva supervises the activities within, seldom descending to the lower level.

As the Great Mother, Eva nourishes and protects her family, providing sustenance and life. She reveals that meeting her children's needs is her primary concern when Hannah, who equates love with play, asks Eva about her love for her children. Eva explains that she never had time for recreation: "No time. They Wasn't no time. Not none. Soon as I got one day done here comes a night. With you all coughin' and me watchin' so TB wouldn't take you off and if you was sleepin' quiet I thought O Lord, they dead and put my hand over your mouth to feel if the breadth was comin' what you talk' 'bout did I love you girl I stayed alive for you can't you get that through your thick head" (60).

Eva's role as Great Mother is further exemplified in her efforts to save Hannah, her firstborn. Hannah has a prophetic dream in which she attends a wedding in a red dress; she later burns to death in spite of Eva's fervent attempt to save her. Seeing her daughter's dress on fire,

> Eva knew there was time for nothing in this world than the time it took to get there and cover her daughter's body with her own. She lifted her heavy frame up on her good leg, and with fists and arms smashed the windowpane. Using her stump as a support on the window sill, her good leg as lever, she threw herself out the window. Cut and bleeding she clawed the air trying to aim her body toward the flaming, dancing figure. She missed and came crashing down some twelve feet from Hannah's smoke. Stunned but still conscious, Eva dragged herself toward her firstborn. (65)

The emphasis here is strictly on the sacrificial role woman-as-mother is often called upon to assumed, a role Morrison will explore in depth in *Beloved.*

Eva is also seen in this role in her more successful effort to save Plum, her youngest child and only son. When constipation threatened his life in infancy, she unclogs his bowels with fingers lubricated with lard, "The last bit of food she had in the world. . . . And now that it was over, Eva squatted there [in the outhouse in the middle of a cold winter's night] to free his stool, and what was she doing down on her haunches with her beloved baby boy warmed by her body in the almost darkness, her shins and teeth freezing, her nostrils assailed" (34). That motherhood calls for sacrifices is clearly the point being made.

Although her role as Great Mother places Eva in a situation that requires her to sacrifice, if necessary, her life for her children's, Eva, as a complete sign of this archetype, must embody the dark side of this role as well. Consequently, she is also cast in the role of "Terrible Mother." Eva, like Eve, is inescapably the taker of life as well as the giver of life. She is, in other words, capable of devouring and destroying that which she has given life. She sacrifices herself, but she is also able to sacrifice her son, if and when necessary, as in the Adonisian myth.

When Plum returns from the war (which makes him a warrior, like Adonis) mired in heroine addiction, Eva is not able to accept his selfdestructive behavior, slovenliness, and diminishment to a mere shadow of himself. She takes away his life by engulfing him in fire, while he lays embraced in the warm thought of her love and the false sense of security induced by his narcotic state.

In what we at first perceive as a merciless, inhuman act, we find, although in exaggerated form, a lesson in the ultimate importance of the self-reliance that Sula must come to realize and accept. Scarred, too, like Shadrack, Plum seeks to escape independence through drugs rather than to act responsibly to establish an order and chart a direction for his fragmented life. His infantile behavior is a metaphor for lack of independence. He wanted to return to the womb, Eva explains, suggesting an act of "Bad Faith" on his part. "He wanted to crawl back into my womb. I ain't got the room no more even if he could do it. . . . And he was crawlin' back, being helpless and thinking baby thoughts and dreaming baby dreams and messing up his pants again and smiling all the time" (62).

As Eva suggests, what Plum sought was not incestuous co-habitation, but escape through rebirth and childhood. He wanted to become a child again, to return to the parental shelter she once offered, to avoid responsibility for self, as well as to be restored and made new. Unable to accept either her son's dependence or his inevitable decay, Eva destroys him. As she reminds Hannah, however, her love for Plum had not abated. She tells her: "I held him close first. Real close. Sweet Plum. My baby boy" (62).

Through Morrison's careful use of tropes throughout the passage we are able to find embedded in the text an excellent use of mythology for Plum's burning might also be viewed as an act of purgation — a rite of purification. The language here is filled with images and symbols of cleansing, renewal, and rebirth: "Plum on the rim of a warm light sleep . . . He felt twilight. Now there seemed to be some kind of wet light traveling over his legs and stomarch with a deep attractive smell. It wound itself — this wet light — all about him, splashing and running into his skin. He opened his eyes and saw what he imagined was the great wing of an eagle pouring a wet lightness over him. Some kind of baptism, some kind of blessing, he thought" (47). The images of wetness and light recall the embryonal fluid of the uterus, and the reference to "Twilight" signifies rebirth, the dawning of a new day. That his will be a more spiritual rebirth than a physical one is suggested by the eagle and the "Wet lightness" that it pours over Plum.

Ironically, then, Plum's death symbolically leads to new life, in the final analysis. In the dominant images of the warm fire and secure bed, we find semblances of the nurturing womb. Eva, in spite of her pronouncements, provides rebirth for her defiled son, suggesting why he remains her "Baby boy."

The passage resonates, on the one hand, with the traditional African's concept of escbatology, or afterlife. Death is perceived as a significant phase in a movement that includes birth, life, death, and rebirth that evolves from the African's cyclical concept of time. Thus, the notion of a world of the "Living dead" (a community of the departed) is prevalent in traditional African cosmology; here individuals are dead in body but not in spirit, especially if they are remembered by the surviving members of their family who remain in commune with him or her. Although death is a major theme in Sula, it, like the notion of evil, is not pursued strictly in the Western sense. Morrison explores such primordial human concerns from an Afro-centric perspective to illustrate the multifaceted responses of black life.

We must note, however, that her angle of vision is not limited to the Afro-centric alone; Plum's burning also recalls Western mythologies death and rebirth. This is most evident in the "deep attractive smell" and "great wing of an eagle" and in the reference to Plum's dirgelike lullaby and the comparison of Eva's movements with those of a heron. Together, they recall the purple-colored (note the significant use of the name Plum) phoenix (and its prototypes as the heron and eagle), whose power lies in its ability to die and resurrect itself.

Building its nest with the sweetest spices (Eva sees that Plum has been drinking what she thinks is a glass of strawberry crush soda), the phoenix sits, singing its sweetest song, (we hear this in his chuckles and Eva's lullaby), while its nest, ignited by the sun's ray (fire) is transformed into a pyre. From the ashes, a new phoenix emerges to transport the remains of its parents to Heliopole, the City of the Sun, for burial. Thus, this myth is often associated with the solar journey, which includes distinct phases of birth (sunrise) death (sunset), and rebirth (sunrise); phases that remain paramount to Eva's son (sun).

With this apparent allusion to the mythical phoenix and to traditional African cosmology, Morrison continues and in fact crystallizes the tropes and themes that will recur from this point on in her collected works, demonstrating not only her willingness to borrow from traditional myths but also to weave her own by merging Western, African, and African-American folk beliefs, mythologies, mysticism, and magic. For example, we find her placing at the center of her literary cosmology traditional notions of the significance of the elements: earth, air, water, fire. We saw them in The Bluest Eye in the failure of the seeds to grow in the earth.

Water images, prevalent in Sula, are for the most part associated with death, as with Chicken Little and the Bottomites who plunge to their death in the cave. But it is also aqua vitae, as in the case of Shardrack, whose vocation and avocation as a fisherman are intertwined with life. Fire, though associated with death, as in the case of Hannah, is also a form of ritual cleansing, and we see this with both Shadrack and Plum. Significant, too, are the natural cycles, such as the solar movement, which in Sula is associated with maleness; lunar cycles will be associated with females in later works. We find significant explorations of the role of womanhood and motherhood, of woman-as-woman, wife, and perhaps more important, as mother — a role that will be associated more with nurturing and nursing (with the mother's milk) than with the mere act of giving birth to children. Most important, however, is the fact that the meanings of these myths are approached from a black woman's point of view.

Thus, one might conclude that in Morrison's canon biblical myths are not necessarily debunked as much as they are expanded. We find ample evidence of this in Eva, who lives up to her name. Like the biblical Eve, she is the mother of life, "Of all living things." This explains the presence of so many different kinds of people living in her home as well as Eva's power to name and classify, visible in her treatment of the Deweys. Morrison expands Eva's character, forcing us to realize that Eva cannot be romanticized for her more benevolent qualities alone. Lighter and darker sides add to her complexity and credibility. She must simultaneously be the mother of Life and Death. Even in biblical mythology Death entered the world when Eve sinned, a point that Edelberg misses.

More important, however, is the fact that with Eva we have the ideal image of total self-reliance. Eva willingly makes choices. It is not coincidental that in treatment and characterization she emerges as a goddess, as builder and ruler of her own house. She builds and rules her dominion at 7 Carpenter's Road, which both in name and number suggests a creative act — the power of self-creation that one would associate with the divine power of a goddess (God created His world in seven days). She is "creator and sovereign" (26), and we see the world from her perspective.

Sula inherits as legacy from her community of women arrogance and self-indulgence: "Eva's and Hannah's self- indulgence merged in her and, with a twist that was all her own imagination, she lived out her days exploring her own thoughts and emotions, giving them full reign, feeling no obligation to please anybody unless their pleasure pleased her. As willing to feel pain as to give pain, to feel pleasure, hers was an experimental life" (102). It is thus not surprising that as an adult Sula "Went to bed with men as frequently as she could" (105), but it is also unsurprising that she rebelled against the traditional role of woman as wife and mother that her untraditional parents indirectly, if not directly, encouraged her to follow. Her promiscuity, however, must be considered an essential aspect of her "experimental life," her independence and self- reliance, not solely as a desire to be amoral.

Thus, in the Peace women — Eva Hannah, and Sula — we find the creative act of inversion, of topsy-turvydom that becomes a positive, creative force in the lives of Morrison's characters. Indeed, they act and feel good about their lives when they sabotage the status quo. In the final analysis, Morrison's Sula is warm, subjective, uninhibited, and irrational. She is a free spirit who is not bound by external mores and values. She declared to Nel:

> ". . . Me, I'm going down like one of those redwoods. I sure did live in this world."
> "Realy?" What have you go to show for it?"
> "Show?" To who? Girl, I got my mind. And what goes on in it. Which is to say, I got me."
> "Lonely, ain't it?"
> "Yes. But my lonely is mine." (123)

Here, Sula clearly suggests that, unlike Pecola, she is account- able to no one but herself for th direction of her life. Her determination to assume existential responsibility for self is indicated by her vociferous declaration: "I got my mind," the creative assertion that wills what one wishes. This act, indeed, given their histories, could not be expected from the Breedlove family.

In the end, however, Sula's untrammelled spirit remains problematic, for she seems to lack interest in assuming any res ponsibility for her fellow human beings. This apparent lack may explain why she dies so early in the novel, although she is never outrightly expelled by the community. Barbara Christian concludes that "Morrison resists the idea that either individual pursuit or community conservatism is enough for fulfillment. Left without a context, the self has 'no speck from which to grow' (103), and deprived of creative spirits, the community succumbs to death and destruction."

Nel Wright

In the midst of Sula's chaotic youth, one constant remained to provide sanctuary: Nel, who throughout their childhood together, had been a complementary force. For Sula, Nel became a confidante, a source of security, especially after Sula overheard Hannah's remarks about love and like. Their friendship became so close that they "Themselves had difficulty distinguishing one's thought from the other" (72).

Yet it must be argued that their relationship was not simply one of being-for-the-other; for there was reciprocity, although ironically during their childhood it was Nel who led and Sula who followed: "They were solitary little girls whose loneliness was so profound it intoxicated them and sent them stumbling into Technicolored visions that always included a presence, a someone, who, quite like the dreamer, shared the delight of the dream" (44).

During their childhood Nel and Sula were "daughters of distant mothers and incomprehensible fathers" (44). Conformity, making things right (as her name "Wright" suggests), was the operative word in Nel's home. In her effort to escape her past, which included a prostitute mother, Helene, Nel's mother, "saw more comfort and purpose than she had ever hoped to find in this life" (15) through her daughter. Consequently, she reared her daughter on principles of obedience and politeness: "any enthusiasm that little Nel showed was calmed by the mother until she drove her daughter's imagination underground" (16).

Nel recaptures her sense of self and aborts the role her properly behaved mother had identified for her when, after a trip down South, she discovers her mother's frailty and fears. "I am me," she whispers. "Me. . . . I'm me. I'm not their daughter. I'm not Nel. I'm me. Me" (24). This self-reclamation, this certainty of identity, becomes a creative act that makes Nel self-reliant. Nel's confidence and Sula's insecurity formed the foundation of the reciprocity that characterized their friendship, providing them with the most important relationship in their lives. For Sula, Nel was "The other half of her equation" (105); together they formed a whole. "They found relief in each other's personality" (45). By the time they reach adulthood, however, the tables turn. Sula displays a desire to live outside the norm, to lead rather than to follow. Nel, on the other hand, succumbs to the expected and becomes a wife and mother through her marriage to Jude Green.

Sula's unconventional standards and life-style, coupled

with the fact that as girls she and Nel had "Never quarreled . . . the way some girlfriends did over boys or competed against each other for them" (72), lead Sula to bed with Nel's husband, after she returns to Medallion. But Sula and Nel are no longer adolescents, and Sula's action serves only to destroy the friendship — the most meaningful experience she had known. Although she had considered Nel "The closest thing to both an other and a self" (103), she discovers that "she and Nel were not one and the same thing" (103). In the end, then, Sula's return is not to the community — that is, to traditional values, for these are counterproductive in her view. She returns to a friendship, which, paradoxically, she destroys.

In her unconventional view of life, Sula makes a distinction between sex and friendship — a view that Nel, in her conventionality, does not share. For Sula, sex, though "Pleasant and frequent," is "Unremarkable," unlike her remarkable friendship with Nel. Admitting to Nel that they were "good friends," Sula, years later, is unable to see the wrong she committed. She tells Nel: "What you mean take him away? I didn't kill him, I just fucked him. If we were such good friends, how come you couldn't get over it" (125).

Nel's marriage to Jude, however, had given her an identity that required her to forfeit the necessary sense of self that remains salient to Sula. Because jude's subsequent departure left Nel with "Thighs (that) were really empty" (95), as Byerman correctly notes, "The loss of Jude is the loss of identity and the loss of life. . . . [Nel] now becomes 'a woman without a man' and unable to raise her eyes. For this change she blames Sula, who, without a sense of ownership, cannot conceive of Jude as an object to be taken."

What is important for Sula is the friendship she had nurtured and developed with Nel in the midst of a world that promised fragmentation. Emphasis is placed on their having been "girls *together.*" It is their togetherness — their friendship together — that led to their sense of individualism. Ironically, the significance of their togetherness is what Nel, who thought she had missed Jude all along, realizes in the end. It is the multifaceted signification of being "girls together" — and above all its loss — that is echoed in Nel's excruciating declaration: "We was girls together . . . O Lord, Sula . . . girl, girl, girlgirlgirl" (149).

Morrison is definite and calculating in her presentation of the depth of friendship between black women. In a conversation with Claudia Tate, she confesses to wanting to write about such friendship: "When I wrote *Sula,* I knew I was going to write a book about good and evil and about friendship. Seemed to me that black women have friends in the old-fashioned sense of the word."

By providing Sula and Nel with the secret of Chicken Little's accidental death, and specifically by having Nel provide the strength and support Sula needed at the moment, Morrison further united them in a manner that would bond them for eternity. Although the action was Sula's, the involvement, as Eva would later point out, was clearly theirs together. After all, Nel suggests the cover-up when she tells Sula, "*Let's go. We can't bring him back*" (146). Eva is thus correct when years later she questions Nel:

> "Tell me how you killed that little boy?"
> "What? What little boy?"
> "The one you threw in the water . . ."

"I didn't throw no little boy in the river. That was Sula."
"You. Sula. What's the difference?"
". . . Never was no difference between you." (144-145)

In the end, then, Sula and Nel are vital parts of the same personality. Together they form a whole in spite of their differences. According to Morrison, although Nel has limitations and lacks Sula's imagination, "They are very much alike. They complement each other. They support each other."

Men in *Sula*

That this unique level of friendship generally does not exist between men and women is suggested in Morrison's treatment of male-female relationships. For the most part, the men in *Sula* are superficial, immature, untrustworthy, and anonymous, as is suggested by their names Jude (Judas), Green (naive), Boy Boy (infantile), Chicken Little(fearful) and diminutive), the Deweys (anonymous), and so forth. The negative aspects of their names are most visible when juxtaposed with the empowering names of the women. The men's behavior, for the most part, is less than heroic — even Ajax's, whose name is obviously borrowed from a Greek warrior. Each leaves a community of abandoned women. This abandorunent becomes the impetus for Eva, the paradigmatic woman who must rebound through assertiveness and self-reliance or be lost, after she and her children are deserted by her husband/their father. She does rebound through the powerful symbolic act of building her own house, establishing her own territory, the sanctum of her mind (consciousness), "sixty feet from Boy-Boy's one-room cabin" (30).

Thus Eva's domicile is more than a "ramshackle house"

with boarders and stray beings, as some critics argue. There would be no "Men in the house, no men to run it" (35). It is not uncommon for critics to claim that the male-female relationships in *Sula* are often marked by mental and physical violence. Hovet and Lounsberry do not offers such a simplistic view, but instead propose more complex courses that may explain the tension in these relationships, including the provocative one that "The 'diminishment' of the black male may be caused by excessive 'mothering,' by both black wives and mother, as well as by social discrimination."

Even self willed Sula becomes a victim when, in her pivotal and at first nontraditionanl relationship with Ajax, she goes against the lessons her grandmother taught her and even her own personal convictions. The results are fatal. At first, the relationship provides not only physical and sexual completion but also what seems like spiritual wholeness in the form of love. Sula is attracted to him because of "His refusal to baby or protect her, his assumption that she was both tough and wise"(10). He is attracted to her because "[h]er elusiveness and indifference to establish habits of behavior reminded him of his mother,"(109) "an evil conjure woman"(109). Unlike her previous relationships, this one gives her "real pleasure," from a gift bearer who showers her with butterflies, wild berries, stolen bottles of milk, and "Meal fried porgies wrapped in a salmon colored sheet of the *Pittrburgh Courier*"(108). At first, reciprocity is the operative word in their relationship. And indeed this should be expected because they consummate their relationship in Eva's house, where individualism formed the foundation. Moreover, Ajax not only speaks to her but also listens and recognizes her brilliance. Assuming that she is tough and wise, he shuns chauvinism and refuses paternalism. she dominates him at times, and in their lovemaking she has an equal share as a contributing partner.

In the metamorphosis that occurs in their relationship, however, Sula confuses love with possession. She transforms Eva's house into a domestic haven where "The bathroom was gleaming, the bed was made and the table was set for two" (113). Perhaps the ultimate indications of change, however, are the green ribbons that she places in her hair and her invitation that Ajax become dependent upon her: "come on. Lean on me" (115). Ajax, a would-be pilot, abruptly walks out of her life, leaving her "With nothing but stunning absence" (115). The depth of the consequence of Sula's deferment of self becomes apparent when she later discovers that she does not even know his correct name: Albert Jack. She concludes: "If I didn't know his name, then there is nothing I did know and I have known nothing ever at all" (117). Sula seems here to learn the lessons Pecola's life had served to teach. Having sought authenticity and verification externally, that is, from her relationship with others, she had become vulnerable to the dictates of others, which led to a greater sense of liminality and invisibility. Failing to continue her course of self-definition by aborting her heretofore uncompromising values, Sula is no longer self-reliant. This, too, brings on her death, which, much like Pecola's insanity, is inevitable.

Shadrack

Shadrack, the Bottom's jester/fisherman, is more successful in maintaining an authentic self. Through him, Morrison explores the experiences of a person who is in the midst of individuation, a process that, according to Swiss psychiatrist

Carl Jung, involves becoming "a single homogeneous being, becoming the unique person that one in fact is." Indeed, Shadrack, like to Bottomites, is interested in finding out what he is about, is involved in a. quest for psychological wholeness.

Before coming to the Bottom, Shadrack had spent a year in a mental institution, where he had been placed after his brutalizing World War I experience left him physically and psychologically handicapped. After witnessing the death of a fellow soldier in an explosion that he survives, Shadrack, like his biblical namesake, emerges from the conflagration. Here, too, we find the image of the phoenix. He is nevertheless scarred by his encounter with death.. A neurotic who believes that his hands have grown to monstrous proportions, Shadrack has no sense of who or what he is. Left practically in a state of tabula rasa, or blankness, he remains unbalanced and suffers from having "No past, no language, no tribe, no source, no address book, no comb, no pencil, no clock, no pocket handkerchief, no rug, no bed, no can opener, no faded postcard, no soap, no key, no tobacco pouch, no soiled underwear and nothing nothing nothing to do" (10). As Ogunyemi explains, Shadrack's "apparent madness is Morrison's cynical commentary on a world gone awry . . . Shadrack somehow survives the fire of war but remains a ghost of his former self."

That Shadrack is faced with fragmentation is indicated by his desire to tie together :the loose cords in his mind"(8). Unable to do so immediately, during a moment of cogitation, he allows his mind "To slip into whatever cave mouths of memory it chose" (8). During the ensuing dream, he sees a "Window that looked out on a river which he knew was full of fish [and] someone was speaking softly just outside the door"(8). Considering this dream a roadmap to his identity, Shadrack sets out to find, upon his release from the institution, the setting he had envisioned. He finds it in Medallion, his former home, which was only twenty-two miles away.

In her development and treatment of Shadrack's effort to cement the "Loose cords" in his mind, Morrison establishes a pattern of action that parallels Jungian ideas related to the definition and function of the psyche and its fundamental components: the self, ego, shadow, anima (female) and animus (male). Most important, she uses Jung's concepts of the conscious and the unconscious selves, which function in a compensatory manner to maintain an ordering and unifying center of the total psyche. Using dreams (and particularly "Big Dreams") as vehicles, the "collective Unconscious," whose contents include "all future things that are taking in shape in [the individual] and will sometime come Consciousness," is continuously engaged in dramatization, Jung argued, which leads to a harmonious relationship between it and the conscious mind. Its archetypes or spontaneous symbols provide the pieces to the puzzle that the individual needs to complete the self.

It is within the realm of the dramatization that the significance of Shadrack's experience during his institutionalization can be best understood. For it is the workings of his collective unconscious, grouping and regrouping its contents in an effort to strike a balance with its conscious mind, that provide Shadrack with the dream and specific images and symbols that, when understood by his conscious mind, set him on the path to transformation and rebirth that result in actualization and wholeness. As we learn from the narrator,

Shadrack's mind slips into whatever "cave mouths of memory it chooses." What the narrator suggests here is that Shadrack's mind is reacting to his experience in such a way that indelible memory patterns can be produced. From this involuntary process, Shadrack is able to secure relevant data that will assist him in striking the balance he desperately needs and seeks.

That Shadrack plunges into the depth of his collective unconscious in search of self is suggested by Morrison's careful use of language and tropes. Such words as *memory* and *cave* can be taken as symbols of the unconscious. Whereas memory is often associated with a place in the unconscious where time and space emerge, of temporary subliminal content, cave is a common symbol for the unconscious itself. Also important are the images Shadrack see: the window and the river. Although it would vary from individual to individual in Jungian analysis, the window might very well symbolize the conscious, that which looks out or is outwardly seen. The river, a body of water, is the commonest symbol of the collective unconscious. Shadrack's dream, then, one might assume, means that he is on a path of seeking harmony between the two important components of the self: the conscious and unconscious, with this descent into the collective unconscious. For Morrison, this would be termed the act of *re-memory*.

Dreams are not only compensator but also, for Jung, prospective or antieipatory: through them the unconscious anticipates future conscious achievements and offers them to the conscious in sketches (rough drafts). Thus, Shadrack's dream might be taken to represent not only his search for psychological wholeness but also a luminous moment that reveals the very vehicle he needs to achieve it. In the final analysis, he realizes that he has a place where the window, river, and voices are. By descending into the unconscious through his dream, Shadrack is able to emerge — to ascend — experience rebirth from a fragmented life and begin to find tangible meaning and order.

Assured of some tangible direction for his life, Shadrack sets out on a journey to self, which not coincidentally is one that he has been involved in all his life: at twenty-two years of age he is twenty-two miles from the setting of his dream, Medallion, the self. As a final indication of his determination to find and accept this self, Shadrack, while briefly incarcerated, forces himself to confront it by looking at his reflection in the toilet bowl in his cell: "There in the toilet water he saw a grave black face. A black so definite, so unequivocal, it admonished him. He had been harboring a skittish apprehension that he was not real — that he didn't exist at all. But when the blackness greeted him with its indisputable presence, he wanted nothing more" (11).

In this symbolic act of self-reflection, Shadrack, at this stage fundamentally devoid of ego and persona, sees his true self in yet another symbolic descent into the unconscious. But in contrast to his dream, which is involuntary, his action here, which involves a confrontation of his physical self, is willful. Significantly, he sees a self that is tied to race, the missing, tangible element that must be restored if the whole self — psychological and physical — is to emerge. In the end, then, it is his lost personal history that he desperately needs to tie the loose ends in his mind. He, like Sula, but unlike pecola, chooses to accept who he is historically rather than try to escape from it.

Accepting the blackness that greets him becomes a creative, existential act that leads Shadrack toward an authentic existence. It provides him with an umbilical attachment to history, collective and personal, and consequently to the needed grounding available to him him in Medallion alone, which we may now clearly see as not only a metaphor for his created self but also, given what we know about the Bottom and its residents, a self that embodies the African-American experience. The toilet bowl and cell thus become tropes for his legacy of oppression and suffering. Ironically, they are nurturing wombs (water is the crucial element), from which his ultimate rebirth will take place.

To reach the desired level of authenticity, however, Shadrack must transcend the one remaining impediment: his fear of death and dying. To do so, he founds National Suicide Day on which to confront both and thus affix some order to his life. Finally achieving a desired level of self-affirmation, shadrack behaves in a manner revelatory of a totally self-derived and controlled individual. Like Sula, he spurns social prescriptions. He walks about with his penis exposed, urinates in front of ladies and girls, curses white people, drinks in the street from the mouth of the bottle, and shouts and shakes in the street.

His unconventional behavior alienates him from the Bottom community, which considers him a lunatic. He lives, literally and figuratively, on the outskirts of the Bottom, suggesting, like Sula's birthmark, his status as pariah, as outsider. What seems true, however, is that his encounter with his deeper unconscious self integrates his anima side, freeing him from the binding effects of the ego, leaving him unsaddled by inhibitions, fears, hiopes, and the ambitions (values) of those around him. And perhaps more important, it allows him to turn his world topsy-turvy. Because he is not being ego centered and is controlled to some degree by his "shadow," or darker side, as his name clearly suggests, Shadrack has to be viewed as immoral or amoral by those who become "the Other," although for him these values are the embodiment of authentic existence and creativity.

Yet Morrison does not suggest through her characterization of Shadrack that he should function as a role model in the Bottom for others. Shadrack carries no symbol of power of authority akin to Eva's scepter-like crutches; nor does he demand that others conform to a life like his. He is, in the final analysis, prophet-as-doer/actor — who, as his biblical name implies, determines the direction of his own life, regardless of the outcome — rather than prophet-as-speaker/ leader, who dictates the actions of others.

This is true even of his action each 3 January. Although his ritual on National Suicide Day has become "Part of the fabric of life up in the Bottom," his is a "solitary parade"(13), in which he converts the Bottom into a ritual ground for his own rite of cleansing and rejuvenation. When the generally passive Bottomites decide to follow Shadrack in "a pied piper's band" (137), they plunge to their deaths. Ironically, as the narrator tells us, "They knew Shadrack was crazy but that did not mean that he didn't have any sense or, even more important, that he had no power" (12). But his power is over self. This reminds us of what Morrison tells Claudia Tate, "If you own yourself, you can make some types of choices, take certain kinds of risks." It is not oincidental that he survives.

It is also unsurprising that the only person to gain insight into Shadrack's complexity is Sula. Like him, she occupies a position as communal scapegoat and pariah. Sula affirms their bond and establishes an intuitive relation with shadrack when, after accidentally drowning a playmate, she goes to Shadrack's cabin to confirm what, if anything, he has witnessed. She is immediately startled by the contrast between the externally chaotic and disarrayed Shadrack and the neatness and order, the restfulness, peacefulness, and secure quality of his simple abode, a symbol of the degree of wholeness he possesses. she thinks, "Perhaps this was not the house of Shad . . . with its made-bed? With its rag rug and wooden table?" (53). When Shadrack arrives to find her there, he welcomes his only visitor ever with a simple "always," an apparent answer to an unspoken question.

His answer may allude to a question of the permanence of life, or so he would have us believe. It could, however, express the opposite, which he would later discover to be true: death is the only given in life. It alone will "always" endure, as year later the incident on New Rive Road would further suggest. Ironically, those who had gone down into the watery grave were attempting to destroy vicariously (undoubtedly now too late) those who in killing their dreams had relegated them to a life deferred. They ended up killing themselves, now physically rather than merely symbolically as in the past.

In the end Shadrack's "always" must also refer to the single most important act of adhering "always" to one's personal convictions. Paradoxically, Sula takes flight, totally unaware of not only the importance of this lesson but the complexity of its implications, as her life with Ajax would eventually bear out. Yet, the imparting of the lesson was of significant importance to Shadrack, who three years before had dreamed about her visit in his dream of the window, river, and voices, doubtlessly those of Sula's and Nel's, outside his cabin door.

Shocked into Separateness: Unresolved Oppositions in *Sula**

Like *The Bluest Eye, Sula* is based on the underlying condition that fragmentation and displacement are the fundamental barriers to the formation of African-American identities. Whereas the first novel probes the pernicious effects of the imposition of external standards on the black community, in *Sula* Morrison more explicitly constructs a system of binary oppositions and simultaneously unravels it. Here, Morrison becomes overtly deconstructive, writing "What the French call *diffférance*, that feminine style that opens the closure of binary oppositions and thus subverts many of the basic assumptions of Western humanistic thought" (Rigney, Voices 3). By moving into the split, Morrison scrutinizes the ambivalent counterforces of fusion and fragmentation.

In this novel, the most important of the oppositions is between self and other. Displaced as they are by the racial dichotomy, characters in *Sula* are drawn into the traditional Western misconception that assumes the existence of a unitary self and that privileges self over other. They assume that they must have an originary self and/or that they can acquire it with or through an other. Morrison thereby directs attention to one potential response to the characters' fragmentation: fusion with another person in the attempt to solidify one's

* From Dangerous Freedom by Philip Page.
Philip Page. *Dangerous Freedom: Fusion and Fragmentation in Toni Morrison's Novels*. Jackson: University Press of Mississippi, 1995.

identity. Whereas the characters in *The Bluest Eye* tend to fold inward in their attempts to define themselves, the characters in *Sula* look outward to relationships with significant others. Such pairs involve parent and child, heterosexual couples, and peers—most fully the relationship between Sula and Nel.

In *Sula* Morrison depicts a rigidly bipolar world, one in which the falsifications and privileging are so extreme that the tensions between opposed terms are overwhelming, as attested by the novel's numerous deaths. As the novel documents this bipolarity and the concomitant tensions, however, it undercuts that system and privileges a fluid, open, and liberating perspective. Sula, forced to become exile and then pariah, personifies this new freedom that dares to reject the old dichotomies and to create a new kind of identity. Both the character and the novel become representative of divisions within the American and African- American cultures.

As in *The Bluest Eye* the world in *Sula* is inverted and the mode is ironic, but in *Sula*, as Deborah McDowell asserts, Morrison strikes a more elegiac chord ("'self" 85n). The dedication to Morrison's two sons looks ahead to their mother's sense of loss after their departure: "This book is for Ford and Slade, whom I miss although they have not left me." The epigraph from Tennessee Williams *The Rose Tattoo* also evokes the pathos of loss, the loss of "glory," both for oneself and in the eyes of others: "Nobody knew my rose of the world but me. . . . I had too much glory. They don't want glory like that nobody's heart." In the novel's first sentence, the narrator grieves for the loss of the Bottom: "There was once a neighborhood" (3). Every chapter includes the physical or spiritual death of at least one African American (Reddy 29), and the plot culminates with Sula's death and the tunnel disaster.

As the novel spans the destructive years from World War I through the Depression to the threshold of World War II in 1941 (the year in which *The Bluest Eye* is set) to 1965 and the civil rights movement, it becomes an elegy for victims of war, poverty, and racial violence. Morrison refers to "The nostalgia, the histoy and the nostalgia for the history" in this novel ("Unspeakable" 222), and Melissa Walker describes it in terms of "Late sixties nostalgia for a lost but not so distant world" (120). After Sula's death, the mourning becomes more poignant, first when Shadrack grieves for his lost friend: "she lay on a table there. It was surely the same one. The same little-girl face, same tadpole over the eye. So he had been wrong. Terribly wrong. No 'always' at all. Another dying away of someone whose face he knew" (157-58). Then the mourning escalates further when Nel cries for her lost friendship with Sula: "We was girls together. . . . O Lord, Sula . . . girl, girl, girlgirlgirl" (174). Like many contemporary African-American novels, *Sula* eulogizes a lost community and a lost past.

The displacements begin with the novel's setting, which begins with the first sentence: "In that place, where they tore the nightshade and blackberry patches from their roots to make room for the Medallion City Golf Course, there was once a neighborhood." As Morrison explains, this lost world is fragmented into oppositions: place/neighborhood, they/ neighbors (and implicitly whites/blacks), nightshade/ blackberry, roots/ MedaWon, houses/golf course, and past/ present ("Unspeak-able" 221). The larger community is divided between town and Bottom, and the division is ironic, based on the fraud of the "Nigger joke" (4) that initiated the racial division of the land, which exemplifies Ellison's "Joke at the center of the American identity" (Shadow 54).

In *Sula* many issues are depicted in terms of opposing values or terms. The present is directly contrasted with the past, and female and male roles are opposed. The Wrights, the Greenes, and the Bottom itself are studies in social conformity, which is set against the individual freedom of the Peaces. The story of Nel and Sula becomes an investigation of the meanings of good and evil, the values associated with monogamy and promiscuity, and the relevance of innocence and experience. By what it leaves out as well as by what it includes, the novel contrasts presence and absence. And, especially through Sula's meditations on her identity, the novel explores the relationship between self and other.

The novel is thus posited on a binary structure. Its setting is divided between the Bottom and Medallion, a black community and an anonymous white town, a neighborhood and a golf course. Its plot chronicles the lives of two opposed characters who grow up in two opposed houses managed under two opposed theories of child-rearing. The character pairings of Nel and Sula are doubled in the pairings of their contrasting mothers (Helene and Hannah) and grandmothers (Rochelle and Eva). As opposed to the differences in these female pairs, the men in Nel and Sula's lives are similar but also paired: each woman lacks a brother or male friend, each has an absent father, and each has her most significant heterosexual relationship with a self-doubting man who departs abruptly (Jude and Ajax). The plot opposes the highly individualized black characters and the nameless, featureless white characters who hover on the fringes. It opposes the sane residents of the Bottom and the insane Shadrack, whose well-ordered cabin represents a further dichotomy with his disorderly behavior. It sets children in opposition to adults, most notably in mothers' lack of love or liking for their children. It contrasts meaningful employment, such as construction work, and demeaning labor in hotels and white homes.

To reinforce this pattern of binary opposites, *Sula* is divided almost exactly into halves, a dyadic structure that is reinforced by the nearly palindromic pattern in which the introduction of characters in Part I is reversed in the dispensation of characters in Part II (Grant 95). In addition, the novel is split between a linear structure, implied by the inexorable march of years in the chapter titles, and a circular one, suggested by the narrator's frame that starts the discourse after the Bottom has already disappeared.

The narrative form of this novel, in contrast to *The Bluest Eye*, also reveals a binary pattern. Whereas in Morrison's first novel the conventional distinction between external narrator and character breaks down in the polyvocal narration, in *Sula*, except for two paragraphs in which Nel narrates directly (105, 111), the distinction between external narrator and characters is maintained. Moreover, the narrator/character distinction is underscored by the opening section, which highlights the narrator's historical knowledge and vast distance from the characters' perspectives.

Correspondingly, the conventional distinction between an external narrator and the reader is forcefully maintained in *Sula*. This narrator, unlike Morrison's chatty narrator in *Jazz*, establishes her credentials and her distance from the reader in the opening chapter and maintains that separation throughout., The narrator rarely permits dialogue between characters, thus retaining tight control over the telling of the story. The narrator manipulates readers, forcing the story onto them, shocking them with sudden violence, making them question their responses to such characters as Eva and Sula, delaying crucial information (such as Jude's adultery with Sula), leaving frustrating gaps between years, omitting important scenes (such as Plum's and Hannah's funerals), not reporting what happens to Eva or Sula when they leave the Bottom, and not relating what happens to Jude or Ajax after they depart. The narrator also shocks readers with mysterious beginnings of chapters (such as "It was too cool for ice cream" [49] or "Old people were dancing with little children" [79]) and teases them by reversing the normal order of things (as when she reports the second strange thing before the first (67). Not only highly controlling, the narrator is also noticeably omniscient, with access not only to many characters' thoughts but also to the collective feelings of the community, for example when she describes the narrow lives of the Bottom's women (122) or the hope that seduces everyone into the last National Suicide Day parade (160).

At the same time that *Sula* is constructed on a system of binary opposites, the novel subverts that structure. Perhaps the clearest example of this deconstructing is the play between linear chronology and circularity. As many commentators have noticed, the novel purports to move steadfastly forward through time, as its chapter titles suggest, but even as it does so, it moves backward and forward, circling or spiraling through time. As Denise Heinze (122-23) and Maxine Lavon Montgomery (128) suggest, the novel's double perspective of linearity and circularity reflects a fusion of Euro-American and traditional African conceptions of time.

This subversion of Western linearity represents Morrison's attack on traditional, white-imposed conceptions. Although McDowell states that "The narrative retreats from linearity" ("'self'" 86), the strategy is not a retreat but the assertion of an alternative. While *The Bluest Eye* primarily laments the imposition of white, dualistic standards, *Sula* confronts such standards, loosens them, and advocates a nonlinear response. That perspective is suggested by Christian, who argues that the novel is about "The search for self . . . continually thwarted by the society from which Sula Peace comes" (Black Women 153), and by Kathryn Bond Stockton, who states that *Sula* confronts "The reign of white gender" that "seduces blacks away from the Bottom's communal bonds into the tight configuration of the couple" (94).

The novel's alternative position leads to its often perplexing openness. Robert Grant documents the novel's emphasis on the lack of a coherent subject and consequently on missing objects (Eva's leg and comb), absent or missed characters (Chicken Little, Ajax, Sula), and objects that evoke missing persons (Sula's belt, Jude's tie) (95-96). These gaps and discontinuities create holes in the text that unhinge any straightforward narration, thereby calling into question traditional means of representation and allowing for greater reader participation. For Grant the novel thereby becomes "a prime 'postmodernist text whose interpretational difficulties are a function of Morrison's calculated indeterminacies" (94). Similarly, the novel raises but leaves "Largely unresolved" the issue of good and evil (Butler-Evans 88), an issue that Morrison has said she deliberately dealt with in a non-Westem, that is to say, nonoppositional, manner. Placing this alternative stance in the context of feminine writing, Barbara Rigney claims that the emphasis on absence, ambiguity, multiple perspectives, and fragmentation creates a novel that, "Like all of Morrison's works, subverts concepts of textual unity and defies totalized interpretation" *(voices 32).*

The deconstructive implications of this open perspective are implied by Hortense Spillers, who contends throughout her essay for the creative openness of *Sula*, and are spelled out in detail by McDowell, who quotes Spillers ("No Manichean analysis demanding a polarity of interest — black/white, male/female, good/bad — will do" ["'self'" 80]). For McDowell, "*Sula* is rife with liberating possibilities in that it transgresses all deterministic structures of opposition." "The narrative insistently blurs and confuses . . . binary oppositions" and "glories in paradox and ambiguity as it creates "a world that demands a shift from an either/or orientation to one that is both/and, full of shifts and contradictions" ("'self'" 79-80).

Like a jazz composition, Sula sounds a traditional Euro-American motif, a structure of binary oppositions. Simultaneously, it plays on that motif, modifying it, refiguring it, subverting it, fusing it with non-Westem values. The result is a complex doubling, or multiplying, of perspectives, content, and form that embodies and challenges both Euro-American and African-American standpoints and that enables Morrison to fret out the fragments in a simultaneously fused and unfused whole.

Whereas *The Bluest Eye* examines isolated individuals who are split from meaningful relationships with community, family, or friend, in *Sula* characters respond to their bipolar world by attempting to create personal meaning through intimacy with another person. Such attempted dyads allow the characters temporary relief from their isolation and thus help them endure the frustrations of their marizinalized and divided lives, but they provide no lasting solution.

As this novel focuses on potential paired characters, it noticeably lacks emphasis on larger groups. There is no triad of intimate women, like the three prostitutes in *The Bluest Eye*,

Pilate-Reba-Hagar in *Song of Solomon*, or Sethe-Beloved-Denver in Beloved. The corresponding group is Eva-Hannah-Sula, but these three women constitute a much less cohesive unit than the other triads, as evidenced by the negation in their relationships (Eva had no time to love Hannah, Hannah does not like Sula, and Sula exiles Eva to the county home). Though tied by blood in a direct matrilineal line, they are a dis-unit, a deconstructed unit. The tensions between their unity and their separateness figure the pervading tensions in *Sula* between *any* structure and its decomposition. The only united triad is the deweys, but their unity is achieved at the expense of each boy's individuality, as suggested by their namelessless. Their stunted physical and mental growth attests to the parodic and inverted nature of their relationship and thus symbolizes the lack of viability of such groups in this novel.

Pairs of characters in Sula frequently attempt unions — most notice — ably between parent and child, in heterosexual couples, and between peers — but such unions are often short-lived and always problematic. As a result, like the frozen blades of grass during the ice storm, the characters remain "shocked into separateness" (152). At the end of the novel, Nel senses the isolation: "Now there weren't any places left, just separate houses with separate televisions and separate telephones and less and less dropping by" (166).

One type of attempted pair is mother and child (men are so consistently absent that no father/child relationships exist). Daughters, such as Hannah and Sula, desire closer relationships than their mothers can provide: Eva has no time or energy to love Hannah, and Hannah in turn, like her friends, expresses her dislike for her daughter. Mother-daughter relations are even more insecure in Nel's family, where Helene and her mother Rochelle are permanently estranged, where Helene's version of motherhood is to mold Nel (literally by trying to reshape her nose and figuratively by eliminating her individuality) into her own concept of white respectability, and where Nel looks upon her own children as a burden. Throughout the Bottom, except for the artificial period when people use their fear of Sula's alleged evil to rally behind each other, mothers (such as Teapot's Mamma) treat their children as difficult objects rather than as loved human beings. Nevertheless, although mother-daughter relationships appear to lack closeness and love, they do so only in comparison to a traditionally white ideal. As in *The Bluest Eye*, where imposed white standards of beauty and value are set against contrasting black standards, here white stereotypes of parent-child harmonies are implicitly contrasted with more fluid communal values. Mothers may not love or like their daughters in the ideal of the Dick-and-Jane myth, but through belief in communal values, even though such values are not ideal, mothers endure, holding their households and the community together.

Mother-son relationships are just as problematic. Like Sethe's murder of Beloved, Eva must murder Plum out of love, when the alternative for him is worse than death, in his case because he has lost his selfhood. Three Bottom sons — the deweys — are divorced from their mothers, adopted by Eva, and in the process lose their individuality and chance for maturity. Although they are fused with each other, like Plum they are isolated from themselves and society. Another Bottom son, Jude, tries to establish a motherly relationship with his wife Nel, and another son, Ajax, does love his mother, but their overpowering relationship (he "Worship[s]" her [126]) seems to prevent him from forming a lasting commitment to anything except airplanes: "This woman Ajax loved, and after her —airplanes. There was nothing in between." As Baker writes, Ajax "Is properly understood . . . not as 'his own man,' but as the offspring of his mother's magic" (*Workings* 153).

Characters also attempt significant relationships as heterosexual couples. Except for the marriage between Helene and Wiley (which presumably lasts because Wiley is so seldom at home), all such pairs (Eva-BoyBoy, Nel-Jude, and Sula-Ajax) are temporary. More successful are Hannah's brief, unthreatening, and mutually satisfying affairs with the Bottom's husbands. More viable is Eva's household and her role as mentor for young married couples. More enduring is the community itself, which provides an alternative form of integration to the couple.

The attempted fusion with another person is most fully exemplified in Sula and Nel's relationship. Critics agree that the two are nearly fused," the critical agreement deriving from the textual evidence of Sula and Nel's near merger into one consciousness. In her pubescent dreams each one fantasizes the presence of the other, a sympathetic female presence with whom the romantic adventure can be shared (51). When they actually meet, their psyches are already half-united: they are instantly like "Old friends" (52), they share "Their own perceptions of things" (55), and they are "Joined in mutual admiration." Later, they have "difficulty distinguishing one's thoughts from the other's" (83), they share one eye (147), and Eva alleges that "Never was no difference between [them]" (169).

Despite this near fusion, Sula and Nel are almost opposites, as suggested by their mutual fascination with the other's house and family. As Baker notes, their fantasies betray their opposing destinies (Workings 146-47): Nel passively "Wait[s] for some fiery prince" who "approached but never quite arrived"

(51), whereas Sula "gallop[s] through her own mind on a gray-and-white horse tasting sugar and smelling roses" (52). Fulfilling those early fantasies, Nel never leaves the Bottom, but Sula, travels widely, and Nel becomes the model of community respectability as opposed to Sula's unconventional behavior. For Nel "Hell is change" (108), but for Sula "doing anything forever and ever was hell." They are like the poles of two magnets, both irreconcilably repelling and absolutely attracting. After years of separation each regains a glimpse of their lost unity: in Sula's moment of afterlife consciousness she thinks of sharing her experience of death with Nel (149), and the final words of the novel depict Nel's epiphany of lost union with Sula (174).

This rich and ambivalent relationship between Sula and Nel suggests that Morrison is experimenting with alternative conceptions of selfhood and friendship. Their closeness calls into question the traditional notion of the unitary self, and their enduring yet strained relationship also questions the stereotype of undying friendship. According to Rigney, they "represent aspects of a common self, a construction of an identity *in relationship*" (*Voices* 50). Such a construction further probes the issues of unity and separateness, of self and pair.

Although Morrison in her authorial detachment can experiment with their relationship and their identities, both Sula and Nel have trouble resisting the conventional illusion that a relationship with a significant other must be total and all-consuming. Each tries unsuccessfully to find that degree of absorption with her mother and her grandmother. Then, after their momentary union as adolescents, their inevitable differences and social conventions drive them apart. Just as the momentary physical bond between Sula and Chicken Little cannot hold, Sula and Nel slip farther and farther apart. That gap begins at the moment when Chicken Little "slipped from [Sula's] hands" (60), and the gap develops into "a space, a separateness" at Chicken's funeral (64). Nel then attempts to substitute an all-consuming relationship with Jude, but this attempt, in its disequilibrium, is shallow. Nel, cautious and conforming, repeats her mistake with Sula, trying to create her identity in fusion with another's. Sula, more active and nonconformist, embarks on a quest, but her quest is similar to Nel's marriage, for she seeks another Nel (Reddy 36), a friend who will be "Both an other and a self" (119), and after her return she seeks union, first with Jude and then with Ajax. Both Sula and Nel seek totalizing unions with significant others, but when such unions do not last, their only recourse is isolation. The counterpart to symbiosis is division (Rubenstein 137).

One consequence of the characters' attempts to find meaning in relationship with another person is that they have difficulties in maintaining workable self-concepts. Their senses of self become entangled with their quests for fulfilling relationships with another, and in the process their identities, their relation- ships, and their communal ties all suffer.

The women of the Bottom are remarkably able to endure nearly impossible conditions, but in doing so their balance between self and other is skewed. As a result, like the characters in *The Bluest Eye*, they need "To clean themselves" on such scapegoats as Shadrack, Sula, and even their own children. Helene loses her self in her need to disassociate herself from her prostitute mother, and she endlessly repeats that loss in such acts as her self-denying smile of humiliation on the train. To compensate for such identity loss, she becomes a complete assimilationist, outdoing Pauline in her self-serving refuge in social superiority, rigid Christianity, and self-denying emulation of the white middle class. Like Geraldine (Baker, *Workings* 139) and Ruth Dead, she effaces her funky self, as Helene Sabat becomes the watered-down, whitened Helen Wright, trying in her self-*right*eousness always to be considered "right." Such conforming characters, lacking a core self, disintegrate into fragments. They are examples of the black middle class whom Leroi Jones (Amiri Baraka) describes as determined "To become *citizens*": "They did not even want to be 'accepted' as *themselves*, they wanted any self which the mainstream dictated, and the mainstream *always* dictated. And this black middle class, in turn, tried always to dictate that self, or this image of a whiter Negro, to the poorer, blacker Negroes" (130). Hannah comes closer to a healthy accommodation between self and other, meeting her own needs for male companionship without sacrificing her dignity or making unrealistic demands, but, like the other adults, she too can make no permanent relationships and is estranged from her child.

Eva is forced by her isolation and poverty to take such ultimate risks as abandoning her children and sacrificing her own leg. Onelegged, she tries to stand alone, without a significant other, but in doing so, like Baby Suggs and Sethe in *Beloved*, she overdoes her independence and willfulness, assuming a goddess-like imperialism that privileges the righteousness of her self and her will at the expense of others. She "creates" the deweys, rescuing them from potentially worse fates but denying them full identity and augmenting her own selfhood at their expense. Similarly, she saves Plum from further despair, but her act of murder is also motivated by her desire to protect herself from the shame and grief of his loss of self. Eva is so busy surviving that she has no energy for the conventional (white) mother-daughter love, and that lack is also a consequence of her over-reliance on self and her lack of recognition, not to mention compassion, for others. Then, her inability to save Hannah from the fire, a reoccurrence of the fire in which she burns Plum, is part of the price she has to pay, a price she pays again when Sula, also ego-bound, rejects her.

The males in *Sula*, displaced by their inferior racial status, never achieve stable selfhood. Tar Baby, Plum, and the deweys lose their identities. They are like Shadrack, whose sense of self and other is shattered in the war. He, however, can provisionally control his fear of disintegration through his obsessively well- ordered cabin and his ritual of National Suicide Day, measures that parallel the Bottom's collective ability to control its traumas by incorporating whatever evils confront it. Other men — BoyBoy, Jude, and Ajax — are more capable of coping with life, but they never attain full integration of self and other. With no meaningful work, they lack confidence and therefore cannot remain in what they feel are half-emasculated roles. Symbolized by Ajax's fascination with planes, each of these eligible males therefore flies from the burden of a permanent role as husband and father. Neither Jude nor Ajax can mature fully because each remains too attached to his need for a mother. Jude does not want an equal partner in Nel but someone who will mother him (Lounsberry and Hovet 128; Reddy 34). He is still a child whose selfhood is ever frail, overwhelmed by the weight of the oppressive economic and social conditions of the male work world and taking refuge in self-pity and the desire to be worshipped. He lacks the psychic resources to resist Sula or to face the consequences with Nel. Denied a complete identity by the white system's refusal of satisfying work, he wants "a someone sweet, industrious and loyal to shore him up" (83). Unable to find or become a self, he chooses Nel in the delusion that "The two of them together would make one Jude." His choice of Nel is a displacement, a vain attempt to replace his mother, to replace his own absent identity, to find "someone to care about his hurt, to care very deeply" (82). Ajax appears to be more secure in his selfhood: hero-like, he bears gifts of life, such as milk and butterflies, and he enjoys a temporary equality with Sula. But his close ties to his conjuring mother do not allow him to make lasting commitments to anyone else. Like Jude, his selfhood and self-confidence are frail, so at the first sign of possessiveness on Sula's part, he takes to the air, and his identity is correspondingly deflated from the heroic Ajax to the mundane Albert Jacks.

The course of Nel's efforts to establish an effective balance between self and other is more complex. Her "exhilarating" but "fearful" (28) trip to New Orleans, including her dis-association from her mother's loss of identity on the train and her liberating encounter with her grandmother, at first enables her to find a sense of self: " 'I'm me. I'm not their daughter. I'm not Nel. I'm me. Me.' " This initial spark allows her to become Sula's partner, each fulfilling the gap in the other's imagination. Her flame of independent selthood gradually burns down, however, under the constant, distorting pressures of racial, gender, and parental influence as well as her own passivity. It falters in comparison to Sula's overwhelming, rebellious self-hood and seems to flicker out with the death of Chicken little, after which even her relationship with Sula is not the same and for which she denies responsibility for over forty years. By the time she accepts marriage with Jude, the fire is cold, and she becomes the supportive, conforming, self-denying woman her mother tried to construct. Her attempts to fuse herself and Jude are specious, based on assimilated values, and, instead of a healthy unity, she only becomes locked in a fragmentary existence.

Nel's rejection of Sula in favor of a socially acceptable role as nurturing wife and mother leaves her with few psychic resources after that role is rendered unacceptable. Her unfulfilled self then is reflected in her inability to love her children, in which ironically she again conforms with the rest of the mothers in the community. She is unable to love or feel compassion for anyone, becoming all too much like her mother. That unfocused self is symbolized by the grey ball of fur that lurks just out of her imaginative vision (94). Like the white ring — also round — on Ruth Dead's table, it is the cloud in which she hides her self-knowledge and self-acceptance. Its semipresence suggests that she at least senses that she is denying herself and therefore all others, unlike such characters as Helene, who have forgotten entirely such denial and such self-knowledge. Although it haunts Nel, the grey ball thus indicates that her quest for selfhood is not dead but merely dormant, waiting to be revived by Eva's uncanny divination of the truth of her responsibility for Chicken Little's death and therefore of her responsibility for her own life. At the end of the novel, too late for Nel to reestablish her intimacy with Sula, she dissolves the grey ball and regains a self, her relation to the other, and the deep, humanizing sorrow that accompanies the revelation.

More than any of the other characters, Sula suffers from the dislocations of self and other. The narrator is explicit: "The first experience [Hannah's denial of liking her] taught her there was no other that you could count on; the second [Chicken Little's death] that there was no self to count on either" (118-19). But, unaware of any other choices, "she had clung to Nel as the closest thing to both an other and a self, only to discover that she and Nel were not one and the same thing" (119). Neither aided by the usual models for self-development nor checked by the usual restraints, and finding that she can neither find an identity in the other nor form her own (either in conjunction with or separate from that other), she drifts into the attempt to make herself. Given the confining conditions of life in the Bottom and given the paralyzing conventions for identity in both the mainstream society and the black community, making oneself is a positive and promising choice. Pilate Dead does achieve a healthy, self-made identity, but Sula must struggle, perhaps because, despite her aggressive self-confidence, she has "No ego," "No center, no speck around which to grow" (119). Unlike Pilate, who knows she must guide Milkman, Sula has no defining project, no focus; she is an "artist with no art form" (121). Along with this lack, the defining moments in Sula's development are negative (Byerman 196; Spillers 202). Just as Cholly's dangerous freedom and fragmented self result from the triple deaths of Aunt Jimmy, his masculinity, and his dream for a father, so Sula's undirected self follows from the triple negation of her mother's rejection, her "Murder" of Chicken little, and Nel's preference for marriage.

Part of Sula's problem is that she cannot live anywhere but the Bottom, where her only communal role is that of the pariah. She can exist only in the eyes of others, only as the nonprivfleged member of another destructive opposition, but she cannot conform because that would eliminate her visibility and hence her existence. Unlike Pecola, who becomes what she perceives, Sula becomes what she is perceived to be. Thus, her birthmark continually changes shape and color, because, like Sula herself, her mark is what others see it to be. When she does lapse into conformity with the community's role of "Wife," her independent selfhood, which Ajax sees and appreciates, vanishes in his eyes, and she becomes nothing to him and to herself. Sula is unable to join herself with any other, yet she is unable to exist independently. As in all of Morrison's fiction, neither fusion nor fragmentation suffices.

It is tempting to fall into the trap of praising or blaming Sula. Deborah Guth lines up previous critics into those who find Sula triumphing and those who find her failing (577n), and Guth herself compares Sula unfavorably to Eva. But such attempts at judgment are misdirected, for, like Claudia, Sula cannot be pinned down to one reading or one value judgment. Spillers articulates the required open-endedness: "We would like to love Sula, or damn her, inasmuch as the myth of the black American woman allows only Manichean responses, but it is impossible to do either. We can only behold in an absolute suspension of final judgment" (202). Like her birthmark, Sula remains open for interpretation.

Sula's resistance to any fixed interpretation parallels her own role in resisting the narrow formulations of self, woman, or black. She strives to remain free of convention, and correspondingly she must remain free of reader's fixed formulations. For Henderson, Sula is a representative of "The self-inscription of black womanhood" (131), an avatar of an alternative identity and role for African-American women. In Henderson's terms, via "disruption and revision" Sula rereads and repudiates "Black male discourse," and I would add all conventional discourse, black and white, female and male. Spillers agrees in principle, arguing that Sula is "a literal and figurative *breakthrough* toward the assertion of what we may call, in relation to her literary 'relatives,' new female being" (181), who "Overthrows received moralities in a heedless quest for her own irreducible self" (185), declaring her independence in her "radical amorality" and "radical freedom" (202).

By this reasoning, Sula is the locus for the creativity of the novel. Like Morrison's text, Sula cannot be fully known, as Morrison creates her with unending play between interpretative possibilities. As the novel posits a world governed by binary oppositions and exerts sustained pressure against that structure, Sula personally opposes the binary world, tries to escape it, experiments with subverting it, and finally yields to it. Both novel and character, by questioning the System and by groping toward alternative responses, make themselves up and concomitantly deconstruct the status quo. *Sula* and Sula remain open, for to finalize an interpretation is to close the book and end the process. Sula thus retains her hermeneutical richness; she is the title character, inviting our interpretations, and/but she is offstage for at least half the book, again inviting but not finalizing our readings. Her birthmark is a synecdoche for this role, like her and like the novel, open for interpretation, mediating between the external object and the internal subject. It, Sula, and *Sula* are "free-floating signifier(s)" (Henderson 130).

Sula's self-created self, her role as pariah, and her confusion over self and other double Shadrack's similar status. When he sees his comrade's head blown away, Shadrack loses confidence in the stability of the other and in the order and permanence of the material world. Similarly, Sula's belief in the order of the universe is destroyed by the blank space in the water above Chicken Little's body. Each event also shatters each character's sense of self: Shadrack has to verify his own existence in the imperfect mirror of the toilet bowl, and Sula's course of self- exploration is displaced into her roles as fugitive and witch. Morrison underscores this subconscious bond between Shadrack and Sula, first in the introductory chapter and then in their encounter after the drowning. At that moment she joins him as an outcast from the social order of the community and the psychic order of integrated selves (Baker, *Workings* 149). His ambiguous word, "always," reinforces the bond between them, implying that always life will be like this, always she and he will be pariahs. On her part she leaves her belt, which further symbolizes the subconscious ties between them. They are a peculiar dyad, linked subliminally by their mutual roles but unable to acknowledge the connection.

As Rushdy notices ("'Rememory'" 310), just before her epiphany at the end of the novel, Nel encounters Shadrack, who "Passed her by" (173), vaguely recalling her but unable to place her. Physically, "shadrack and Nel moved in opposite directions, each thinking separate thoughts about the past. The distance between them increased as they both remembered gone things" (174). The novel moves from the potential and magical union of Sula and Nel, by way of the subconscious, almost telepathic empathy between Sula and Shadrack, through numerous troubled relationships including Sula and Nel's, to this state of mutual isolation. But in the next sentence "suddenly Nel stopped" because "Her eye twitched and burned a little," a trace of Sula's presence in its recall of Sula's birthmark over her eye. The unspoken, unrecognized encounter with Shadrack is the catalyst for Nel's realization that she misses Sula, and Shadrack's presence thereby precipitates her belated mental reunion with Sula, which dissolves her grey fur-ball of guilt and self-denial.

As critics have noticed, Nel's cry is ambiguous. In it she finally finds her voice, but her cry is wordless, void of representational meaning. Margaret Homans contends that the cry "exemplifies the paradox of separatism in language" (193), whereas Keith Byerman finds that the cry's lack of conventional structure makes possible the natural and human order of circles (201). For him Nel achieves true humanity in her cry, but for Spillers, the cry merely expresses remorse and may suggest "The onset of sickness-unto-death" (197). Nel's cry echoes Sula's orgasmic cries — "she went down howling," during which she "Met herself, welcomed herself, and joined herself in matchless harmony" (123). Henderson argues that for Sula this "Howl, signifying a prediscursive mode, thus becomes an act of self-reconstitution as well as an act of subversion or resistance to the 'network of signification' represented by the symbolic order" (133-34). Each woman's undifferentiated utterance, coming at a moment of internal fusion, constitutes a cathartic release: Sula finds and accepts herself and Nel dissolves her fur-ball, a sign of her self-acceptance and internal harmony. Nel's "fine cry" (174) places her close to Claudia MacTeer's final position — saddened, experienced, self-knowledgeable, and a potential spokesperson.

As in all of Morrison's novels, the ending resists closure. In this novel, destruction and death predominate, and the attempt to create meaning through significant pairs is always problematic. Yet characters do survive, and, strangely and inexplicably, psychic bonds do exist. Shadrack edges slowly toward emotional health through his tenuous relationship with his friend and through his grief for her. Sula, in her moment of post-death consciousness, thinks of Nel: "It didn't even hurt. Wait'll I tell Nel" (149). Nel, after years of repression, self-hate, and isolation, is mysteriously linked to Sula by way of Shadrack, which enables her to rejoin humanity in her "fine cry — loud and long" (174).

Conscious, direct, total union is futile and even destructive, but indirectly, without obsession or compulsiveness, meaningful relationships can endure. Just as the binary opposites are necessary, the independence of each individual must be acknowledged and preserved. The temptation is to think in terms of either/or — either I am separate or I am united, either the oppositions are opposed or they are merged — but this novel and all of Morrison's novels urge that alternative configurations are possible and necessary. Sula and Nel can't know each other's every thought, Nel and Jude can't make one Jude, Sula can't possess Ajax; but Sula's and Nel's lives do intimately affect each other's, and Shadrack can mediate between their souls. Sula, Nel, and Shadrack form a peculiar but compelling triad, subconsciously fused and necessarily fragmented.

From a social and cultural perspective, Morrison's pre-occupation with divided entities in *Sula* reflects the endemic divisions within America. The gaps between pairs of characters signify the deep-seated fractures between opposed values in the larger society, particularly between blacks and whites. As with other binary pairs, Morrison juxtaposes the two races in direct confrontation, and the racial tension remains simmering, not breaking out into a race riot but contributing to the pervasive violence within the book. The two races constitute another binary pair, and the novel delineates the results of their difficulties in achieving a viable relationship.

This unfolding split is present in the tensions between the black residents of the Bottom and the whites who menacingly surround them. As opposed to *The Bluest Eye*, where the dominating white culture is present only indirectly in such forms as images of white beauty and values, in *Sula* nameless white characters repeatedly appear, always negatively with respect to blacks. The "good white farmer" tricks the gullible ex-slave into accepting infertile land in the hills, and in 1965 nameless whites reverse the trick. Other anonymous whites exert economic and political power over blacks: they withhold meaningful jobs, harass Tar Baby, arrest Ajax, and bury Sula. Enacting that power structure, the four Irish boys make sport of bullying Nel and Sula as they attempt to displace them. Whites abuse their status in their ridicule and humiliation of blacks: the white conductor treats Helene like "The bit of wax his fingernail had retrieved" from his ear (20-21) as he coerces her into mortifying submission. Whites overtly consider blacks as less than human, as when the bargeman who finds Chicken Little's body wonders "Will those people ever be anything but animals" (63), and then, ironically, desecrates the corpse. The pervasiveness of his brutality is reinforced by the sheriff's opinion: "Whyn't he throw it on back into the water" (64).

Another long-standing division in American culture, still present in the twentieth century, separates the idealized, agrarian past and the industrial present. The American myth promised a new beginning, an Edenic garden where the evils of urbanization and class conflict would be transcended, but the realities of slavery, the Civil War, and increasing industrialization meant the gradual fading of this Jeffersonian ideal. Racial division is fundamental to this failure: a racially segregated society intensifies rather than eliminates class hierarchy; the melting pot fails when cultural islands form (Spiller 16). Despite the fading of the agrarian myth, it retains its force in the twentieth century in the form of nostalgia for an ideal rural past. In *Sula*, Morrison evokes this sentiment by placing the narrator in the near-present, wistfully recalling the old days when the Bottom was a neighborhood, one that, despite its problems and its faults, was preferable to its obliteration. But Morrison is also ironic, for the past that the story recalls is far from idyllic: in contrast to the American agrarian dream, the African-American agrarian past is characterized by violence and hardship. In the Bottom there are no waving fields of grain, no "Two chickens in every pot," and, no matter where she travels, Sula finds that "There is no promised land of freedom to look toward" (Reddy 37). Nevertheless, that agrarian past, un- comfortably close to slavery, must be remembered and reclaimed, as Morrison delineates more intensively in *Beloved* and *Jazz*.

The sense of ironic displacement, begun in the novel's preface, deepens as Morrison leads readers to the Bottom via Shadrack. Sent to serve in World War I, "When blacks as a social group were first incorporated into a modern capitalist system" (Willis 85-86), Shadrack is blasted into isolation by experiencing his comrade's decapitation. The dead soldier is physically divided just as Shadrack becomes mentally divided; the soldier's physical loss of his head is transformed into Shadrack's mental loss of contact with the outside world. Together, the physical and mental displacements suggest the displaced situations of blacks: Reddy argues that Morrison's "definition by negation . . . places Shadrack the returning soldier in relationship to his enslaved ancestors" (33). In the Bottom, Shadrack and the other residents are still on the bottom of American society, largely forgotten, and "Under erasure" (Gates, *Figures* 202).

The Bottom, even more thoroughly than the Ohio neighborhood in *The Bluest Eye*, inverts the American dream. As Baker claims, it symbolizes "The Afro-American Place," a place that is outside and below history, a place, in contrast to the commemorative implications of the white Medallion, that objectives the difference between white and black ("When" 254-55). Still, it is a "Place," as the novel's first sentence reminds us, a place where neighborhood is possible, where communal values at least exist and can be supportive, where one's double-consciousness becomes an essential ingredient for survival. In the narrator's present time, no amelioration of the inversion has occurred: "Things" only "seemed" "Much better in 1965" (163).

The American dream has always been inverted for African Americans: if Europeans were to be regenerated in America (Marx, *Machine* 228), Africans were exiled to it; if America meant freedom to Europeans, it meant imprisonment to Africans; if America promised unlimited mobility to white settlers, the only mobility for slaves was as fugitives; if America meant a new place for Europeans, Africans had no place of their own. R. W. B. Lewis characterizes the new American hero as emancipated from history, undefiled, and able to stand alone (5), none of which applies to the enslaved African American. In Fisher's terms, the existence of slaves and then of ex-slaves rendered inviable the American myth of transparency ("Democratic" 85).

In addition to the double-consciousness that results from being both within and outside mainstream culture, another result of racialization in America is that for African Americans the search for identity has been especially intense, even "desperate" (Ellison, *Shadow* 297). The first major form of African-American writing, the slave narrative, is a response to this need. The theme is also evident in the passing novel, for example James Weldon Johnson's *The Autobiography of an Ex-Coloured Man* and Jesse Redmon Fauset's *Plum Bun*, in which the unsatisfactory choices confronting light-skinned African Americans are examined. The question of identity also dominates most African-American novels of the twentieth century, such as Zora Neale Hurston's *Their Eyes Were Watching God*, Richard Wright's *Eight Men* and *Native Son*, Ellison's *Invisible Man*, and Ernest Gaines's *The Autobiography of Miss Jane Pittman*.

One form that the search for identity takes in American fiction, black and white, is the pattern of escape and return. Typically, the American hero is stifled by the community, must leave it to pursue his or her self-development, but returns to the community with his or her acquired experience. This return, however, is usually problematic, which, according to Marx (*Machine* 363-65), results in the often unresolved endings of American novels in which the hero is unreconciled with or even alienated from the community. Such endings are usually double endings in the sense that the departure/return cycle is fulfilled and yet a loss is inflicted. Hester Prynne is accepted by the Salem community and Pearl is brought into the human community, but in compensation the other "Hero," Dimmesdale, and the "villain," Chillingworth, are exercised. Ishmael returns to tell the tale, but Ahab and the rest of the crew must be eliminated. Huckleberry Finn is integrated into the community but, a kind of double hero, prefers perennial escape. Doubleness especially marks African-American novels. For example, the narrator of *The Autobiography of an Ex-Coloured Man* is torn between the two lives open to him; like Sula, Janie Starks returns to her community as an outcast, but internally she is fulfilled and serene; and Ellison's invisible man withdraws from the community to a questionable isolation.

Sula extends this rich tradition of white American and African- American heros. Unwilling to subsume her identity into the mold allowed by the black community and the dominant society, she creates her own self, which gains her at least freedom and self-satisfaction ("I got my mind . . . I got me" [143]), but which leaves her isolated and incomplete. Like her chameleon birthmark, she is an optical illusion that varies according to the observer. In Pilate, the mark of difference (the lack of a navel) becomes the germ for a true self, but Sula's birthmark, instead of making her a genuine subject, makes her always an object. Except for her childhood friendship with Nel and her ambiguous relationship with Shadrack, her interactions with other people therefore tend to be negative. She gains a self, but, unable to gain harmony with community and cosmos, she cannot achieve lasting fulfillment. A pioneer, she forges a new path, but, like so many American heros, she cannot be absorbed by the community.

Sula's fate thus resembles that of many African Americans. African Americans are split off from mainstream American culture, and she is split off from the community and the larger society. She has the mobility of all Americans but she has only a marginal place. Neither slave nor free, she is caught in the racial enclosure of negation (Gates, *Figures* 54). Unlike Pauline, Helene, and Nel, she refuses erasure, refuses the impossible attempt to achieve transparency, but in that process, double- consciousness leads, as it does for Pecola, not to health and stability but to a mental state of morbidity and apathy similar to the condition described by Du Bois: "an almost morbid sense of personality and a moral hesitancy which is fatal to self- confidence" (164).

Like other classic American heros, Sula escapes and returns, and, like them, her return is problematic. She has to escape because her first attempt at an identity through companionship fails when Nel chooses the conforming role of housewife. She must return because without the negative self-definition supplied by the Bottom she has no identity, hence the anonymity of the cities she has drifted through. Upon her return, her position is more ambiguous than that of most American heros, for her place in the community is defined only negatively. Although her self-creation represents a significant advance over Cholly, who is also "dangerously free" but cannot create his own self, Sula remains too free, too radical, too resistant to assimilation. Rejecting assimilation, she opts wholly for the other extreme of non-conformity, not realizing that this too is a bipolar opposition to be deconstructed, not accepted. She insists on absolute independence, refusing to negotiate the two extremes, refusing to bend to be absorbed within the confirning limits of community, and finally accepting a fixed position in opposition to convention. But, like one-legged Eva, she cannot stand alone, so she abandons her attempt at independence when she tries to possess Ajax — in other words when she succumbs, Nel-like, to the other pole, the social pressures of domestication.

In a fictional world that emphasizes paired characters, Sula cannot survive because she finds no enduring relationship with any other character. that she does not, and that no one else does either, suggests that the quest for identity through such relationships, while privileged by the dominant society and by the black community, is impossible in this environment. In the Bottom, external pressures overwhelm any possibility of

Sula and Nel (or of any two people) working through the convoluted process of forming such a relationship. Similar pressures plus their own internal needs, disrupt Jadine and Son's attempt at fusion, whereas Sethe and Paul D and Violet and Joe Trace are able to build satisfying relationships, even while both cases document the complex difficulties of such a process.

Like similar antisocial heroes, Sula — radical, funky, anarchistic, chaotic — must be exorcised for the community to survive. The community endures for twenty-five years but is impoverished by the loss of this energy, as Nel realizes that post-Bottom, post- Sula Medallion is spiritually weakened. Without the pariah to clean themselves on, the members of the community slip into the doldrums. Yet Sula is not entirely forgotten, as her death is connected to a strange, sad, nostalgic fruition for Shadrack and Nel.

Although the attempt to find identity through a relationship with another person is an illusion, that fundamental division between self and other must be investigated, as Morrison continues to do in her next four novels. the violence of *Sula* is, necessary to loosen the rigidity of the bipolar structures. Only by questioning such structures, by accepting the inevitability of separation, and by attempting to bridge the gaps, can one understand the division and therefore one's self. Accepting the grief unblocks the repressed emotion and allows the soul to be reborn and to soar, even if it "Howl[s] in a stinging awareness of the endings of things" (123) and even if it soars in "circles and circles of sorrow" (174). For this novel, however, the epiphany comes too late, too late to retrieve what has been lost, too late for Nel or Sula to continue her self-development. Such retrieval, development, and unification is reserved for Morrison's next hero, Milkman Dead.

*Sula**

After completing *Sula* in 1973, Morrison says that she knew she was a writer. And as an indicator of talent, depth, and stylistic innovation, *Sula* assures Morrison's literary reputation. Superficially, the novel seems a continuation of themes and structures introduced in *The Bluest Eye*. Again, Morrison uses paired female characters; themes of identity, love, and responsibility; a vivid sense of community; shifting narrative perspectives; and rich use of irony and paradox. But *Sula* challenges readers in ways *The Bluest Eye* does not, primarily because of Morrison's presentation of evil and the structures she employs to reveal its polymorphic nature.

Divided into two roughly equal parts, with a prologue followed by chapter titles consisting of dates, *Sula* appears to move in a straightforward progression from 1919 to 1927 and then from 1937 to 1941, with "1965" as the novel's epilogue. But the events of various chapters don't necessarily occur during the dates indicated; indeed, the text spirals and laps back on itself, accruing sometimes changing or contradicting meanings as it goes. This demands the reader's concentrated effort, for Morrison here dramatizes her talent for using language as "Both indicator and mask." *Sula* insists that readers put aside conventional expectations to enter a fictional world deliberately inverted to reveal a complex reality, a world in which evil may be a necessary good, where good may be ex-

---

* From *Toni Morrison's World of Fiction* by Karen Carmean.
Karen Carmean. *Toni Morrison's World of Fiction*. Troy, New York: The Whitston Publishing Company, 1993.

posed for its inherent evil, where murder and self-mutilation become acts of love, and where simple answers to ordinary human problems do not exist. *Sula* has drawn many critical essays that have attempted to give it'a systematic, philosophically centered reading. But it defies single authoritative readings in theme and structure (although existential, Manichaen, and "Other" readings come close) mainly because this is a novel about becoming and changing, sometimes in clear process, sometimes not.

Sula's prologue begins by emphasizing place, indicating that the neighborhood of the Bottom, destroyed to make room for a golf course, will play a significant role in this narrative. The Bottom is more than a setting, however. Morrison often uses community as an active character in her work. From the very start we are made immediately aware of a mythological dimension, drawn into an imaginative place where nature and people interact, as they often do in folk and fairy tales. Beginning with the end of the Bottom, Morrison introduces a pattern of inversion which she quickly succeeds with others. This includes the anecdote about the origin of the Bottom as a "Nigger joke," when a white slave owner rewards his diligent slave with poor, hilly land where living will always be difficulty This "Joke" based on deceit and motivated by greed, becomes an important structural and thematic thread in *Sula*, for all of its elements bear directly on the lives of the Bottom's inhabitants. Behind the scenery, as it were, is the white man, controlling the literal disposition of the land and the slave's perception of it through the manipulation of language:

> "see those hills? That's bottom land, rich and fertile."
> "But It's high up in the hills," said the slave.

> "High up from us," said the master, "But when God looks down,
> It's the bottom . . . of heaven best land there is' (5).

The "Joke" effectively isolates the slave and ensures his economic failure while reinforcing the owner's sense of superiority. At the same time, however, the slave gleans some measure of success from his choice, developing a sense of humor as grimly ironic as his daily existence. Thus while the white folks hear the later inhabitants' laughter, they remain ignorant of the pain somewhere under the eyelids" (4).

Isolated by location, race, and economics, the Bottom develops into a neighborhood, sharing some values with nearby white Medallion and developing its own distinctive attitudes as well. Chief among them in the novel is the neihgborhood's acceptance of evil, which seems a form of passive acceptance: "They let it run its course, fulfill itself, and never invented ways either to alter it, to annihilate it or to prevents its happening again. So also were they with people" (89-90). This sense of endurance, superficially so stoical, perhaps even rational in the face of oppression, may also be a form of fatalistic indifference or fear. In any case, it becomes self-defeating, because it may be concluded that their "view of survival and of Nature exists only on the physical plane and is rooted in the fear of dying rather than in a desire to live." Fear leads Shadrack, most prominently, and other characters as well, to create external structures and focus on these instead of actual causes. Thus National Suicide Day, Shadrack's means of imposing order over fear, not death, becomes the structure which eventually assumes its own independent importance. This need for finding an objective correlative for fear will lead the community to focus its fear and hatred on the River Road, the tunnel, and on Sula for their perceived inherent evil while remaining blind to the mysterious and protean nature of evil.

Another character motivated by fear is Helene Wright. Hers is a fear of life, suggested by her attitude toward sexuality. Raised by her grandmother in a house guarded by four Virgin Marys, Helene is cautioned against "any sign of her mother's wild blood" (17). Helene escapes New Orleans' sultry atmosphere and her prostitute mother's shadow by marrying Wiley Wright and moving to Ohio, where she sets a standard for communal rectitude, a standard she later imposes on her daughter Nel. But Helene's existence seems more a denial of a former life than an affirmation of an improved one, especially when her veneer of dignity dissolves into a "Brilliant smile" aimed at a loathsome white conductor who denigrates her at the beginning of a trip back to New Orleans. Helene's smile, a flirtatious appeal for understanding, allows Nel to see her mother in an entirely new context. No longer a woman "Who could quell a roustabout with a look" but instead an image of "custard," Helene reveals an unsuspected side. The "custard" and "Jelly" Nel associates with her mother suggest more than weakness (22). They reveal the nature of Helene's sexual fear.

Nel's trip to New Orleans gives her a glimpse of another, more complex reality rife with paradox and denial. Her grandmother's parting injunction, "Voir," is a message to see and inspect (27). Helene refuses to translate for her daughter. Nonetheless, Nel returns to the Bottom aware of her separate identity: "I'm me. I'm not their daughter. I'm not Nel. I'm me. Me" (28). Contemplating her separateness, Nel wants two things out of life, to be "Wonderful" and to leave Medallion (29). Now she is prepared to ignore her mother's objections and become best friends with Sula.

Sula's upbringing in her grandmother Eva's house is the most significant factor in developing her attitudes, her perceptions of life forming in the irregular house her grandmother designs. A microcosm of the Bottom, Eva's house contains all the elements of the larger community: love, lust, generosity, possessiveness, evasiveness, duty, tenderness, denial, and deceit. Both life- sustaining and moribund, Eva's house is a monument to her twisted sense of responsibility, a sense warped by dire circumstances.

Abandoned one November by her husband Boy Boy, Eva struggles to feed her three starving children until, sensing futility, she leaves them with a neighbor and disappears. Eighteen months later, Eva returns, with one leg missing but with notable prosperity, to reclaim her children and build her own home. Precisely how Eva loses her leg becomes the topic of speculation in the Bottom, though it is suggested that Eva sacrifices it in a train accident for an insurance settlement. Whatever the case, Eva's experience changes her from a passive victim to an active manipulator. Her motive shifts from love to hatred: "Hating Boy Boy she could get on with it, and have the safety, the thrill, the consistency of that hatred as long as she wanted or needed it to define and strengthen her and to protect her from routine vulnerabilities" (36). Finding an embodiment of evil, a locus for her hatred, Eva participates in the community's use of fear and hatred as a defining, strengthening, and protective emotion, and her reaction brings her positive results. Later, the residents of the Bottom will hate Sula, and their reactions against her will temporarily lead to caring relation- ships. Eva's hatred also frees her from conventional solutions to routine problems. She becomes "creator" and "sovereign" of her home, directing the lives about her with unquestioned authority (30). In effect, Eva assumes godlike proportions, her removed authority indicative of emotional distance, her power over life and death unchallenged.

We see the results of Eva's authority throughout the novel, especially in relation to male characters: the deweys, Tar Baby, and Plum. All receive Eva's care and all, to some extent, become her victims. Eva's rescue of the deweys from indifferent mothers is fraught with paradox. While they doubtless benefit from whatever care they receive, these boys, originally so different in age and physical features, live down to Eva's leveling assessment: "What you need to tell them apart for? They's all deweys" (38). As if Eva's initial dismissal of individuality arrests their development, the deweys never grow to physical or emotional maturity. Tar Baby, a white man boarding in Eva's house, receives similar treatment. Intent on drinking himself to death, he finds the shelter and indifference to his habits he requires in Eva's house.

This isn't so with Plum, Eva's only son, who grows up "floated in a constant swaddle of love and affection" (45). Here is another verbal paradox, with "floated" and "swaddle" suggesting Plum's perpetual infancy is brought to an abrupt end with military service in World War I. A year after his return to the United States, Plum appears in the Bottom with a "sweet, sweet, smile" induced by his heroin habit (45). Like Shadrack, Plum seems to have suffered a psychic war injury which he cannot relate. His silence and ever deeper withdrawal into drug induced euphoria finally spur Eva into action.

The scene during which Eva sets fire to Plum is suggestively political. Plum's drug habit along with military service and his discharge without adequate treatment echo Shadrack's premature release from a veteran's hospital. Both become casualties in a war which brings African-Americans no gain whatsoever. Thus the cherry pie and *Liberty* magazine assume ironic meaning and widen the significance of Plum's death. As the agent of death, Eva acts primarily out of love. Tears stream down her face as she tightly holds Plum. Grieving yet resolute, Eva's choice of death by fire echoes other mythic literary deaths and suggests purification and even rebirth, particularly with the references to "a wet light" and "some kind of baptism" (47). But Plum neither rises from his own ashes nor does he emerge from the flame strengthened and sanctified. He is extinguished by his own mother. No one questions Eva's act, certainly not the community which never believes the rumors it circulates. Only Hannah can summon the courage to ask her mother why she killed Plum. The response Hannah hears in "Two voices" suggests at least two reasons. Eva's primary motivation is to allow Plum "To die like a man" instead of retreating further into druginduced infancy (like Tar Baby), and here Eva's motive becomes self-protective, not liberating (72). Dreaming that Plum is trying to reenter her womb, Eva saves herself ("Godhavemercy, I couldn't birth him twice") and her idea of what Plum should be (71). Her act both destroys and saves.

Doubtless, Eva's notion of manhood relates to her practice of "Manlove," a love of maleness for its own sake," which she passes on to her daughters (41). Here, too, we trip over another paradox. Though "Prejudiced about men" to the extent that she flatters their egos and criticizes wives she deems short of domestic devotion, Eva never allows herself to become the mere object of masculine attention (42). What can be truthfully said is that she is like Hannah in that both "exist as sexually desiring subjects rather than objects of male desire." But "Manlove," the privileging of men, binds Eva to the community, cementing her to an unchallenged tradition — unchallenged, that is, until Sula reaches adulthood.

Structurally, Morrison prepares her readers for her title character through her use of inversion and paradox. Sula's delayed appearance also suggests the importance of all that precedes her in life: the Bottom, Shadrack, Helene, Eva. Thus when readers first encounter Sula savoring the "Oppressive neatness" of Helene Wright's house, we know her background yet little about her (29). Morrison will continue this pattern throughout the novel, removing Sula from narrative action — with calculated results.

Just as Helene is surprised by Sula's acting contrary to expectations, readers should not anticipate conventional behavior from this elusive character. Morrison created Nel and Sula to be a whole: "Each has part of the other. . . . But each one lacked something that the other one had." This lack, like Sula's absences, serves to define her and is first dramatized in the novel when Sula hears her mother saying, "I love Sula. I just don't like her" (57). Hannah's statement unwittingly severs a significant bond with Sula. Sula is conscious only of "a sting in her eye," but the event essentially points out Sula's difference from her mother (57). Sula and Nel immediately strengthen their union in a wordless ritual, loaded with sexual implications. But the hole they dig, both womb and grave, signals both their union and dissolution.

Chicken Little's death, which immediately follows, becomes central to the narrative because it serves to bind the girls closer together. This accident occurs at a critical age for these twelve year olds, pointing out their moral development. With Chicken's unexpected disappearance, Nel registers the first reaction: "somebody saw" (61). This apparent fact prompts a fearful yet determined Sula to investigate. Her discovery of Shadrack's unexpected neatness momentarily distracts Sula until she observes him in his doorway. Sula cannot voice the frightening question ("had he?"), and Shadrack gives her an answer ("always) full of ambiguity (62). When Sula returns to Nel, the one on whom she depends for thought, Nel denies Sula's responsibility: "It ain't your fault" (63). Not only that, Nel seems equally distressed about Sula's missing belt, somehow equating one with the other. Nel's response suggests her own lack, a denial of her responsibility, despite the fact that she clearly represents communal responsibility throughout the novel. Her reaction seems self-contained, even detached. By contrast, Sula's soundless grief is eloquently directed at Chicken's misfortune, not her own. Absolved of responsibility, she nevertheless loses something central to her becoming whole. The test points out clearly what happened to her: "ever since her mother's remarks sent her flying up those stairs, ever since her one major feeling of responsibility had been exercised on the bank of a river with a closed place in the middle. The first experience taught her there was no other that you could count on; the second that there was no self to count on either. She had no center, no speck around which to grow" (118-119). Sula fails to see this for many years, of course. It's far too early for such sophisticated introspection. But her later actions, especially her cool observation of Hannah being burned, underscore Sula's difference, a difference later termed "evil" by the community when it watches the result of this lack.

The contrasting characters of Nel and Sula seem to retain their balance for years to come. Indeed, Sula returns after a decade's absence knowing that she has missed Nel all along.

It is Nel, not Sula, who has separated, despite the fact that Sula has been physically absent. Yielding to Jude Green's need for a "Hem," a someone "sweet . . . to shore him up," Nel discovers a feeling stronger than her friendship (83). And in marrying a man who believes that the two can make one whole and complete Jude, Nel virtually extinguishes her possibilities for developing an independent self.

The images attached to marriage in *Sula* are far from complimentary, with this social institution literally signaling the death of the female imagination and individuality. "Those with husbands," the text says, "Had folded themselves into starched coffins, their sides bursting with other people's skinned dreams and bony regrets. . . . Those with men had had the sweetness sucked from their breath by ovens and steams kettles" (122). Jude's concern all along is with himself, not Nel, as he longs for confirmation of manhood denied him through racist employment restrictions. In acceding to Jude's urging, Nel joins the community's valuation of females as significant support, not independent beings. Accepting her role as wife and mother, Nel never questions the quality of her life. Any urge to examine, any incentive to leave the Bottom, or even rebel against its traditions, leaves with Sula. It does not, however, return with her.

Following Sula's return, Nel briefly rediscovers another way of seeing: "It was like getting the use of an eye back, having a cataract removed" (95). But she is alone in celebrating Sula's reappearance. From the beginning Sula irritates the Bottom with her individuality, her refusal to accept a woman's role. Without calling attention to the fact, Morrison gives Sula license to act as she pleases. Significantly enough, Sula can be said to behave "Like a man. She's adventuresome, she trusts herself, she's not scared. And she is curious and will leave and try anything." Because of this "quality of masculinity," she is seen as a "Total outrage." Thus It's not surprising for a community held together in part by traditions largely maintained by and relating to women to label Sula "devil" and "Pariah" (117, 122). To the Bottom, she is the embodiment of evil. And what actions illustrate the nature of her evil? She places Eva in a nursing home, and she selects sexual partners from among married men. The rest is rumor.

Sula's reason for Eva's removal to a nursing home is based on self-defense. Immediately after entering Eva's house, Eva brings up two issues wholly antagonistic to Sula. She shows no gratitude (to Eva) and she has no husband or children. Their ensuing argument illustrates deeply opposed ideologies, with Eva maintaining a traditional view of Sula needing a husband and babies to "settle" her and Sula vigorously asserting her right to make herself and not be made by others (92). To any conforming pleasure, Sula says she's not yielding. "I'll split this town in two," she declares to Eva, "and everything in it before I'll let you put it [the fire of individuality] out!" (93). The fire image occurs naturally enough to Sula. Knowing that Eva has burned Plum, Sula fears her. She later tells Nel about this fear, but Nel, like the rest of the community, refuses to believe the rumors of Eva's murder of her son. From Sula's perspective, putting Eva in a nursing home prevents another murder — Eva's or Sula's.

As for Sula's method of satisfying her sexual needs, Hannah's similar acts should be recalled. Of course, Hannah's sexual acts did not antagonize the women of the Bottom. The difference stems largely from Sula's refusal to flatter male egos and thus seemingly devalue the men and, by extension, their wives. Sula's motives, however, are different from Hannah's, who simply refused to do without some "Touching every day" (44). The sexual act becomes for Sula an act of self-exploration and affirmation. Even Sula's early romantic fantasies forecast her sensual self-exploration, as she spends hours "galloping through her own mind on a gray-and-white horse tasting sugar and smelling roses in full view of a someone who shared both the taste and the speed" (52). Later, sex becomes a free fall into "a stinging awareness of the ending of things: an eye of sorrow in the midst of that hurricane rage of joy. There, in the center of that silence, was not eternity but the death of time and a loneliness so profound the word itself had no meaning" (123). In this state, Sula experiences her deepest feelings, deep enough to bring "Tears for the deaths of the littlest things" (123). Her sexual partner is relatively unimportant. He merely serves as the means to her end, "The postcoital privateness in which she met herself, welcomed herself, and joined herself in matchless harmony" (123). Sula is consequently more intimate with herself than is ordinarily true of others, more knowledgeable about herself, more attuned to her own needs and desires. In the end, this inner intimacy, far from being evil, assumes a purity, signified by her association with rain.

Nel, on the other hand, has envisioned sex in terms of tangles and webs, snares for a struggling self as well as for others. Her concept of love and female sexuality is rooted in possessiveness. Thus when Sula, innocent of possessive love, takes Jude as a lover, Nel feels personally betrayed. So attached is her sexuality to her husband, Nel mistakenly believes that it departs with him. Though she grieves sexual emptiness, she fears looking at other men. Nel cannot see herself as Sula so clearly envisions her, a spider dangling by her own spittle, "More terrified of the fall than the snake's breath below" (120). Unlike Sula, Nel fears change. She tries to hide from the fact that change is a necessary part of life. Without Sula's influence in her life, Nel's imaginativeness, her sensual enjoyment is replaced by a "Little ball of fur and string and hair" (109). By excluding Sula from her life, Nel successfully isolates her friend, but the result appears like an ironic form of suicide.

Meanwhile, Sula finally meets a man who admires female independence. Bored by clinging women, Ajax is initially drawn to Sula because he thinks that besides his mother "This was perhaps the only other woman he knew whose life was her own" (127). Equally weary of men unable to respect her intelligence, Sula finds attractive Ajax's "refusal to baby or protect her, his assumption that she was both tough and wise" (128). Surprisingly to Sula, Ajax prefers her in the superior sexual position during love malting. In this position, Sula imaginatively mines the layers of Ajax's being to discover his essence, thinking in terms of precious metals, semi-precious stones, and life-giving loam. But their love affair ends when Sula resorts to the conventional domestic signals: a clean bathroom and table set for two. Worse, though, is Sula's invitation for Ajax to "Lean on" her (133). Instead, he pulls her under him one last time before going to Dayton, leaving Sula stunned and empty.

Sula's thwarted affair with Ajax emphasizes the varying concepts of female love in the Bottom. She might have become, like Nel, subservient to a husband who sees his wife as someone to absorb his pain and bear his children. Or she might subscribe to Hannah's practice, which allows sexual pleasure but denies emotional ties. Before reaching adulthood Sula has rejected the former choice; otherwise she would never have left the Bottom. And after loving Ajax, she finds Hannah's approach equally unsatisfactory. Both concepts preclude mutual responsibility, the former by making women entirely responsible for domestic harmony, the latter by negating emotional connections. Sula's aborted love affair also dramatizes how her capacity for affection is consistently stifled. Looking back, she could trace a pattern of emotional connection followed by loss. Chicken dies, Nel denies her, and Ajax leaves. Looking at Ajax's drivers' license and seeing the name Albert jacks, Sula discovers that she never knew the identity of her lover. "and if I didn't know his name," she thinks to herself, "Then there is nothing I did know and I have known nothing ever at all since the one thing I wanted was to know his name . . ." (136). In Eva's fonmer bedroom, facing her own as well as the evidence of her grandmother's futile expression of love, Sula might reflect on the insolvency of human relations. Unlike Nel, she doesn't expect either reward or punishment for her acts. She believes that "Being good to somebody is just like being mean to somebody. Risky. You don't get nothing for it" (144-45). Still, confronting death, Sula seems satisfied that she at least lived her own life, that perhaps her way has been good.

Sula dies as she lived — alone. Alive, her impact on the Bottom had been ironically positive since in reacting to Sula's presence adults became more cherishing of their elderly parents, mothers more vigilant over their children, and wives more caring with their husbands. Their actions, however, seem generated more from spite than love. Consequently, after Sula's death, the Bottom's residents revert to their former habits of neglect. No one claims that evil dies with Sula. The community's projection of evil on one resident and subsequently on a public works project proves ludicrous from the beginning. Signalling the fact that Sula's nature is not actually evil are her eyes, "clean as rain" (52). What, then, is her "Problem?" An omniscient observation concerning the essence of Sula's nature suggests that she was dangerous, like Cholly Breedlove, because of an "Idle imagination": "Had she paints, or clay, or knew the discipline of the dance, or strings; had she anything to engage her tremendous curiosity and her gift for metaphor she might have exchanged the restlessness and preoccupation with whim for an activity that provided her with all she yearned for" (121).

Sula's energy and intelligence go unrecognized and unemployed, ignored by a community too busy foisting its guilt and failure on her. This is distressing, as is the fact that Sula cannot overcome overwhelming odds to discover the necessary form of self-expression. Here, then, is an example of true evil in the story, coming from the waste of Sula both by herself and those around her. Without Sula upon whom to focus blame, the people of the Bottom shift to a tunnel, part of a local federally funded road project which has raised and then frustrated residents' hope for employment. Here we see further examples of evil in the forms of sexism and racism. What may be concluded is that if the story indeed "considers the ways in which society denies women the possibility of autonomy and independence," then the tunnel suggests the larger frame of how white Medallion (and by extension the United States) denies the same to an entire race." joining Shadrack on National Suicide Day, residents march to the tunnel and assault it with bricks and lumber. Of those who enter, many die as the tunnel collapses with Shadrack standing above " . . . ringing, ringing his bell" (162). That the tunnel, which becomes a grave to so many, has been built by whites seems no accident.

The image of Shadrack presiding over the Bottom's death brings to mind John Donne's famous statement: "any man's death diminishes me, because I am involved in Mankind; And therefore never send to know for whom the bell tolls; It tolls for thee." The obvious point of this image is to affirm the interrelationship of all. Throughout *Sula* we are reminded of the impersonal interest with which the white community observes occurrences in the Bottom, interest similar to that of Nel and Sula as they watch Chicken and Hannah die. As observers, all remain fascinated yet detached from the fatal activity before their eyes. These reactions emphasize their inability to empathize with and their denial of responsibility for others. Significantly, it is Nel, representing the community, who has never consciously admitted her interest and role in Chicken's death. A visit to Eva in 1965 offers her a glimmer of truth as she is forced to review her role. What bothers her is that Eva "didn't say *see*, she said *watched*." An inner debate follows: "'I did not watch it. I just saw it.' But it was there anyway, as it always had been, the old feeling and the old question. The good feeling she had had when Chicken's hands slipped. She hadn't wondered about that in years. 'Why didn't I feel bad when it happened? How come it felt so good to see him fall?'" (170). The more Nel ponders these questions, the closer she comes to recognizing that Sula and she are intimately bound, despite her feeling of separateness, her relief over surviving.

Morrison presents a parallel catharsis to emphasize the importance of communal responsibility. Blaming Sula and the tunnel will not improve conditions any more than personal evil can be exercised by death because the human community's problems remains more fundamental. As she does in *The Bluest Eye*, Morrison alludes to the human soil, the conditions for growth and development critical for nurturing healthy human beings through love unblighted by possessiveness or self- sacrifice, love allowing feelings for oneself as well as for others. Seeing the painful, disfiguring effects of love, Sula creates herself in her own image, becoming totally "free." But she does not become "free" in a positive way. About personal freedom Morrison herself has said that "Ideally" it means "Being able to choose your responsibilities. Not not having any responsibility, but being able to choose which things you want to be responsible for. In shunning responsibility for the creation of a healthy community, white Medallion and the Bottom become culpable, not Sula. After all, she has little choice of her growing environment. Indeed, the extended neglect of children throughout the novel is a recurring reminder of communal dereliction. Chickeni the deweys, Ajax, Teapot, and Sula herself are allowed to grow with little supervision or care. No wonder that the children who survive become as self-centered as their adult examples. Sula's solipsistic approach may seem to be more extreme than that of others. But when we see the widening rings of denial moving out from her to the Bottom to Medallion and the rest of the United States, we begin to fathom the political depth of this novel. Sula at least wholly claims her life, including its failures, while others deny their human connections in favor of simpler, safer ways.

The community of the Bottom never recognizes its moral insolvency, never sees the role it plays in its destruction. But Nel is given a belated chance for self-recognition. Her glimpse of truth is brought about first when Eva, to whom Nel has paid a duty call, confuses Nel with Sula and soon thereafter asks how Nel managed to kill Chicken. Nel's assured moral rectitude melts as she begins to see that everyone might have been wrong about Sula, that what Sula stood for was not necessarily bad. In an exchange just prior to her death, Sula has pointed out her position to Nel:

> "How you know?" Sula asked.
> "Know what?"
> "about who was good. How you know it was you?"
> "What you mean?"
> "I mean maybe it Wasn't you. Maybe it was me" (146).

Years later, Nel sees that Sula might have been right. Moreover, Nel acknowledges that there was spite behind communal actions, not love or moral conviction. And when she understands this, Nel also recognizes that Eva was right to confuse her with Sula. She sees that despite their difference, they were identical in their disclaimer of responsibility.

The story ends with the beginning of Nel's painful comprehension that much of what she has believed in has led her away from herself instead of leading her to truth. Morrison's dramatization of tradition's unperceived barriers to self-discovery reflects her belief in the need for experimenting with life, of breaking rules, not simply out of boredom or curiosity but because there is no other way to explore possibilities. Sula discovers the terror and thrill of the free fall into life through her own creative capacity for invention. Nel, on the other hand, values duty and tradition more than self. Taught to believe in the virtue of self-sacrifice, she denies her own possibilities and becomes dependent on others for her life's meaning, and even, as Sula points out, for her own loneliness. Trying to read *Sula* as an either/or proposition, that either

Nel or Sula must be right, is unnecessarily simplifying and distorting of this novel, for Morrison all along intends both characters to command our attention. Like the characters, labels of "good" and "evil" become confused because "One can never really define good and evil. It depends on what uses you put it to. Evil is as useful as good is." And though what remains of the Bottom will never know that Sula was not what they thought her to be, at least Nel breaks through the barriers of traditional moral certainty to recognize a Sula she hasn't seen for a long time: "'We was girls together,' she said as though explaining something" (174). Her reference to girlhood recalls a time of their greatest possibility, a possibility Nel rejected in favor of conventional ideas about womanhood which in turn blinded her to the truth of Sula.

Nel's grief brings the novel to a close, but like most elements of the novel, it paradoxically opens up her own possibilities. Thus in a way, the novel is open-ended. Finishing *Sula*, we have to consider carefully what we in fact do know. Our conventional expectations, after all, have been challenged through omission, contradiction, paradox, irony, and speculation, through a fusion of supernatural and realistic, and through a lean prose conjuring gothic events. By the end, we are prone to have given up any dualistic thinking in favor of the fluid, multiple process Morrison's novel gives us. The novel and the title character require imaginative exploration into the nature of life and art. Ultimately this means that, artistic structure notwithstanding, we are asked to respond to the free fall into individual consideration instead of relying upon literary conventions.

편저자_김명주

충남대 영어영문과 졸업
미국 웨스턴미시간대학교 영문학 석사
미국 뉴멕시코 주립대학교 영문학 박사
충남대학교 영어영문학과 교수

“Does Christianity Narrow the Artistic Vision in Literature?”
“인문학의 위기와 노드롭 프라이의 문학적 상상력의 옹호”
“포크너의 종교성과 『8월의 빛』 외 다수의 논문

Sula

숱라

1판 1쇄 찍음 • 2003년 2월 20일
1판 3쇄 펴냄 • 2010년 10월 15일
편저자 • 김 명 주
발행인 • 정 현 걸
발 행 • 신 아 사
인 쇄 • 예지인쇄
출판등록 • 1956년 1월 5일 (제9-52호)
서울특별시 은평구 녹번동 28-36번지 2F
전화 (02)382-6411 • 팩스 (02)382-6401
홈페이지 • www.shinasa.co.kr
이메일 • shinasa@chol.com
ISBN 89-8396-216-X (93840)

정가 **12,000** 원